The Jordans and The Slovers

They had come to Indiana to start a new life!
The Jordans were Virginia aristocrats
—the best blueblood the new world had to offer.

The Slovers were as uncivilized and
as primitive as the wild land
they had come to conquer.

It wasn't long before the womenfolk were at
each other's throats.

It wasn't long before Eric Jordan was sneaking off at
night with the lovely, young Slover girl.

It wasn't long before they both found themselves
at the mercy of a man they despised,
Caleb Lewis, "the white Indian."

A Moving, Passionate Novel of the American Frontier

Books by Dale Van Every

WESTWARD THE RIVER
- THE SHINING MOUNTAINS
- BRIDAL JOURNEY
- THE CAPTIVE WITCH
- THE TREMBLING EARTH
- THE VOYAGERS

Published by Bantam Books

THE SCARLET FEATHER

BY DALE VAN EVERY

This low-priced Bantam Book has been completely reset in a type face designed for easy reading, and was printed from new plates. It contains the complete text of the original hard-cover edition. NOT ONE WORD HAS BEEN OMITTED.

THE SCARLET FEATHER

A Bantam Book / published by arrangement with Holt, Rinehart & Winston, Inc.

PRINTING HISTORY

Holt edition published March 1959
2nd printing........March 1959
Bantam edition published April 1963

Bantam Books are published by Bantam Books, Inc. Its trade-mark, consisting of the words "Bantam Books" and the portrayal of a bantam, is registered in the United States Patent Office and in other countries. Marca Registrada. Printed in the United States of America. Bantam Books, Inc., 271 Madison Ave., New York 16, N. Y.

THE SCARLET FEATHER

October

Pale gleams flickered among the upper boughs of the immense overhanging trees, but none filtered down into the pool of darkness in which lay the two gently rocking barges moored side by side against the bank. The moon, continuing its slow rise from the wooded horizon, silvered an ever-increasing expanse of the river and fringed with shadowed detail the other wall of forest along the farther bank. The border of radiance rippled nearer until at length it overran the squat scow-like hulks of the moored craft and, dispelling the darkness in which they had been shrouded, accentuated the loneliness of their situation. For the Ohio, down which they had come, was a lonely river, coursing through the solitude of a wilderness that stretched away without seeming end, unmarked by human habitation nearer than the Shawnee towns half a hundred miles to the north or the Cherokee towns twice a hundred miles to the south.

Of the thirty-two people aboard the two craft only sixteen-year-old Betsey Slover was awake to note the sudden faint brightening. Shimmers of light slipped along the cracks in the deck shed in which slumbered the five other members of her family, the two Jordan cows, and their own four dogs. She twisted to peer out between the boards beside her head. Slanting across her glimpse of the shining river was the nearer end of one of the mooring lines, glistening with patches of tiny ice crystals where its wetness had frozen in the night. It seemed to end in mid-air where its glitter was cut off by the edge of the shadow cast by the dark forest on the bank. She lay back in the straw. Deliberately she touched her fingertips to her straggly hair, her thin, pinched face, her meager breasts, and then, with a sigh of satisfaction, to the gracious swelling of her distended belly. She welcomed her so early approach to woman's full estate as nothing short of a miracle sent by heaven. But instead of another of the little kicks and jerks which in recent weeks had so much delighted her there came the knife thrust of her first pain. She clutched at her mother, lying beside her in the straw. After a round of discontented grunts and snorts Polly Slover opened her eyes.

"They's started," announced Betsey eagerly.

"Yer sure?"

"Real sure."

"How fast they comin'?"

"Cain't tell yet." Betsey caught her breath, trembled, and breathed again. "Thet was another one."

"Long's thy'se not hittin' yuh no harder'n thet—'twill be a while yet."

Polly rolled over and resumed snoring. A half hour later Betsey clutched her again.

"Thet last one was right bad," she reported.

Polly thrust an exploring hand under Betsey's blanket, nodded resignedly, and reached over her to prod Betsey's younger sister, Lina.

"Light me a candle."

Lina, only half awake, obediently crawled away over the huddle of recumbent men and animals to the embers of the cooking fire on the square of sheet iron before the shed doorway. The light of the candle as she returned played over her touseled mop of flaxen hair and the mature roundness of her body under the ragged linsey-woolsey gown. She was fourteen, but despite the womanly contours of her figure, her utterly placid expression gave her more the look of an overgrown child of four. Polly peered at Betsey's pain-contorted, perspiring face.

"Fetch me thet axe handle."

Lina handed it to her. Polly began pounding on the blanketed forms about her in the straw.

"Git yerselves up and out o' here. And take yer dogs with yuh."

Her husband, Olen, gigantic, shambling, bearded, and Jarot and Jacob, nearly as big and bearded as their father, growled mild protests, gathered up their bedding, and stumbled out, dragging the whimpering dogs. Other and more vehement growls of protest arose as the aggregation pushed in under the tarpaulin stretched over the sleeping space on deck occupied by the three Lymans, the two Jordan male Negroes, and the Jordans' eight hired boatmen.

"Go to hollerin' loud's yuh feel like," Polly counseled Betsey. "Hollerin' don't make it no easier but it makes the time go faster."

Betsey essayed a tentative groan. Her breath, taking her by surprise as it was suddenly expelled by the next cramp, turned the groan into a low, animal-like howl.

In the main cabin of the other barge, Agatha Jordan lifted her head to listen. Beside her in the bunk her husband, Duncan, at once turned toward her, as though always aware of her even in his sleep.

"That Slover girl," whispered Agatha. "Her time must be on her."

She started to get up. Duncan caught hold of her.

"Childbirth's no novelty in that family. Polly claims she's had eighteen."

"I wouldn't doubt it. She likely started when she was no older than this poor little Betsey. But don't you notice how much colder it has turned?"

Duncan waited for Betsey's second cry to diminish to a moan.

"I am paying the closest attention but I seem to have been left behind somewhere."

"I only want to make sure the children are warm."

"Ah. How could I have lost sight of how inexorably with you first things come first." He was still holding to her. "But I have a better idea."

"What's that?"

"You stay here and keep a place warm for me to come back to."

She dropped back on the pillow with a secure wife's low laugh of drowsy assurance.

"Then hurry."

He thrust his feet into felt slippers, wrapped his greatcoat about him, and felt his way across the dark cabin to draw aside the blanket hanging before his mother's bunk. There could be no question that she was warm. She slept under a mountainous feather bed with her head encased in a knitted nightcap and her throat swathed in a woolen scarf. Moonlight from the porthole illuminated her angularly handsome face, which had come, as she aged, so increasingly to resemble his own. He smiled. She had been fiercely determined to accompany them on their westward journey and having had her way, had become as fiercely determined to remain as comfortable as at home.

Duncan edged open the door of the second cabin, lighted by its dim night lantern. All his children were asleep—Eric with his new long rifle under the covers with him—except eight-year-old Cam. Thryza Carter, his mother's ward, was sitting on the edge of Cam's bunk. She saw him at the door but, drawing her quilted dressing gown slightly about her, continued to give Cam her sympathetic attention.

"Then is Betsey yelling like that just to make everybody sorry for her?" Cam was asking. "How much does it hurt, Tracy?"

"I can't say, dear. I've never had a baby."

"Why not? You're old enough. You're six years older than Betsey."

"Are you forgetting that I am not married?"

"Neither is Betsey."

"You don't know that. She may have had a secret marriage back in her mountains before she left."

There came another and more strident cry from the other barge.

"But does it really hurt more than anything else in the world? Geneva says it does."

"Geneva likes to talk. If it was as bad as that wouldn't you imagine mothers would stop having babies? But they keep right on—and are happy to—just as your mother has."

Duncan advanced into the light.

"Go back to sleep, Cam," he ordered. "And stop pestering Tracy." His smile warmed as he looked down at Tracy. "How unapt that we should all have taken to calling you Tracy. We should invariably say Thryza, very distinctly."

"Why, Papa?" demanded Cam. "Why is Thryza a better name than Tracy? It's harder to say."

Duncan looked away from Tracy's dark hair which now in the night flowed over her shoulders in a curling disorder denied it by day.

"Because Thryza has a special meaning. It means 'pleasure' —and that is what she has been to us ever since she came to live with us."

Tracy looked up at him, her gray eyes under their black brows wide and calm.

"Trite as it may sound, Duncan," she said, "I have to say the pleasure has been mine."

"What's trite mean, Papa?"

"It means it's long past time for you to go back to sleep. And you, too, Tracy."

Duncan went out to the circular brick fireplace on deck, threw more wood on the coals and, after a quick, almost surreptitious, glance around, sat on a stool and took from his pocket the small leatherbound daybook he had carried during the war. Fresh paper had been inserted to provide space for a journal of his new enterprise, but it seemed to him that this expedition to found a settlement in the western wilderness was, at least for him, but a continuation of that other conflict with the past. He turned to the first page and contemplated the familiar roster of the company of which he was as much the necessarily responsible commander as during those years with his regiment.

His mother, Louisa. His wife, Agatha. His children, Eric, Ken, Cam, Chris, and Susie. His brother, Garett. Garett's wife, Olivia. Tracy, almost the same as one of the family. The four Negroes, Ned, Clem, Hebe, and Geneva—all that remained of the hundred the Jordans once had owned. Frank Lyman and his sons, Mark and Luke. The Slover family. Ten adult men. Eleven with Eric, who at fifteen was so nearly a man. Eight women. Six children. And soon now this child of Betsey's. Another name to be added to the roster. The first, God willing, of many more.

He closed the book hastily as Garett came out and held wide the blanket draped about him to warm his gaunt nightshirted figure at the fire. Duncan looked at his brother inquiringly. Garett had been a semi-invalid since a musket ball had lodged in his spine at Yorktown in what had turned out to be literally the last half hour of the war. Garett shrugged and grinned.

"Don't always be eying me as though you doubted I'd see the next dawn. No worse night than usual. Though I have to admit that caterwauling next door is no sleeping potion. Pity the damsel couldn't have held off a few more hours. How much more appropriate had she managed to celebrate your first day on the soil of your new principality with so auspicious an offering. Never mind—she's young and may be at it awhile. The worthy Slovers may yet gain their footnote in history. What was the first white child born in Virginia—Virginia Dare, wasn't it? This Slover offspring can yet be the first on the baptismal records of Reveltown, or will it be Revelburgh?"

Duncan stirred uncomfortably. "Ours is a small company. We may well welcome every addition to it."

"How true. While I—own brother of the lord proprietor—remain childless. Yet I try, and try again. A process, I may say, with its own intrinsic rewards. Speaking of children, was there some to-do in your nursery just now? Seemed to me I heard Tracy's voice.

"Only Cam. She was asking questions."

"About the biological phenomenon in the next barge, no doubt. Remarkable child. What a thirst for knowledge."

Olivia, her pale young face flushed, came darting out.

"Garry," she cried. "Come back to bed this instant. Do you want to catch your death?"

"My ever faithful mate," said Garett. "Her anxieties for my welfare know no limit. Though I must confess it something of a boon to one in my enfeebled condition to have the capacities of a Casanova perpetually attributed to him by the one in the best position to judge."

The intensity of her fury sharpened Olivia's classic, cameo-like features into ugliness.

"You can be so utterly unspeakable."

Garett flung the blanket about his shoulders with a dignity that might have attended the arrangement of a toga.

"Very well, my sweet. Your banners wave triumphant, as always. I shall return to our coach. And no more this night will I prowl."

He went in. Olivia remained by the fire, breathing hard.

"He is a sick man," said Duncan.

"It's not for you to sort out the blame. You're not the little father of the whole world. I'm sorry, Duncan. Sick or well—I love him. You must realize that. How could I stand it another minute if I didn't?"

"And he loves you."

"I do believe he does. I have to."

Olivia drew another long breath and turned wearily toward the door through which Garett had gone. But when she reached it, she straightened and her step quickened. Duncan shoveled coals from the fire into a brazier and carried it into the children's cabin. Cam was rebelliously silent but she was holding her head off the pillow in her anxiety to listen. Tracy lay beside her.

"Simplest way to keep her quiet was to move in with her," said Tracy.

"A most unjust reward for the transgressor. Clap a sack over her head, if you have to, and get some sleep."

The other children, burrowed deep in their beds, had not awakened. When he came out Agatha was at the fire, staring resentfully toward the adjoining barge. Betsey's cries had become piercing.

"Can't you have their boat moved off a ways?" she demanded.

"As a special token of our neighborly sympathy?"

"Why pretend? Listen. Sounds like a cat in a sack. No doubt the girl's in pain but I don't like all this sluttish yowling right outside the children's window."

"When you came out with me this year instead of waiting

until next—as we at first planned—you must have guessed the many realities of the natural world to which they would be subjected. And what is more natural than childbirth? For my part I think the closer they get to natural living the better it will be for them, as it will for us."

"Whenever you start talking about this settlement of yours—of ours, I suppose I should say—you don't sound like you. You sound as though you were reading something out of a book."

"Then I will say no more." He slipped an arm around her. "Except this: Mrs. Jordan, would you now do me the great honor of going to bed with me?"

Her black eyes, often so brilliant and hard, softened. "With the greatest of pleasure, Mr. Jordan."

In the cabin doorway she lifted her head from his shoulder.

"My God," she whispered. "Here come all the Lymans."

She attempted to shut the door quickly but Duncan caught it, pulled away from her and returned to the fire. Frank Lyman clambered over the rail into the Jordan barge. Clutched in his arms were his blankets, his sack of personal effects, and his chest of carpenter's tools. One by one he dropped each of his several burdens to the deck at Duncan's feet. His purse-lipped scowl of indignation seemed as durable and established a part of him as his shock of bristling white hair, his square red face, his squat sturdy figure, his work-gnarled hands. His two sons, swinging over the rail after him, dropped their loads as deliberately. Mark was a head shorter, Luke a head taller, neither had white hair and their faces lacked as yet the granitic lines time had cross-hatched on their father's but their expressions of righteous disapproval quite matched his. They took their stand a half step behind him. All three eyed Duncan defiantly.

"Never," Frank pronounced, "never will we set foot in that boat again."

He stiffened, waiting for Duncan's remonstrance. Mark and Luke edged more nearly abreast of him.

"Can't say I blame you much," said Duncan. "If I'd realized how crowded we'd turn out to be I'd have hired a third boat in Pittsburgh."

"It's been a deal worse than crowded," said Frank. "It's been like bunking in a backhouse. So far we put up with spending the nights in a tangle o' niggers and water rats—and them boatmen o' yours is the dirtiest-mouthed critters I ever did have to listen to—but when the Slovers and all their dogs come crawling in on us just now——"

"Why don't you turn in here by the fire for the rest of the night? Tomorrow it'll all be over. We'll be getting off these boats."

The onward march of Frank's protest was thrown out of step by Duncan's studied failure to take offense. Mark assumed his father's pause was a signal to take his turn at pressing their grievances.

"They ain't got the first part of an idea who might have fathered that brat she's having. She herself no more than any the rest of them. From the way they all been talking among themselves—and trying to count up on their fingers—it could of been most anybody that wears pants that ever come within eight mile of their cabin."

Luke cleared his throat and spat in the fire. "That's only the outer peel off the onion. Their place was a stop-off for pack trains, so it could of been most any mule-skinning scalawag between Pittsburgh and Richmond ever to come through their valley. But if you was to ask me, I wouldn't doubt it could of been either o' them mush-headed brothers o' hers—or maybe that real no-count, her old man—the way they all hutch together at night like a litter of rabbits."

The unction with which his sons had voiced their views set Frank off again. "When you picked up them Slovers on our way over the mountains and brung them along with us it was plain they was real trash. Me and my boys—we seen that straight off. It was plain then and it's plainer now. They're lower than trash. They're out-and-out heathen. They can't read nor write. They can't get out three words without one of them being foul. Not one of them has ever once been to church. Why they ain't never in their lives even seen a church. They ain't no better than a pack of savages."

Duncan's tone remained carefully casual. "But don't you see, Frank, that is precisely why we need them. Olen Slover grew up on the frontier, as did his father and grandfather before him and his sons after him. They're genuine bush people. They're used to getting along in the woods—not only to hunting and trapping and tracking but to making do with whatever is at hand. And Olen left behind him five married sons who, if all goes well, may come out with their families next year. We need more people. Most of all, at first, this kind of people."

Frank snorted. "The only thing we need less than Slovers is more Slovers. I don't know how you feel about your family. But me, I know how I feel about mine. I brung up my two boys to fear the Lord and to never take His name in vain and to know right from wrong and to keep their backs turned to all evildoers"

"That will do, Frank. There are several subjects on which I do not need your advice. Now will you tell me what's behind all this claptrap about the Slovers? Why are you trying so hard to pick a quarrel with me? What's your real trouble?"

Frank placed his fists on his lips and began to teeter back and forth on heel and toe.

"We got more troubles than the Slovers—that's a fact. I'll tell you what's one big one. I don't like where we're going. This Revel Creek ain't a good location."

"What's wrong with it?"

"To begin with, it's too far off by itself. It's as far as you can get from the last Virginia settlements one way and the first Kentucky settlements the other."

"You knew that before you left tidewater."

"Back there I had no more idea what this country out here was going to be like than that brat o' Betsey's has about the world he's coming into. But along the way I been talking to folks—back at Wheeling and Pittsburgh—folks that know this country. Worse than being too far off by itself, your place is on the Indian bank of the Ohio."

"Where then would you prefer to go? Have you made up your mind to that, too?"

"I have. On to Kentucky where there's more people. There ain't near enough of us by ourselves to stand off the Indians was they to come at us."

Duncan clasped his hands behind him, wheeled to frown out over the moonlit river, and then wheeled back to face the Lymans.

"I could try to remind you of any number of things, Frank. That the war with England is over. That the Indians have realized there's nothing for them to do but make peace, too. That yesterday you saw with your own eyes General Washington himself surveying his land on the Kanawha no more than a day's run from our site. That if anyone knows what he's about he certainly does. That I must be sure of what I'm doing or I would not have brought my mother, my wife, and my young children out with me. But what's the use of trying to reason with you? We've been over all this before. I invited you to come out with us because I thought that since you and your sons were Continental veterans and respected citizens in your community you could take a leading part in our new one. But let's forget all that, along with the bargain we struck back in Virginia. Tomorrow we'll get to Revel Creek. As soon as we're unloaded, Bill Granger is taking his barges on downriver to winter in Louisville. I'll outfit you and you can go on to Kentucky with the barges."

"But we come out with you. We'd of stayed home if it hadn't looked like a good idea to throw in with you."

"You were either wrong then or you're wrong now. Take your pick. Anyway, I'm staying at Revel Creek."

Frank scowled at his sons as though it had been their fault that the argument had come to so unsatisfactory a culmination. They looked away. He grunted sulkily.

"You don't leave us no out. I ain't never yet gone back on a bargain. We'll have to stay, too."

"Good. Now try to get some sleep."

In the cabin Duncan wearily dropped the greatcoat, kicked off his slippers, and slid into bed.

"You handled him just right," whispered Agatha. "Still it makes me sick that you should have to spend half the night blathering with a clown like Frank Lyman. With the river so close, I kept expecting you to tell him to jump into it."

"A pleasure I could not afford. He's a carpenter. One of his boys is a mason and the other a smith. We need him."

"We don't need to cater to him as though he were governor of Virginia."

"Have you forgotten the war?"

"What about the war?"

"That we fought so that we could call men free and equal. You may not have noticed much difference in the East but in this country out here every man is fully convinced he is as good as any other."

"I can stomach Frank Lyman—just. But are you trying to say that out here there's nothing to choose between us and people like the Slovers?"

"The time can come when you'll be glad they're one of us." His lips were touching her cheek so that she could tell that he was smiling. "Maybe we should have stayed peacefully in Virginia and reconciled ourselves to staying poor."

So often they were well into a discussion before she discovered he had not been arguing with entire seriousness. The discovery was always disconcerting but she was never able to help herself. There were too many subjects which she could not even pretend to take lightly.

"No," she said. "I'd have been happy to—for us. But not for the children. There's their future to think of. They just mustn't stay poor."

"How about me? I may be getting on in years, but don't you think I've still some future?"

She laughed softly and pressed more closely into his arms. "Nobody has to think about you. You're quite able to help yourself." She drew back from his kiss and lifted her head to listen. "She's stopped screaming. Do you think it's over?"

Betsey could feel herself floating upward out of the depths. She was not climbing. It was a kind of slow swinging, like the pendulum of the Jordans' clock. The pain was gone. All was as dark as the pit into which she had slipped. She thought to lift her hand to her dry mouth. The hand did not move. She wondered if she were dead. The possibility seemed more restful than alarming. She opened her eyes. The candle had burned down to a stump. The cows were on their feet. Lina was bending over. Then she saw her mother sitting on a box. On her lap was a bundle wrapped in sacking.

"Maw," she whispered.

Her mother raised her head. She did not look excited. She just looked old and tired.

"Yuh got yerself a boy," she said. "A boy most as big as you be."

"Give him to me," said Betsey.

"You jest lay still. You've had yerself a bad time. Quick but real bad."

"Give him to me."

Betsey struggled to lift herself but still could not move. Lina pulled back a corner of the blanket and Polly laid the bundle beside her. Now she could move her hands. She plucked at the sacking. The small naked body rolled against hers.

"He's cold," she gasped.

"We're all cold," said Polly. "It's a right cold night."

Betsey could feel herself slipping back into the darkness. She was terrified. Not for herself. She no longer mattered. But for the child who needed her, who had only her. She fought to stay with him, to watch over him, to save him.

Again she was swinging slowly upward. This time the glare hurt her eyes even before she had opened them. It was broad daylight. A steady burning pain enveloped her loins. The shed was empty except for the cows. She could hear the splash of oars. The barge was moving. On deck people were shouting back and forth. All the other blankets had been heaped over her. She was warm. And he was warm. She peered under the blankets. His eyes were tightly closed but his lips were moist and quivering. One of his two tiny fists opened and clenched again. He struck out jerkily with one leg. She pressed her cheek to the soft damp top of his head. She could feel the pulse beating in it. He was alive and strong. The tide of happiness pouring into her had all the sweep of the great river. All that she had suffered through the time before he had been conceived—and since—was as nothing compared to this reward.

"Maw," she cried.

No one answered. No one came. Outside people were still shouting. She could hear her father swearing as jubilantly as the time he had run down and axed the wounded Indian. It was odd that they should find so much of interest out there when the center of so much greater interest was in here.

"Maw," she called.

Lina appeared in the doorway for a moment.

"We're a-gittin' in," she announced. "We's most there."

Until now Betsey had felt little concern about where they were going or when they might arrive. The place had no importance. No more than had had the home back in the Virginia mountains that they had left. But now this new place took on suddenly a very great importance. It was about to become his home.

"Lina," she called. "Lina."

Lina was good-natured. She might come. Finally she did.

"Help me up," commanded Betsey. "I have to see."

Pain tore at her with claws of fire. Clutching the child against her, with Lina's help she struggled to the doorway and looked out. A long murmuring grunt of appreciation escaped her. The hard frost in the night had contrived a change in the world without to match the change in her inner world. The immense and interminable forest had been transfigured, its dun grays and faded greens turned into a blaze of color—to scarlet and gold, to coral and topaz and amethyst, to orange and saffron and lemon, to unnamed and unnamable shades and hues and tints. Small white clouds scudded across a bright blue sky, arching over the wide river, which sparkled in the sun with reflected flashes of the sky's blue and white as it flowed on around islands which were like heaps of jewels and between banks that were like walls of gigantic flowers.

Ahead, the Jordan barge was turning toward a stretch of the shore on which the forest seemed even more brilliantly aflame than elsewhere. It rounded a point on which stood a single shimmering sycamore and nosed on into the estuary of a small side stream. The second barge followed. Suddenly Olen dropped his oar and came loping into the shed.

"Whereat's my rifle?" he yelled. When he was truly wrought-up the ordinarily almost limitless range of his profanity tended to become curiously diminished. "I'll be a corn-holed muskrat if'n there ain't four buffler knee-deep in thet there crik right there by the first bend."

Duncan, standing in the prow, seized Garett's arm and pointed.

"Look. There's the rock on the bank he told about."

"A most convenient site to disembark," said Garett. "Our own Plymouth Rock, as it were."

Duncan jerked away from him and leaped from the rail to the long flat rock. Behind the rock rose a low mound sparsely covered with pine and oak, and beyond the mound stretched a patch of meadow beside which an old beaver dam had widened the stream into a pool. The three Slover men plunged past him and on to the meadow. In the anxiety of each to get in the first shot all began firing without pausing to aim. The dogs at their heels began to bark. The buffalo ran into the woods across the stream. The Slovers and their dogs ran on after them. Duncan scrambled to the top of the mound and looked about him. The scene was as familiar to him as the words on the yellowed pages of Corbit Revel's twenty-year-old letter.

"Exactly as he described it," he declared. "Even to the flat rock where boats can unload. Some of these trees are bigger than he said but once we cut them the mound will make a perfect building site—just as he said it would."

He turned to see that it was Tracy, first of the others to follow him up the slope, who stood beside him. Crisply curling tendrils of her black hair danced in the breeze, there was a faint flush under the usually smooth ivory of her skin, in her gray eyes were little flecks of lights which must have been gathered in from as far away as the sunlit ripples on the stream. She was poised on tiptoe to see more widely, her tense young body vibrant with the instinct to run to meet a new experience. The pulse of vitality in her made her presence seem to him a happy complement to his own excitement. She took one swift glance around at the stream, the pool, the meadow, the circumference of iridescent forest, and looked back up at him.

"How wonderful that you should see it first in all this color," she said, "as though it had adorned itself for you."

"For all of us," he said quickly. "We're all in this together. We must never forget that." He raised his voice. "Eric, bring me my map case." He grasped her arm and pointed. "I drew a map, based on Corbit's description. There should be a falls less than a mile upstream. I must see first off if I'm right. If so, I shall make a measured line from here to there the base line for my survey."

"I'll get the case," she said. "Eric couldn't wait to try his new rifle. He ran off after the Slovers."

Ken ran lightly across the meadow and into the woods. Almost at once he all but bumped into Eric. He had not intended to follow so closely since there was considerable question about Eric's accepting his company. Ordinarily he did not admit that the five years' difference in their ages endowed Eric with absolute authority but this was a special occasion. Possession of the new rifle clearly placed him for the moment beyond challenge.

"Don't make so much noise," said Eric. "Wild animals have ears same as we have—better ears."

Relieved that he was not sent back, Ken began to tiptoe. Eric resumed his slow forward progress, glancing down repeatedly at the priming of his rifle before again peering ahead.

"The Slovers waded across the creek back there," Ken whispered.

"That's the reason I didn't," said Eric. "No use looking for game in country that four buffalo, three hunters, and a pack of dogs just ran through. Now stop talking. Only reason I'm letting you come along is I maybe can use your help packing in what I shoot. But I'll never see anything to shoot if you keep gabbling all the time. So either stay quiet or go back right now."

"I'll stay quiet," Ken promised.

"And don't keep so close. I don't want you joggling my arm when I have to take aim."

They left the more open forest, where often there had been wide vistas through the serried ranks of trees which spread their canopies of foliage high overhead, and pushed on into an area where there was more undergrowth. Eric paused at each bush and peeked carefully around it before advancing again.

"Is your gun loaded?" asked Ken.

" 'Course it's loaded. And double-charged besides. 'Case we run across a bear."

Ken plucked at Eric's sleeve and pointed. Off to the right and beyond a fringe of shrubbery was a little forest glade. In the glade a young doe was grazing. She lifted her head and cocked her big ears forward. Eric's hands froze to his rifle while the rest of his body began to shake. The doe whirled and rose into the air in a long soaring bound. When her hooves touched the ground she soared again as though on wings, and, descending, dropped from view behind a laurel thicket.

Eric jerked up his rifle in the general direction of the thicket and pulled the trigger. He had failed to wait until the gun butt was well settled against his shoulder and the kick of the double charge spun him so far off balance that he lost his hat and dropped the rifle. He clutched at them and glared at Ken.

"I told you not to joggle my arm."

Beyond the laurel thicket there was a sudden spasmodic rustling and threshing. Eric all but dropped his rifle again. His transport of chagrin became a transport of triumph.

"I hit her," he cried. "I hit her."

The boys ran around the laurel. The doe was trying to pull herself along by her forelegs. Her hind quarters were dragging on the ground. Her mouth was agape, her tonge hanging out, her eyes distended.

"I broke her back," exulted Eric.

Ken came to an abrupt stop and then edged slowly nearer, his face paling as he stared.

"Look," he said. "Look at her eyes. She hurts—she's afraid —and she doesn't want to die."

"But that's what's coming to her," said Eric. "Right now."

He held the muzzle of his rifle back of the doe's ear and pulled the trigger. The lock clicked drily. He had neglected to reload. Horrified that he had committed the novice's most elementary crime he began frantically to do so. Ken was taking no notice of his brother's ignominy. All his attention was concentrated on the animal's torment.

"Don't get so close," panted Eric. "Haven't you ever heard a wounded deer is dangerous? They got hooves sharper than knives. They can cut you to pieces."

Again he lifted the rifle. This time the piece fired. The doe's forequarters collapsed, she beat her head several times against the ground, and lay still. Her eyes were still open. One of them, filled with sand, continued for a moment to twitch. Ken backed away. A sob burst from him. He turned and ran back toward the boats. Eric drew his hunting knife, knelt, and began sawing exultantly at the doe's throat.

Betsey awoke again. The child's body clasped against hers was hot and wet with sweat. She raised herself in the straw and threw off some of the blankets. There was much trampling and thumping in the other barge. But there were no nearer sounds and she was alone in the shed. Even the cows were gone. She was content to be alone. She opened her dress and pressed the child's mouth to her breast. His lips were moist and warm but he made no effort to suckle. She pinched the nipple to make it stand out. He still showed no interest. It could be too soon for him to be ready. She gave up the attempt. The effort of throwing off the blankets and lifting him up had inflamed the pains. As they slowly subsided she drowsed again.

When once more she roused, the sun was at the cracks in the other side of the shed. One bar of light fell across the child's face. It was thin and wrinkled and had a bluish cast. He was no longer sweating. He was dry and hot. His breathing was fast and had a strange rasping sound.

"Maw," she cried. "Maw."

No one answered. Hugging the child to her, she crawled to the doorway. No one was near except the boatmen. They were in the other barge which was tied up to the flat rock, heaving boxes and barrels out on the bank. They were scowling and swearing as though in a temper about something. There were many people up on top of the mound. She could see all three Jordan women. But her mother was nowhere in sight. Then she saw Lina. Lina was kneeling on the bank downstream a little way, washing her hair. She was forever washing some part or other of herself. She took a queer pleasure in it.

"Lina," called Betsey.

Lina came slowly along the bank, wringing out her hair which was so light in color that it looked almost white, even when wet, and made her big brown eyes look almost black. When she swung her bare legs over the rail the boatmen turned to look. Lina paid no attention. She paid so little attention to anything that she seldom seemed more than half awake.

"Where's Maw?" demanded Betsey.

Lina was staring at the baby. "Whut ails him?"

"Could be"—Betsey had difficulty getting out the words—"could be he's sick."

"He don't look right, fer a fact."

"Go git Maw."

"Maw's over by the pond fishin'."

"Go git her."

"She won't come. Not right straight off, fer sure. Yuh know whut Maw's like when she gits to fishin'. Well, she's never run acrost fishin' like this before. She's got more trout piled around her in the grass than yuh could git in four bushel baskets. She's a-whoopin' and hollerin' like a wild woman."

"Go git her."

Lina set out. Betsey hitched nearer the rail so that she could watch to make sure she kept on. The boatmen again straightened to stare as Lina clambered over the heaps of cargo strewn along the bank. The inert weight in Betsey's arms suddenly became rigid. She pulled the child's face back from her shoulders. The mouth was stretched in a wide, hideous grin. He began to twitch and jerk. The tremors became more rapid, more violent. A froth gathered about the unnatural grin. She gripped him against her, struggling to restrain the spasms, and rocked back and forth, moaning.

"Have you seen my father anywhere around?"

Eric was leaning over the rail almost at her shoulder but his voice seemed to come from an immense distance.

"What's the matter with your baby? What makes him act that way?"

Belatedly the meaning of the first inquiry penetrated the darkness of Betsey's terror. Eric's father was one set apart. He was the company's acknowledged head. Whatever the difficulty, everybody else always looked to him for the answer. If anyone could help her, he could.

"Go find him," she cried. "Find him quick. Tell him my baby's sick."

The convulsion passed. The little body was limp again. He still breathed for there were bubbles in the wisps of froth clinging to his lips. She could see Eric running up the slope to the top of the mound. Now he was talking to his mother. There were many other people up there. But no one came back down the slope.

"I shot a deer."

Eric had wanted news of such consequence to be reported first to his father. But he could no longer hold it back.

"How wonderful," said Agatha. "And so soon, too. Where is it?"

"It was too heavy for me to carry by myself after Ken ran off. And . . ."

Bill Granger came puffing up the slope. After an impatient glance around, he singled out Agatha as the most likely among those present to represent authority.

"My boys need help, ma'am, gittin' them boats unloaded."

"Colonel Jordan is surveying," said Agatha. "The moment he returns, I'll tell him to see you."

The bargeman stood his ground. "The deal, ma'am, was thet the boats was to be unloaded right off so's we could git us on downriver with 'em. And if you folks had good sense you'd not want to see yer stuff just dumped off on the bank.

You'd want it piled and covered with tarps—case it rained."

"Mr. Lyman," Agatha began, "would you mind . . ."

Frank was standing by waiting to speak up.

"We're helpin' your niggers set up your tent, like you asked us to. And long's there's so much work to do, what about them Slovers that's off hunting?"

Agatha saw complexities looming with which she had no wish to grapple. "Where's Garett?" she asked Olivia.

Olivia, too, was waiting.

"He's asleep down there back of that big pine. He had no sleep last night and I don't feel he should be disturbed."

Louisa rose from her camp chair and leaned on her stick.

"Ned, Clem. You go with Mr. Granger and do whatever he tells you to." She bestowed upon Frank a gracious smile. "Meanwhile, Mr. Lyman, will you not as a personal favor to me finish setting up the tent without their assistance?"

"Yes, ma'am," said Frank grudgingly. "You put it that way and there ain't nothing else I can do."

Tracy released her fingers from the grip of Ken's and rounded the corner of the half-erected tent. She had not needed to watch Eric's face to realize how much he had been cast down by the failure of his triumph to attract more attention.

"Come on," she whispered. "I'll help you bring it in."

"You will?"

He brightened with incredulous delight. A chance to impress Tracy was for him only second to an opportunity to impress his father. They hurried down the slope and across the meadow.

"It's not far," said Eric. "I'd have got it in easy if that crybaby Ken had stayed to help me."

"He's not a crybaby. He just happens to be fond of animals. Don't you remember how sad he was when your father wouldn't let him bring his dog along?"

"Yes, I remember. He cried then, too. But Father was right. The wagons were so overloaded we all had to leave stuff behind. And that dog of his was really no good. He couldn't hunt. And he was most too old and fat even to walk."

"But Ken didn't cry that day at Redstone the oar mashed his finger."

"No, he didn't," admitted Eric judicially. "Ken's all right, in lots of ways." He looked thoughtfully at Tracy. "You're always standing up for one or the other of us."

"Of course. You'd all stand up for me, wouldn't you?"

"Forever and ever." Eric reddened at the boldness of his declaration and hastily changed the subject. "The deer's right over there. I've already tied the feet together and cut a pole so we can carry it in on our shoulders."

"Hunter-style," agreed Tracy.

"Yes," said Eric, his enthusiasm restored. "And maybe Father'll be back to see us come in."

Betsey still rocked back and forth. She had shaded the child's face from the sun with a corner of the sacking and was afraid to lift it to look again. She saw Cam running down the slope, her pigtails flying. Cam climbed the rail and paused only to get her breath.

"Is he worse?" she inquired.

"Go 'way," said Betsey.

"I know something's the matter with him. I was there when Lina came to tell your mother he was sick."

Betsey stiffly turned her head to see if her mother was coming.

"Your mother said she'd be along in a minute. But then she got a big fish on her line and waded right into the pond after it." Cam paused only to catch her breath again. "Then Lina saw the sun shining on Aunt Olivia's mirror hanging on a tree and went up to look in it. And your mother went on fishing. So then I went up and told my mother about you. And she told Geneva to come down and see what's wrong with your baby. Here she comes now."

Betsey's eyes narrowed as she watched the portly old Negro woman waddling deliberately along the bank. She felt a mountaineers' scorn for all Negroes. It was a prejudice returned in kind. Geneva heaved herself over the rail and squatted beside mother and child.

"Les' have us a look at him," she said, trying to speak kindly.

"No," said Betsey.

Geneva pulled Betsey's hands away, turned back the sacking and pressed a black forefinger against the child's throat.

"The Lawd be my shephud," said Geneva. "He's daid."

"No," cried Betsey.

"When they starts out thet pewky-like," said Geneva, still trying to be kind, "it's best fer 'em when they goes quick, 'stead o' hangin' on and sufferin'. Now jus' yuh let me have him and I'll wash him up and lay him out fer yuh."

"No," screamed Betsey. "No. No. No."

November

It was another mild sunny day with the smoky haze of Indian summer softening the sheen on the river and wreathing the wooded folds of the hills beyond. The first brilliance of the forest's October color had passed, but most trees were still clothed in their fading leaves. In this pleasant pause in the onward roll of the seasons the wilderness, usually so harsh with its creatures, was lavishing upon them instead a feast of fruitfulness. Walnuts, hazelnuts, chestnuts, pecans lay on the ground in windrows. Pawpaws, buffalo berries, red currants still clung to their brittle stems. There was no plant too lowly to flaunt a sliver of sun-cured stalk or wisp of ripened seeds. Thrifty squirrels and mice scurried about laying away their winter stores. Geese and swan and innumerable lesser waterfowl, winging down from the North, lingered to feed along stream and river. Turkeys became too fat to fly. Bear gorged on the dried, sugary clusters of wild grapes. Buck deer, shedding the last velvet from their new-grown antlers, leaped with the vigor of long weeks of plenty into the frays accompanying their amours. The does they sought, beginning to shun their no longer spotted fawns, were sleek and smooth and rounded. Even the wolves ceased their hungry howling in the night.

The morning air was sweet and clean and bracing whenever a stir of wind off the river carried away the odor of spoiling meat and fish from the Slover drying racks in the meadow. In their first excitement over the prevalence of game the Slovers had taken far more than could be eaten and thereafter had neglected their initially earnest project of smoking the surplus for winter use. They had presently tired of the easy hunting but the Lymans had kept on with the enthusiasm of neophytes, crashing about in the woods from dawn to dusk. Only after dwelling on the need for days had Duncan succeeded in getting work started on the erection of log cabins to replace their temporary shelters. The Jordans still occupied tents on the flat top of the mound, except for Garett whose tent, at Olivia's insistence, had been set up out on the point where his rest, either by day or night, might be less disturbed. The Lymans had shifted bales and barrels to make room for a sleeping alcove in the tarpaulin-covered heap of cargo still on the stream bank. The Slovers had thrown together a brush and pole lean-to over the opening into the cavelike hollow in the base of the huge old sycamore at the foot of the mound on the side toward the meadow, a site which on the one hand spared them the too-frequent effort of climbing the slope and on the other relieved them from some of their neighbors' critical comment on their housekeeping.

This day began as usual with Duncan's assembling everybody for what he took care to call a "town meeting." He struggled to maintain the illusion that all had an equal responsibility for arriving at decisions just as he insisted upon terming the half-constructed pair of log cabins crowning the mound "the station."

"We are all in this together," said Duncan, using the phrase with which he faced his every attempt to reason with them. "And I'm sure that by now we're all agreed that this is a satisfactory location—better even than we had hoped—in fact, a nearly ideal site. We must all realize how really fortunate we are in gaining possession of it ahead of the great rush of land-hunters bound to flock West next year. However, this but gives us the more reason to keep in mind that if we're to have roofs over our heads before winter sets in we'll need to get on faster with the job than we've been doing. So let's examine the way we've been going at it to see if perhaps our plan can be improved upon. We started in with the thought, Olen, that you and your sons would take care of felling the trees and cutting the timbers we need. That is, that two of you would take turns at that every day while the other one hunted, since we still need fresh meat. My Negroes, Clem and Ned, are standing by to drag the logs up here. That's the hardest work but they're glad to do it. You, Frank, with the help of your sons, have undertaken to do the actual building. I, for my part, am helping wherever I can be most useful—at least part of every day, for we're also agreed, I believe, that it's important for me to finish the survey so as to determine the borders of our grant. This has been our plan, but at the rate we've been going so far, we'll never have homes by Christmas. Have any of you any suggestions that might help? You, Frank?"

"Nothing wrong with the plan." Frank looked sourly across the circle at the group of Slovers. "We'll build just as fast as the stuff's brought up to us."

"And you, Olen?"

Olen's mouth widened into his habitual amiable and placating grin which was so little in keeping with the gaunt, hawk-nosed ferocity of his countenance. His answer came in a high whining voice that was even less in keeping.

"Yuh bin mighty white with us, Kunnel. We ain't fergittin' thet."

"Thank you, Olen. But what I mean is—does the work plan suit you?"

"Whutever yuh say, Kunnel—thet's good enough fer us."

Olen rolled his eyes at Agatha, pleased that he had made two complete statements untainted by any of the profanity to which she so much objected.

"Good," said Duncan. "Now then, let's see the chips fly."

The Slovers set off for the woods at an unprecedented dog-trot. Nevertheless, when Duncan came back to the station toward noon, Frank was reclining against the half-built wall of the main cabin ostentatiously taking his ease. Mark, equally idle, was seated on a stump part-way down the slope toward the array of drying racks around the Slover sycamore. Ned and Clem were lying on their backs taking turns gnawing at a cold haunch of venison. As Duncan approached, Frank rose, portentously crooked one stubby forefinger, and set off down the slope toward the woods. Duncan, wearily guessing what to expect, followed.

"You come along, Mark," said Frank. "Where's Luke?"

"He went off down toward the woods a while back," said Mark, jumping up to accompany them.

Frank kept to the track left by the Negroes' timber dragging, on into the woods toward a stand of straight young pine flanked by a clump of cedar and another of walnut, which had been selected as the most suitable nearby source of building material. Ahead there was no ring of axe or whine of saw. Frank came to a stop, stood aside so that Duncan could see past him, and with smug satisfaction watched Duncan's face.

Jacob was stretched out beside his axe, sound asleep. It was a Slover byword that there was no limit to Jacob's need for sleep. He had been known to sleep standing up in the rain or on his knees in a canoe, but it was accepted that he much preferred his present position—flat on his back in the sun with his arms flung wide. A little beyond him Jarot sat on the ground with his back against the trunk of a pine he had felled but not yet trimmed. Duncan glanced with passing interest at the curious musical instrument in his lap over which he was bent. He had heard Slover references to "Jat's mandiddle" but had never before caught a clear glimpse of the object. Jarot had contrived it by fastening together with bits of rawhide the sound box of an old violin, the neck of a cast-off mandolin, and a homemade bone bridge for the six strings of a guitar. His fingers were plucking the strings so gently that only a whisper of sound came forth and that little without recognizable key or rhythm. All the same he was sweating with the intensity of his concentration. From time to time he took a deep breath and his lips writhed as though he were resolved also to sing, but if so his ballad was entirely inaudible.

Duncan kicked the moccasined soles of Jacob's feet until Jacob stirred and disconsolately opened his eyes. When he saw who had awakened him he pushed himself painfully upward, accompanying the effort with alternate apologetic grins and patient groans, first to his knees and then to his feet, picked up his axe, and began sadly to swing it. Duncan called to Jarot but Jarot remained deaf. He was more lost to the world than had been Jacob in the depths of his slumber.

"Yippee," yelled Jacob piercingly, and followed the cry with a drawn-out imitation of an Indian war whoop.

Jarot slowly and vacantly looked up. His eyes met Duncan's but there was a distinct interval before any light of recognition dawned in them. His gradual recovery from the trance into which he had fallen was like a return to this earth from the distance of another planet. Finally he began sheepishly to blink, laid aside his mandiddle, snatched up his axe, and resumed trimming the pine. He was not afflicted with Jacob's congenital laziness. When he did work, he flew at it with furious energy.

Agatha started from her chair and looked again. Cam was inching along on knees and elbows between the drying racks until she had reached a vantage point where she could peer through a crack in the hollow sycamore into the interior of the Slover domestic establishment. Agatha's lips tightened upon sighting this most flagrant exhibition yet of Cam's perpetual curiosity. With swift silent steps she ran down the slope, caught the culprit redhanded, and snatched her away. Out of earshot up the slope she halted to indict her prisoner.

"Aren't you ashamed? The very idea—creeping up to peek into people's houses—and right in broad daylight, too."

"That's not a house. It's a hollow tree. And I only wanted to see what they were doing in it."

"Why should you need to know what they were doing?"

"Well, I saw Lina go in there and so when after a little while I saw Luke sneak in, too, I——"

"Oh," gasped Agatha. She repressed her indignation in order first to satisfy a mother's need to ascertain precisely how critical had been an eight-year-old daughter's exposure to worldly experience. "And what do you think they were doing?"

"I know what they were doing. I could see. He was trying to get his hand down into her dress or up under it."

"Which do you mean?"

"I mean both. When he reached in at the top she just laughed, but when he reached underneath she slapped him."

"Is that all you saw?"

"Yes. Because it was just then that you came and jerked me away."

Agatha concealed her relief. "You've been a bad, bad girl. Now go straight to bed and stay there until I tell you you can get up."

Cam ran to the children's tent, her eyes filling with tears of vexation at the injustice of her punishment. Ken and Chris came running from the other way to meet Agatha at the top of the slope.

"What's Cam done, Mother? What's Cam done now?"

"You two go down and play by the pond and stay there till I call you. And take Susie with you. Don't let her get in the water. Clem. Ned. If you must gnaw on that bone take it somewhere else. Geneva. You and Hebe have been wanting to look for chestnuts. Go look for some."

Agatha's pent-up indignation found release when she turned to face Duncan striding up from the wood lot.

"Something's happened, Duncan, that you'll just have to do something about. You must see that a stop is put to it immediately. I just caught Cam watching Luke Lyman carrying on with Lina down there in that Slover hovel——"

"Which am I to do something about, Cam's spying or Luke's courting?"

"It's no laughing matter. It seems to keep slipping your mind that we have young children. And that even out here in these miserable woods there are certain elementary decencies that must be remembered."

"You may have hit upon something of a social problem,

but wouldn't it seem one better dealt with by the two families involved? Luke is a grown man—not to speak of his sanctimonious father—and the Slover girl has parents. In what way is it our affair?"

Frank, followed by Mark, was coming up the slope from the wood lot.

"Then I'll speak to Frank Lyman myself," said Agatha.

"I'd prefer you did not."

Louisa straightened in her chair under the oak which had been left to shade the area between the two cabins-to-be.

"Duncan is right, Agatha," she said. "He has to keep hounding these poor clods to get any work at all out of them and it would be too bad to confuse them by his being obliged to lecture them on their morals as well. But you, too, are right, Agatha. Something must be done about it." She looked toward the approaching Frank with a smile of welcome that at once made him suspicious. "Mr. Lyman."

"Yes, ma'am," said Frank, advancing uneasily.

"Would it surprise you, Mr. Lyman, to know your son Lucas is at the moment engaged in the seduction of the younger Slover girl?"

Frank did not flinch. "It would not surprise me, ma'am. 'Cause I'd know it ain't so. Luke's been raised to stand off from dirt. He's a good clean boy, Luke is. And he's given his promise to a fine honest young woman back in Virginia, as you'll see for yourself, ma'am, when she comes out to marry him next year. And if this ain't enough to satisfy you then I'd have you remember that none of us Lymans would go nearer one of them mangy Slovers than we could reach with a ten-foot pole."

"Your fatherly trust becomes you," said Louisa. "But I gather your other son is not so certain."

Frank looked at Mark. Mark's consternation was at a peak only to be scaled by a righteous young man suddenly confronted by the full-panoplied horror of public exposure.

"You may recall, Mr. Lyman," continued Louisa inexorably, "that I suggested the enterprise was under way at this moment. To be precise, in that big hollow tree right down there."

Frank cast one agonized glance at the sycamore, succumbed to doubt, and began to run down the slope. Olivia moved forward into the circle of spectators.

"Good Lord," she murmured, "let's hope Cam was telling the truth."

"The child may have certain faults," said Louisa, "but idle gossip is not one of them."

Frank circled the drying racks, lowered his head, and charged into the brush-and-pole lean-to. An instant later there burst from the hollow tree a muffled roar of rage. He reappeared, dragging Luke by the hair which he wore clubbed at the back of his neck. Luke wrenched free, saw his retreat toward the meadow cut off, and began to run up the slope. Looking apprehensively over his shoulder to gauge his father's pursuit he did not realize until he had reached the top that he was to be here confronted by the phalanx of Jordans. He turned toward the wood lot trail, bumped into Mark, and came to a full stop. His father seized him again. Luke shook him off. His panic passed and he was possessed by a rage of his own.

"You'd never of popped in on me like you did if that driveling sneak Mark had stood watch for me like he agreed to, like I always did for him when he took his turn."

"You swivel-tongued, tittle-tattling bastard," yelled Mark.

"Mark," howled Frank. "Mark Amos Lyman." His culminating sense of outrage at the revelation his older son, too, was guilty, held him at a loss for words but not for long. "You that left a wife and two little children at home. You that's head of a family. You that's got your own name on a pew. You . . ."

But neither of his sons was listening. They had begun to fight, flailing at one another awkwardly with their fists. Duncan and Frank separated them.

"Get out o' my sight, the both o' you," roared Frank. "You're too old for me to whop. And too low for me to look at. Get out o' my sight."

Mark and Luke shambled down toward their nook in the cargo pile. Frank looked bleakly at Duncan and then at Louisa and then again at Duncan.

"You've proved me a fool," he said. "But you'd best go to thinking on what I've said right along about your taking up with riffraff. I said right from the start we'd all rue the day. But I was weak and give in to you and your smooth talk. So now retribution has come to me. As it will come also to you. As sure as God punishes sin."

He stalked off after his sons.

"I hate to echo anything Frank Lyman says," said Agatha. "But I have to, Duncan, in this instance."

"What precisely would you have me do?"

"I'd have you call in Olen and Polly and talk to them like a Dutch uncle. Tell them that so long as we all have to live together there are certain civilized rules they will have to abide by. Either that or they will have to move out. And don't smile while you're saying it."

"I'm no more amused by a whiff of the gutter," said Duncan, "than you are. But the particular situation has apparently corrected itself."

"We're going to be cooped up with them all winter," protested Agatha. "We don't intend to behave like animals, and we can't sit watching them behave that way."

She broke off as Tracy came out. Tracy looked soberly at Duncan and Agatha.

"I've been talking to Cam," she said. "She has more to tell. She's already so excited I'm wondering about making more of it. Yet it's a story which you should hear. Shall I repeat it?"

"By all means," said Duncan.

"According to Cam this incident today was only the last of a number of other meetings between Lina and either Mark or Luke. The first one Cam knows about took place the day after Betsey got up after her illness. She noticed Betsey whispering to Mark just before starting off into the woods with Lina, presumably to gather firewood, and then heard Mark tell his father he'd left his hatchet somewhere and would have to go look for it. The next day it was Luke, and from then on both went. It was always a different direction and always until today into the woods where Cam could not follow—you having forbidden her ever to wander out of sight of camp."

"Cam's hit it," exclaimed Olivia. "That Betsey. She's determined to make all the trouble she can. She's had this terrible grudge against everybody ever since her baby died."

"At any rate," finished Tracy, "Cam thinks Betsey is always present—just as she certainly was today in the hollow tree."

"How truly deplorable," observed Louisa, with a certain relish. "Supervising the corruption of her little sister. Really—such people."

"As so often before," said Duncan, taking his wife's hand, "you have me on my knees. Anybody seen anything of Olen and Polly recently?"

"Cam will know," suggested Louisa.

Tracy came back from Cam's bedside to report that Polly had been fishing above the pond, that about an hour ago Olen had appeared at the edge of the woods across the stream, had beckoned to her, and that she then had gone into the woods with him.

"First time I've ever heard of his taking any notice of her," said Olivia, "except when he gets drunk and beats her."

"A possible ray of light on the general enigma of Olen," said Duncan, "might be that only when drunk does he feel himself anything like the man he looks."

"Don't put it off another minute," urged Agatha. "Send Eric to find them. He's always looking for an excuse to track anything or anybody."

"Eric went hunting right after breakfast," said Tracy. "He said something about knowing where a bull elk had been bedding down nights."

"In any event we know how to find Eric." Duncan went into his tent and came out with a campaign relic, a Hessian silver trumpet. "He's agreed never to wander alone beyond the sound of this."

Duncan blew three sharp blasts. Scarcely had the notes ceased to echo when, to his slightly surprised satisfaction, there came an answering whistle from Eric. Three minutes later Eric burst from the edge of the woods across the stream, ran across the pine that had been felled to form a foot bridge just below the old beaver dam, and came panting up the slope.

"What do you think, Father," he gasped, more breathless from excitement than from running. "I met the most extraordinary man in the woods this morning. I was stalking an elk and I didn't even know he was there—I mean the man—until he was right at my elbow. His name is Caleb Lewis. Wait until you see him. We talk about woodsmen, but he's the real article. Alongside of him these Slovers look like farmers. He's camping right there in the woods just across the creek."

"Extremely interesting, Eric," said Duncan, "but——"

Eric rushed on. "Come and meet him, Father. You've never in your life seen anybody like him. He handles a rifle as if it were a part of him—his hand or his arm—not something you pick up and set down again. He doesn't keep looking all the time to see what might be around him in the woods. He doesn't have to look to know what's there, all the way to the squirrel sticking his head out of a knothole in the top of a tree forty rods off. He moves along slow and easy, almost as though he's lazy, but when he wants to he can spring like a panther. You know how wide the creek is up there just below the falls? Well, he took the pack off his squaw's back and, with that under one arm and the hind quarters of a deer he'd just shot under the other, and his rifle balanced between them, he jumped across the stream in one easy hop."

"His squaw?" said Agatha. "Is he an Indian?"

"Oh, no. He's as white as we are. He even shaves every day. He's not covered with whiskers like the Slovers. But he's been around Indians a lot. He was taken captive by them when he was seven."

"I can see a full tally of his virtues will take some time," said Duncan. "Meanwhile would you emulate your hero's woodcraft by showing me how quickly you can find Olen and Polly for me?"

"Oh, they're right over there where Caleb is camping. He'll be glad to have me take them off his hands. They're all the time talking and he doesn't like to talk much."

"If he doesn't like to talk," said Olivia, "how'd you find out so much about him?"

"That was mostly just from watching him. Of course, Polly kept pestering him with question. She had a stepsister who married a Lewis who moved to the Greenbrier after the French war. The Greenbrier was where Caleb was taken by the Shawnee back in '62. She claims maybe he's some sort of a relative, a third cousin by marriage or something."

"Out of all the immensity of this wilderness," said Louisa, "our first visitor must turn out to be another Slover."

"Oh, Caleb doesn't look at all like one. He stopped answering Polly's questions, and you could tell what he thought by the way he'd look at Olen and then at Polly. Anyway, all his own people were killed when he was taken, and it was so long ago he probably can't remember too much about them."

"Once and for all," said Duncan. "Will you go tell Olen and Polly I want to see them?"

"Yes, sir. Right now."

Eric ran back down the slope and across the stream.

"Fascinating as all this is becoming," said Olivia. "I must tear myself away and take Garry his lunch. It's so hard to get him to eat anything and if I'm late with it he'll snatch at that as another excuse."

In the cook-tent she prepared a tray with a square of wheat bread, a pat of butter, a slice of baked ham, a mug of the milk which was reserved for the children and Garett, and a plate on which were spaced the separate and distinct temptations of a bit of comb honey, a dill pickle, a scrap of cheddar cheese, and a spoonful of plum chutney. As a final touch she laid a spray of golden aspen leaves alongside the dishes on the tray. She hummed as she worked and she was still humming when she entered the tent out on the point. Garett was lying on his back on his cot with his fingers interlaced behind his head. He ceased staring at the canvas above him and stared at her.

"Is that merely a buzzing in my ears, or can it be true that that cheerful sound came from you?"

"Of course from me. It's a fine day and I've brought a fine lunch. If you weren't looking so grumpy I'd finish the sentence and say to a fine husband."

"Something remarkably untoward must have happened to put you in so good a humor."

"You don't think seeing you again after all these hours away from you is enough to account for it?" She finished arranging the tray on a bench beside the cot. "Now, as we say to Chris and Susie, if you'll eat I'll tell you a story. You're quite right. Something has happened."

Garett sat up on the edge of the cot and nibbled at the piece of bread.

"You sparkle with promise. Spare no unhappy detail."

"Now that Betsey is up and around again she's taken to undermining the station's moral props. By using that really quite luscious Lina as bait she's managed the downfall of both Mark and Luke. It would not appear that they put up much resistance. Frank just now caught them, literally in the act, and he's beside himself. To cap it all it was Cam's spying that uncovered the scandal, so Agatha's in a state, too. Even the all-wise Duncan is upset."

"Have Mark and Luke been the only victims?"

"Who else could there be? Certainly not Frank or Duncan. And not Clem or Ned, I hope."

"I'm surprised you do not suspect me."

"No, Garry. Not you. That Lina may be a very tidy morsel. And so available. But that would be much too simple and direct for you. Yours is a more complicated itch."

Garett crumbled the rest of the bread into shreds. "Itch. What a word. How expressive. How inelegantly vulgar. And yet one that leaves me more than ever confused. However depraved, what hope have I ever to sin with her? She regards all Jordans as celestial beings. And why have I been only recently accused?"

"You were away at war while she was growing up. And when you came home you were not well. Then there was all that worry about the estate. You had so much on your mind."

"Chiefly you, I trust you'll admit."

"I will. But since we left we've all been thrown so much together and you've had so little to do but sit and brood."

"Still chiefly about you."

"I know that. That's what makes it so awful."

"Makes what so awful?"

"I can see the way you eye her whenever she's in sight. I

can tell when you're thinking about her—as you were when I came in—as you are right now. I know how often when you make love to me you are wondering what it would be like, if just once, you tell yourself, it could be she in my place."

Her voice failed her. She sank to her knees on the floor between his knees, threw her arms around him, and buried her face against him. He held to her tightly. She lifted her face to look up at him imploringly through her tears.

"Oh, Garry, my dearest darling."

He did not reply. Words were no longer expected of him. Already they were again in the grip of that recourse to physical deliverance which was the one proved consolation of their marriage.

Duncan was seated in a camp chair under the oak with Louisa and Agatha on either side of him. Olen and Polly were standing before this extemporized court, smirking with anxiety to accommodate themselves to its requirements but as yet unable to fathom the exact nature of the original charges.

"Them Lyman boys ain't had no women around handy fer quite a spell," said Olen. "Yuh can't hardly hold it agin 'em fer gittin' sort o' jumpy."

"Thet Lina's big fer her age," said Polly. "It's about time she fixed to git herself a man. I tuk up with Olen here when I was no older'n her. She's some purtier'n I was, too. Yuh don't have to fret none about her. She won't have to fiddle around long 'fore she'll git herself somebody."

"You keep missing the point," said Duncan. "Nobody's talking about ordinary courtship. What we are talking about is Betsey's taking men to her younger sister, superintending the business, as it were, and doing it over and over again. That's what we think you should put a stop to."

"Betsey's had her a real bad time," said Polly. "The fun o' lookin' on is about all she's up to. She ain't yet in no shape to have none by herself."

"What's the use, Duncan?" said Agatha. "These people haven't the slightest idea what we're trying to get at."

Polly was more than ever baffled by the note of disdain in Agatha's tone. Her mechanical grin became a shade less servile. "If'n yer so hog-wild to git at all the ins and outs whyn't yuh tackle Betsey and Lina theyselves?" Without waiting for their assent she raised her voice. "Betsey. Lina. Git yerselves up here."

Betsey and Lina emerged from the lean-to as promptly as though they might have been waiting and watching for the summons.

"Should Betsey really be making that climb?" inquired Louisa.

"She's real tough, Betsey is," said Polly. "She's got pains—and she don't sleep much—but when it comes to gittin' around she's most as spry as ever."

The girls reached the flat top of the mound and moved forward, staring. Betsey's pale eyes were hot with suspicion and resentment but Lina's big dark ones were placid and only mildly curious. It was she who was the center of Jordan attention but no defendant could have faced any court with the appearance of an easier conscience. Her hair was streaming down her back and she was continuing absently to run a wooden comb through it. The movement drew the front of her ragged cotton gown across the pleasant roundness of her young breasts.

"The creature's really oddly attractive," whispered Agatha. "Even clean. But so terribly young. Those ineffable Lymans."

"Don't try to distract me," said Duncan. "Judges are supposed to keep an open mind."

Betsey and Lina advanced to a stand beside their parents.

"Betsey," said Duncan, "did you bring word—not once or by accident but again and again this past week—of where your sister was waiting, or, at least, was to be found?"

"I fetched 'em to where she was. Else how was they to know whereat to look fer her?"

"Had you no idea at all that what you were doing was bad?"

"Whut's so bad about it? The way thet Mark and Luke they come a-gallopin' like dogs arter a rabbit?"

"If you didn't think it was bad," asked Agatha, "then why hide in the woods?"

" 'Cause Mark and Luke they was skeered o' gittin' caught."

"And today when you invited Luke to the hollow tree you hoped he'd be caught. Is that it?"

"Thet surely is it." Betsey hawked and spat to emphasize her ill will.

"So your main thought was to bring us down a peg or two?" asked Duncan.

"I was plenty sick o' seein' you-uns up here so gawdalmighty sure yuh was too high up fer trouble to git near."

"And you, Lina," said Duncan. "Do you, too, have no idea that what you let Mark and Luke do was bad?"

"Why?" Lina stopped the comb in mid-air while she considered the question. "All I let 'em do was fool around a mite."

"What do you mean by that?"

"Oh . . . wrassle and tickle and—and feel some."

"Some?"

"Thet's right. Some down there, and all they wanted up here." In her placid readiness to make herself quite clear Lina indicated first in the area of her legs from mid-thigh downward and then the inside of her gown from the waist upward.

"But why did you let them do that?"

"It never done me no hurt. And it made them feel real good."

"And that's all you let them do?"

"Yes, it was."

"And still they kept on coming, whenever Betsey let them know?"

"They kept on a-hopin', I expect."

"And you kept on disappointing them?"

"Thet Mark and Luke—I don't like 'em too much. Leastways, not thet much."

"Nonsense," said Agatha. "It's simply incredible that grown men would get so excited and then stop at that. The girl's surely lying."

At last a charge had been made which Polly could grasp. The last trace of her fawning amiability vanished. Suddenly she blazed with rebellious rage, her husband and daughters gaping at her, petrified by astonishment.

"Whutever fetched the likes o' you out to this country?" she stormed, "will yuh tell me thet? There ain't no place out here fer you. Whut do you know about whut it's like to hunt fer yer supper? Nor whut it's like to git yer guts clawed out by a b'ar? Nor be snowed in so long yuh go to eatin' yer moccasins? Nor see Injuns axin' yer young-uns in yer own dooryard? This here ain't no country fer the likes o' you. You'd best git yerselves back wherever yuh come from. You—yuh snake-tongued, whey-faced bitch. You and yer mush-mouthed man."

"Duncan," said Agatha. "Are you going to just sit there and listen to her insult us?"

"Hear her out," said Duncan. "We've been free enough with our insults."

Polly, panting and gasping, took a step nearer Agatha. Her thin gray hair had fallen down over her face. The rolls of fat on her cheeks, her bosom, her hips, even her arms and legs, heaved and tossed. She was already exhausted by the violence of a passion to which she was so unused, but her eyes still glittered.

"Yer so set on stickin' yer nose 'twixt other folks' legs—

yuh might's well git yerself a real good sniff. Betsey was only usin' them dough-faced Lymans fer teasers. They wasn't who she was gunnin' fer. Lina never laid still fer neither o' them. There was only one she done thet fer. Thet was fer yer boy, Eric."

Agatha sprang up. She was livid.

"You're lying, all of you."

"We-uns got no call to lie. We got nuthin' to cover up. Lyin's fer the likes o' them thet has."

Agatha looked frantically at Lina. "Lina. Did you and Eric ——"

Lina's eyes, round and wide with childlike calm, met hers. "Yes, ma'am. Twicet."

"You're just saying that, because you want to hurt us."

"Thet was whut Betsey wanted. But thet never was why I done it."

"Then why did you do it? What made you treat him so differently from them?"

"I already said I wasn't so partial to them. But him." Lina's smile was warm and confiding. "I like him."

Eric had put his new skill in woodcraft to practical use by crawling unnoticed within earshot of the tribunal. Having heard his worst fears confirmed, he crept away again, made the edge of the woods, circled the wood lot, and plunged away into the recesses of the forest. The blasts of the Hessian trumpet, repeated at intervals as long as daylight lasted and with greater urgency after darkness had fallen brought no response.

After a sleepless night Duncan and Agatha made their way down to the hollow sycamore at dawn to negotiate peace with the Slovers. An embarrassingly repentant Polly, scrambling from her blankets to receive them, all but groveled at their feet. The Slovers, too, had known a desperate anxiety in the night as they contemplated the imminence of winter and the prospect of being cast out by their patrons. They were as ready as Duncan and Agatha to let bygones be bygones and were instantly eager to accede to Duncan's petition. In this vast wilderness an army might search for days without finding one lost boy. The one hope was that his wanderings might be tracked by experienced woodsmen. The three Slover men grabbed their rifles and set out. In late afternoon they returned but without Eric.

"His tracks they run off plain's a buffler trace," reported Olen, " 'til he come to the crik just below the falls. They wasn't no tracks across the crik nor nowhere's else arter thet. Me and my boys we circled fer most ten miles and never picked up ary other sign." He correctly interpreted the anguished, suffering glance exchanged by Duncan and Agatha and added: "We-uns shoved a pole plumb around the bottom o' thet hole below the falls. He ain't nowheres in thet."

Tracy, listening, backed away. From across the stream came the sound of chopping. With sudden decision she ran down the slope, across the pine log, and on into the woods. The sound of chopping had ceased but she soon came to the camp of Caleb Lewis. There was already a cleared area around his campfire and the first tier of logs of a small cabin stood beside the bark shelter in which his blankets were spread. He had a short length of the split half of a pine log set up on a sawhorse of crossed stakes and was squaring it with the blade of his axe. The axe was so sharp that, when he took the bit in his hands and pushed it against the wood, long even shavings started curling up as though he were using a draw knife. She ran to him.

"Mr. Lewis."

He was fair but so sunburned that at a little distance he might almost have passed for an Indian and his face was so without expression that any guess at his age might range from twenty-five to forty. When he looked around at her she could see what Eric had meant about his eyes. They were a yellowish hazel and they seemed to take in at one glance everything about her, from the pins in her hair to the shoes on her feet.

"Yes, ma'am?"

He resumed his shaping of the pine block.

"I'm Tracy Carter. I come from the station over there. We've a lost boy—a fifteen-year-old boy. He's been gone in the woods since yesterday afternoon. There have been men from the station out looking for him but they can't find him. You're so much more experienced in the woods. Won't you find him for us?"

He kept on thrusting the edge of his axe against the pine, producing the long, curling, pleasant-smelling shavings. She had spoken impetuously, emphatically, her voice tense. Yet he appeared not to have heard anything she had said. She was suddenly struck by a fear that he might already have used the only two English words that he knew, but then, made the more nervous by the discovery of her own nervousness, she recalled Eric's account of the man's talk with the Slovers.

"Won't you?" she repeated.

"I might."

"Oh, will you please?"

He kept on thrusting the edge of his axe against the pine block, producing the long, curling, pleasant-smelling shavings.

"There's only an hour or two left before it will be dark again," she urged.

"First I plan to finish this."

Now that he had brought off a sentence of several words she noted that there was an odd spacing between them, as though it might have been so long since he had spoken English that he needed to take thought in order to be certain of his use of each. Yet it was not as though he were recalling the language of his early boyhood. His accent was more English than western American. The deliberateness of his speech served also to give a decisive finality to his remark. She strove to restrain her impatience. However eccentric his behavior she dared not risk vexing him.

The Indian woman came out of the woods carrying a log on her back. It was a burden to tax a strong man but she bore it with apparent ease. She was stocky and young with a broad, good-natured, not unpleasing face. Her leather dress was smudged by earth and smoke and pine bark but her hair and skin were clean. She came to a stop and without laying down the log waited for Caleb to notice her. He went on working.

"Your wife," suggested Tracy, "seems waiting to be told what to do with that log."

After a moment he looked around and spoke in Shawnee, as impersonally as one might address a horse or a dog. The Indian woman lowered the log to the ground, took a hatchet from her belt, and began notching the ends.

"Her Shawnee name amounts in English to something like Daisy," he said to Tracy.

He spoke again to the Indian woman. She straightened and the absolute impassivity which had marked her former occasional glances at Tracy was succeeded by a sociable smile. She advanced and stretched out her hand. Tracy shook it.

"How do you do, Daisy."

Daisy and Caleb turned back to their work.

"Do you plan to spend the winter here, Mr. Lewis?"

He did not reply.

"Colonel Jordan's grant is all on the other side of the stream. I am sure he will not object."

This observation seemed to interest him as little as had the question.

"Mr. Lewis, it will so soon be dark. There is so little time to look for him before he will have to spend another night in the woods."

"I have no need to look for him. I know where he is."

"You do? Then take me to him. Take me to him at once."

He turned over the pine block and began squaring the other side.

"Then while we're waiting—I'll run to tell his parents he's safe. They've been in agony."

He spoke to Daisy, giving her certain directions which seemed to have absorbed his entire attention. A gust of near panic brushed Tracy. He seemed abundantly able to understand and to speak English and yet he was also able, whenever he chose, to withdraw behind a barrier of Indian inscrutability.

"But you said you'd find him for us."

He lifted his axe and tried the edge with his thumb. Then, as though the pause had reminded him of her presence, he spoke to her again.

"He came to my camp last night after walking in the creek all the way down from the falls so that your people could not track him. He wants me to take him to the Shawnee so that he can live with them."

"Are you out of your mind? You cannot do that to him."

Daisy had finished notching the log. Caleb laid aside the axe and moved around the fire to help her lay it in position on the wall. Tracy followed.

"He comes of a gentle family. He has brothers, sisters, parents—all of whom love him."

Caleb returned to his axe. Tracy, still following him, laid hold of the end of the handle.

"If you're like some of the others who've spent their lives in the woods, if you feel people like us don't fit in out here, then let me tell you this: We've as much right to be here as you have. More, because we'll make something of this country and your kind never will."

He had made no effort to release the axe from her grasp. For a second time he looked at her. This was a longer and more searching scrutiny and was centered on her face and more especially her eyes.

"No need for you to try to guess what I am thinking," she cried. "You have only to listen. I'm trying hard enough to tell you."

"You are too old for him."

"Don't be absurd. He is a child and I am a grown woman."

"You are not married?"

"No. But why all this talk about me? It is Eric who counts. He ran away because he did something bad and is ashamed to face his father."

"He has mentioned you more often than he has his father."

"What maggot can you have in your mind? You are possibly

so ignorant of civilized people that I cannot begin to guess. But for Eric's sake I will try to explain, little as it can concern you. I am not a Jordan, though I have been accepted by them almost as though I were one of the family. I was adopted by Eric's grandmother when I was orphaned at twelve. When they lost their property during the war and decided to come west it was only natural for me to come with them. They asked me to come and I wanted to come. There is nothing—nothing, I tell you—that I would not do for them after all they have done for me. I do not know that you can understand anything I am saying. But I have been something like a nurse to all the Jordan children. And after that a little like a governess, and finally, more like a much older sister. I am fond of Eric. I think he is of me. Now where is he?"

"Eric," called Caleb.

A hundred feet away there was a pile of brush, accumulated by Daisy in the course of felling and trimming trees. The pile shook and Eric crawled out of it. He stood up, clutching his rifle, and took a stride away.

"Come here," said Caleb.

Tracy was blinded, for a second, by rage. From the first he must have had no other intention than to deliver up the boy. He had been leading her on to continue and to embroider her fervent appeal, possibly out of simple boorish curiosity, possibly as no more than a passing diversion. But she could not now afford the luxury of anger. She must think first of Eric.

He had halted at Caleb's call but he did not look around. He still leaned toward the woods as though pausing only to draw a deep breath before resuming his flight.

"Eric, come here," called Tracy. "Please—I want to talk to you."

The sound of her voice set him off as by the pull of a trigger. He plunged into the woods, in his frenzy to escape crashing headlong into thickets and colliding with trees. Caleb looked inquiringly at Tracy.

"Would you?" she begged.

Leaning his axe against the block he started in pursuit, running so lightly and silently that only his toes appeared to touch the ground, and yet with such incredible rapidity that in an instant he had disappeared in the forest. The sounds of Eric's blundering flight ceased and presently he stumbled into view, the lifting of his feet seemed to require a separate effort at each step. Caleb strolled behind him.

Eric kept on toward her, ever more slowly, looking everywhere except at her. His face, which had been scarlet, whitened as he approached. He came to a stop before her, let his rifle slip to the ground, and clutched at the wood block for support.

"Eric," she said, "look at me."

He only hung his head the lower.

"Why are you so afraid to talk to me?"

"I know how you feel," he whispered.

"What makes you so sure of that?"

Eric's voice steadied a trifle, as though in the opportunity to dwell on his guilt there were a shadow of relief.

"I know how you feel about anything that's mean or low. Your nose always wrinkles just as if you were smelling something bad."

"Would you like to hear what I really think?"

The impulse to make another break jerked him up and around. But Caleb stood behind him. Eric leaned back, heavily, against the block.

"It would help if you would look at me," said Tracy.

He dug his chin deeper into his chest.

"I think you've been wicked. I think what you did with Lina was bad. It made you like her kind of people and you must never forget that you're not that kind. But the grief you caused your father and mother by running away was worse."

"I couldn't stay. Not after what I did."

"What you'd done was certainly shameful. Still, it was the kind of a mistake grown men sometimes make. It was the running away that was a child's mistake."

One small corner of Eric's abject misery was lifting. He squirmed unhappily.

"Betsey said it was a chance to show how much more of a man I was than Mark or Luke."

"We've all seen how hard you've been trying to be a man. But just to be any kind of man isn't enough. You must want to be the kind of a man your father is. Keep thinking of that, when you go back now and are standing there face to face with him."

"I can't do that, Tracy. I just can't."

"Of course, if you're afraid of everything that's not easy for you . . ."

He stiffened slightly. She had saved striking the right note for just the right moment.

"Do you think he'll beat me?" he asked, clutching at so simple and dramatic an expiation of his sins.

"I hope so. But I doubt it. He's been too heartbroken while he's thought you lost."

"And you don't think—I mean—you——"

He was still unable to meet her eyes. She took his face in her hands and gently forced him to look at her.

"I'll be as much your friend as I've ever been." She released him and gave him a push. "Now scamper."

Beginning to weep, he set off at a run toward the station.

"Thank you, Mr. Lewis," said Tracy coldly.

She followed Eric. Caleb stood watching her as she walked away. His lips parted in a contemplative grin which, for one instant, showed a gleam of his white teeth. Daisy, covertly watching his face, was startled, as though she saw in it a betrayal of something in him she had never before suspected. Then, chuckling, she went on with her work.

December

Indian summer's pleasant haze was abruptly dispelled by a wintry gale that tore the last leaves from the trees and left their bare branches coated with sleet. There followed day after day of gray cloud and piercing wind. The ground hardened. The pond froze over. A powdering of snow gave the meadow the sterile look of a salt marsh. Packs of wolves, howling gruesomely in the night, each night ranged nearer. The gaunt lifelessness of the denuded trees now permitted gaping glimpses into the forbidding depths of the wilderness. No longer did the circumference of forest seem a comforting wall within which nestled the station in peace and seclusion. It had become a disturbingly open door through which cold winds whined.

The sudden change in the weather was more compelling than had been Duncan's exhortations. With the immediate need of winter quarters so sternly emphasized, Jordans, Lymans, and Slovers alike, chastened by their several recent personal adversities, ignored their differences and joined forces. Duncan postponed the last lap of his surveying in order to share the labor. Garett found tasks within the reach of his strength. Even the Slovers set their axes to ringing. The Lymans were workmen who knew their trade. With ample materials at hand the walls rapidly rose and the roofs spread to cover them.

It was Duncan's intention that the two buildings erected this year were to form two of the sides of what when completed next year would become a quadrangle adaptable to defense if the need ever developed. The main structure, therefore, was ell-shaped. In the longer side the major space was devoted to a large kitchen to double as keeping room for the Jordans and common room for the station. Behind the great fireplace at one end were two small bedrooms for Duncan and Agatha and for Louisa and Tracy and behind the twin fireplace at the other end a bedroom for Garett and Olivia and a spare room, termed by Duncan the office, by Agatha the sitting room, and by Garett the throne room. In the loft over the kitchen were bunks for the children. At the corner of the ell beyond the office was a storeroom, extending at right angles from which was the shorter wing of the main building with quarters in the first section for the Negroes and in the second for the Lymans which also housed their blacksmith and carpenter shop. Next to the Lyman apartment was a gap in which eventually the gate to the station would be fitted and beyond that a detached cabin for the Slovers.

The day the tents were taken down, giving him an unobstructed view of the new buildings, Duncan stood off contemplating with satisfaction the smoke curling from the several chimneys.

"Decided yet," asked Garett, "whether the seigniory is to be officially known as Revel Station, Revel Creek, or Revel Manor?"

"Corbit would have called it Revel Hundred," said Duncan.

"Not bad." Garrett appeared to give the suggestion solemn consideration. "Not too piddling. Not too pretentious. Not bad at all."

The Slovers gathered up their rifles and axes and sack of seed corn, constituting at once the hard core and the sum total of their belongings, and moved to their new cabin. The hollow sycamore and lean-to became a barn for the two cows, adjacent to the dried grass in the meadow and capable of being barred at night to keep out the wolves.

To reward the diligence with which all had labored, Duncan proclaimed a housewarming. The haunches of Eric's first buffalo were set to roasting in the two great fireplaces and a keg of whisky was broached.

"Here's to the flowing bowl," said Garett to Duncan as they looked on from a corner at the festivities. "Behold the varied gifts it bestows. It loosens my usually so taciturn tongue. It renders you even more eminently reasonable. It brings the glow of fond reminiscence into Mother's eyes. It widens Agatha's smile to include Olivia and Olivia's to include me. It wafts Tracy to a yet higher and more cerebral plane. It exalts Frank by virtue of his adamant refusal to touch it. It stirs Mark and Luke to so manly a resolution to outdo each other that they do not falter until both are sick. It satisfies Jake's deepest yearning by putting him to sleep. It draws from Jarot strains of music more ineffable than earthly ear can detect. It sharpens Betsey's malice and sweetens Lina's charity. It causes Polly to flame like a bride when she regards her shaggy mate. But consider Olen. For him it does the most of all."

Olen was emitting wolf-like howls, leaping into the air to strike his moccasined heels together, and repeatedly announcing:

"Ain't no sunnabitch here I can't stuff his elbow in his ear."

The hoarse challenge was accompanied, however, by a grin of loving kindness lavished upon whoever chanced to catch his uncertain eye.

"You, Garett," said Duncan, "are getting drunk."

"I'm trying hard," said Garett. "And 'twould do you as much good."

"Before the night's over my whoops may rival Olen's," promised Duncan. He looked toward the door. "Caleb Lewis does not even send his regrets."

"He's a stiff-legged dog. May he continue to keep his distance."

"I don't agree with you. If we are to have a near neighbor how much better to have a friendly neighbor."

"Caleb was off hunting when you sent me over there this afternoon, father," Eric put in. "Maybe Daisy didn't understand what I meant. Maybe he's back now. Want me to go see?"

"If you like."

Eric put down his tumbler of rum and water and eagerly ran out. The door of Caleb's cabin opened promptly to his knock, letting out a wave of warm air fragrant with the mingled scents of oak fire, bubbling meat, and sweet grass. Eric was startled to discover that in the evening seclusion of her home Daisy wore but a knee-length fawnskin petticoat. By smiling signs she indicated that Caleb had not yet returned. Eric ran back through the darkening forest and was again startled when he came upon Lina waiting for him in the shadow of the station gateway. There was enough twilight left for him to see the color in her red cheeks and dark eyes. She was smiling at him as warmly and sympathetically as when last they had been alone together.

"Whenever yuh happen to look my way you jump like a bee jest stung yuh," she remonstrated softly.

"I promised them," he said, edging around her.

"To keep off from me?"

"I had to."

She was not offended.

"I know about how they tuk on. But no call fer yuh to

take it so hard. I ain't a-holdin' nuthin' agin yuh. Time'll come when you'll be yer own man."

"I promised," repeated Eric desperately.

He bolted past her and on toward the clatter of voices and laughter in the kitchen. His father and Garett, their heads together, were singing Anacreon without, however, attracting any attention from anyone else in the room. His mother was leaning over Olivia, laughing at the charcoal sketch Olivia was doing of Frank's enduring scowl of universal condemnation. Tracy was kneeling beside his grandmother's chair, providing a favorite audience for Louisa's favorite recollections. None of them seemed to notice his return or Lina's placid reappearance behind him in the same doorway. Ned and Clem were removing another joint of buffalo from its spit, but the company had already done so well that there was no second rush to the carving block. At a grudging nod from Geneva they began eagerly to slice off generous portions for themselves.

Olen fell down. From Polly burst a sudden squeal that might have been either a laugh or a cry. As though this were a signal, all five of the still upright Slovers instantly flung themselves upon the prostrate Olen. Subduing the convulsive threshings of his great limbs and heeding not at all his bellows of protest, they lifted him and bore him off to their cabin. Under cover of the commotion the Lymans withdrew, Frank weighed down by his unflagging disapproval and his sons by their belated remorse. Garett lifted his glass.

"I pronounce the house warm." He drank and threw his glass into the fire. "And my bed warmer."

Olivia sprang to guide and support his slightly unsteady steps, but he waved her aside. He bent to press a good-night kiss on the top of Agatha's head and another upon his mother's but when he bowed over Tracy's he appeared to miss his aim and instead nuzzled the kiss lingeringly among the curls at the nape of her neck. He straightened, smiled benignly into his wife's whitening face, and lifted her hand to his arm.

"Now, my sweet," he said, "let us hence. All further favors are reserved for you."

Olivia jerked her hand from his grasp.

"Olivia," said Duncan, "can't you see that he is quite drunk?"

"He's never quite drunk. He's never quite anything—except unbearable." Olivia glared at Garett. "There is one favor I can do myself. That is to spend the rest of the night right here."

She crossed to a bench against the wall and planted herself

on it firmly. Cam had for the last hour kept in the background, trusting to postpone the moment she might be made to follow the two younger children to bed. But now she darted to the ladder leading to the loft.

"I'll move Susie in with me, Aunt Olivia. Then you can have her mattress."

"Thank you, Cam," said Olivia. "Eric, will you bring it down to me?"

Eric looked to his father for guidance. Garett grinned around at the others.

"Don't be misled," he advised them. "We are merely enkindling our ardor, after the fashion of Polly and Olen."

"This constant squabbling," said Agatha, "in front of the children—of all of us, for that matter—I find very tiresome."

Olivia leaped up and sank in a deep curtsy.

"Our most humble apologies, Your Majesty."

Louisa twisted in her chair with a glance of reserve at Agatha. "I am sure we are all finding this tiresome."

"And quite unnecessary," said Duncan, also eying Agatha.

"Hark to the Arcadian echo of our amenities," said Garett.

From the Slover cabin came another bellow from Olen followed by a screech from Polly. The sounds were muffled by distance yet oddly distinct in the cold night. All had unconsciously turned toward the door as they listened. The door opened. Caleb stood in it. Peering over his shoulder were Indian faces. He stepped forward into the room. Five Indians followed and ranged themselves behind him. They blinked in the candlelight but from their narrowed eyes quick sharp glances shot this way and that. They seemed to Duncan immediately to have perceived that there were no weapons in the room aside from their own. His, Eric's, and Garett's rifles were leaning in a corner of the office.

"Are they wild Indians, Papa?" whispered Cam loudly. "Are they going to scalp us?"

They did not look too wild. None had feathers in his hair, horns on his head, or paint on his face. One even wore a battered, bell-crowned hat and another a cocked hat with a remnant of lace still clinging to it. But they smelled of smoke, sunflower seed oil, the cold night air, and, damply and pungently, of the animal hides in which they were clothed. Their bulky shapeless figures wrapped in buffalo and rabbitskin robes, their dark expressionless faces, their very silence and immobility made their sudden intrusion that of creatures altogether alien.

"Good evening, Colonel Jordan," said Caleb, speaking slowly and distinctly. "When I returned to my house tonight

Daisy told me you had asked me to visit you. Since these old friends were already visiting me I asked them to come with me."

"They are as welcome as you," said Duncan.

Caleb stood aside and indicated each of his companions in turn.

"My Shawnee friends are Stone Kettle, Beaver Tail, Night Walker, Bone Polisher, and John Turtle."

Across every Indian face spread an immediate broad grin which appeared curiously childish by contrast with their former sinister stolidity. They leaned their rifles against the wall beside the door. In grave succession they ceremoniously shook hands with Duncan. The last, John Turtle, continued, however, to beam as though this were a social occasion of particular pleasure to him and proved able to accompany his handshake with a word of greeting.

"How do, bruder," he said.

The Indians thereafter continued to shake hands, neglecting no one present, including Eric, Ken, Cam, and the four Negroes.

"My friends had a special wish," said Caleb to Duncan, "to see this place you had built on their land."

"It is now my land," said Duncan.

Caleb, seeming not to notice the amendment, glanced appraisingly about the room. "You started slowly but you have not done badly."

"I am glad you approve," said Duncan. "Geneva, see that our guests are served something to eat."

Serving was not required. At Geneva's reluctant gesture of invitation each Indian whipped out his knife and began helping himself from the joint on the block. They began to laugh and nudge one another and talk among themselves and to stuff enormous hunks of meat into their mouths. So far no one of the whites in the room had moved from the position into which he had frozen when the Indians had entered. Each watched Duncan, waiting for a cue from him.

"You have been our neighbor for some weeks," said Duncan. "I fear we have been so occupied we have been remiss about making friends. Mr. Lewis"—he began indicating the others in the room—"my mother, my wife, my brother, Garett, his wife, my sons, Eric and Ken, my daughter, Cam, and Miss Thryza Carter."

"I have met Mr. Lewis," said Tracy distantly.

Caleb had merely nodded at each presentation, though his glance at each successive member of the Jordan household had been as intent as when upon his entrance he had observed the internal structure of the building.

"Won't you sit down, Mr. Lewis," said Agatha.

Caleb sat on the end of the bench beside the long table and, appearing to have said all that was necessary to say, began to stare at the women, first at one and then, as directly and as unabashedly, at the next. Garett, moving around the table, drew Duncan aside.

"Our dusky guests' preoccupation at the trough," he murmured, "and their captain's with his appraisal of our womenfolk seem to offer the chance of a moment's word with you." He glanced through the loophole at their shoulder at the dark and silent Lyman apartment and the dark but not so silent Slover abode. "Observe our fellow defenders. We could have all had our throats cut by now and they'd be none the wiser. Think we should call them over?"

"No, I don't," said Duncan. "We still may get out of this without real trouble but we most certainly won't if all of them come stumbling in."

Garett nodded his agreement and turned back toward the room.

"Ah," he said. "The fair Olivia is getting in her licks."

Olivia had placed before Caleb a plate of buffalo tongue, buttered beans, and corn cakes spread with honey. He began to eat, ingoring the silver she laid beside the plate and instead, using his hands and his own knife. Olivia sat down across from him and laced her fingers beneath her chin, watching him intently.

"We've been looking forward to meeting you, Mr. Lewis. We've been simply dying of curiosity."

He raised his head and stared at her. Her bright smile faded.

"Your husband is sick?" he asked.

"Not really. He is recovering from a war wound."

"You have no children?"

"No."

He resumed eating, appearing to have exhausted the subject. Cam leaned on the table at his elbow.

"Why didn't you bring your wife with you?"

"I have no wife."

"Your squaw, then. Why didn't you bring her?"

He looked again at Olivia while giving Cam an explicit reply.

"I will tell you about Daisy. She is an Iowa captive—a slave you Virginians might call her. The Kickapoo who took her traded her to the principal chief of the Shawnee for a barrel of whisky. Because he is my old friend, he loaned her to me to help me out this winter."

"How very convenient for you," said Louisa.

"Then you are going to stay here all winter?" Eric asked eagerly.

"Yes," said Caleb.

The Indians, having glutted even their extraordinary appetites were beginning to range about, to inspect garments, whether hanging on the wall or on people, to examine and to handle various utensils and implements. Night Walker picked up a mug in which whisky had been served, sniffed it, and looked expectantly at Duncan. Caleb rose abruptly.

"We will go now," he announced.

The Indians picked up their rifles and docilely preceded him out into the night.

"Whew," said Garett. "A most singular visitation." He grinned at Olivia. "And did you get your comeuppance."

"Duncan," said Agatha. "You must think of some way to get rid of that man. We just can't have him living so near."

"Wouldn't it appear that he might make a more comfortable friend than enemy?"

"Cold comfort," said Louisa, "in having packs of Indians trooping in and out of our house at all hours."

"Something of a dilemma," admitted Duncan. "But it's not a choice we have to make tonight."

His discreet spying at the first streak of dawn established the fact that the visiting Shawnee had already departed and that Caleb and Daisy were again at work on the enlargement of his clearing. The same next morning brought the most authoritative advice on the problem of Caleb that the entire frontier could have offered. George Rogers Clark came ashore to call at the new settlement on the north bank. The great western hero was pleased to learn the station's founder was the same Colonel Jordan who had served with him in the Virginia campaign of 1781 against Benedict Arnold. But he was in too pressing a hurry to get on upriver to attend an Indian council at Fort McIntosh to linger longer than to take a shrewd look around and pay his respects to the Jordan ladies. Duncan, off in the woods finishing his survey, very nearly missed seeing him at all. Eric tracked his father and brought him back just as the General was shoving off. The two men squatted under the sycamore on the point. A small mongrel dog on a leash in Clark's beached bateau kept barking so sharply that they had need to raise their voices.

"You've made a good enough start," said Clark. "But if it was me I wouldn't lose much more time getting a stockade up around those two open sides."

"I do not intend to. I've had a little trouble keeping my people at work."

"Best way to keep folks at work is to lock up the grub and dole it out as they earn it."

"You do not expect the peace to last?"

"You never can count on Indians—one way or t'other. Depends some on the English, too. If they go on keeping their garrison in Detroit and their stinking traders in every Indian town it might not be too long before the hard-nosed ones like the Shawnee get to forgetting they lost the war."

"But when I came through Pittsburgh I understood the Iroquois were ready to cede this whole country out here."

"That's what they did. At Fort Stanwix a month ago. But the Iroquois ain't so important as they used to be and they ain't the Indians who live out here. The Delaware and the Wyandot—who do—they're coming to Fort McIntosh this month to sign some sort of a treaty. But the Shawnee, who live the closest of all to you, are still holding off. Maybe they'll come in. Maybe they won't."

"I've a title from the Shawnee."

The dog's continued barking was making conversation more and more difficult. Clark ordered one of the boatmen to bring him ashore and tie him to a bush at a little distance. The dog ceased barking and began to howl plaintively.

"Heard him yipping on an island we were coming past yesterday evening," explained Clark. "Some no-count mover must have pitched him off there. You were saying about a Shawnee title."

"An uncle of my mother's, Corbit Revel, who was then a trader with the Ohio Indians, was granted this land by the Shawnee in 1774. He died before he could develop and bequeathed the grant to us."

"I missed knowing Corbit. He was just before my time. But I've heard some about him, mostly good. He was about the only white man honest enough to string with the Shawnee during Lord Dunmore's war."

Clark paused and looked off along the stream bank. Ken, drawn from the station by the dog's cries, had crept to the bush and was making friends with the outcast. The puppy ceased to complain and began happily to lick the boy's hands and face.

" 'Course that was quite a while ago," resumed Clark, "and

could be the Shawnee might not feel so good about seeing you settling in here the same as they might have their old friend Corbit."

"Nevertheless, it's a perfectly authentic grant. And it's even within the area reserved by Virginia for Virginia veterans. By next spring Harmar's Federal troops will be out here and the Shawnee will have no choice but to recognize my deed."

Clark was looking off again.

"That boy and that dog surely do cotton to one another."

"Ken had to leave his dog behind him when we left home."

"This one's about as no-count as they come but a boy can find use for most any kind of a dog. Got any objection to my giving it to him?"

"I'd be delighted," said Duncan. "Ken, come here."

Ken approached, endeavoring politely to conceal his greater interest in the dog's company.

"The General wants to know if you'd like him to give you that dog."

A sun of enchanted surprise rose in Ken.

"Yes. Yes, I would." He turned to run, remembered, and turned back. "Thank you, General Clark. Thank you—very much."

He ran to the bush and began fumblingly to untie the dog.

"Harmar's soldiers won't be much help," said Clark. "There won't be enough of them to do more than hole up in a couple of forts. And they'll be less than no good here on the north bank. Congress keeps buttering up the Indians by passing laws forbidding settlement north of the river and if Harmar pays you any attention at all he may try to move you out."

"Are you suggesting then that we give up this station? Is that your advice?"

"It surely is not. Wherever our people get a settlement started I want to see it stick. I got a place myself on the north bank—down by Louisville. No, sir. You hang right on here. 'Case next summer things start to look bad, I'll make out to get word to you in time."

The two men rose.

"It's been a great pleasure to see you again, General," said Duncan, as they shook hands. "I'm eternally grateful for your counsel. Oh, I'd almost forgot a lesser but more immediate problem. There's a squatter moved in across the creek—there where you hear that axe. He's not on my land. But he's a great friend of the Shawnee. He used to live with them and he has an Indian woman living with him now. His Shawnee friends visit him and he brings them to call on us."

"What's his name?"

"Caleb Lewis. What I'm trying to decide is whether as a neighbor he's an asset or a liability. Should I try to make friends with him or try to get rid of him?"

"I'd like to have me a look at him."

"It's too bad to take more of your time."

"I always got time to size up a white man that's partial to Indians."

"Ken," called Duncan. "Run tell Mr. Lewis that General Clark would like a word with him."

Presently the axe in the woods fell silent. Caleb appeared on the crossing log and came striding along the stream bank out to the point. Ignoring Duncan's presentation he came to a stand in front of Clark. The two men, almost the same height and build, identically clad in weathered buckskins, each leaning on his rifle, eyed one another.

"One of my boatmen's gone sick," said Clark. "Thought you might help me out."

"For how long?"

"Far's the Muskingum. You could cut off through the woods and be back here by the third day from now."

"I might spare that long."

Caleb walked off fifty yards and called out. From the woods across the stream came Daisy's reply. He addressed her briefly.

"Telling her what to do while he's away," interpreted Clark. "Cut wood days and keep her door shut nights."

"I hate to see you going to so much trouble," Duncan protested again.

"I'm doing it for me as much as you. Whenever a white man is as thick with Indians as he is I don't want to lose time getting him figgered out. I want to know if he's working for the English, the Shawnee, or nobody but himself. By this time tomorrow I ought to have seen enough of him to make me a pretty fair guess. I'll let you know what it is."

With the puppy by turns tugging at the leash and jumping to lick his hands, Ken circled the foot of the mound and kept on to the farther edge of the meadow. He required seclusion and leisure to examine his prize. The dog was mainly yellow, with black rump and ears and a grizzling of white on muzzle and belly. He was the size of a fox terrier, though with shorter legs and a shaggy coat that made him seem larger than he was. His moods alternated between the two extremes of the most aggressive belligerence and the most fawning affection. When Ken stooped to pat him he dissolved into wriggling ecstasies of response. The next second, he had spun about to face the unknown, bristling and rigid, his ears flattened, his teeth bared, his throat resonant with fury, his eyes fixed in a sidelong glance upon the threatening approach of an enemy visible only to him.

Ken's first concern was the leash. A tethered dog was not his dog. He hesitated, however, to risk untying the leather thong. The dog might not yet realize he was his dog. He might not intend to run completely away, but if he ranged far in these unfamiliar woods he might not know how to get back. While Ken grappled with this problem, the cows ceased to graze on the frozen grass of the meadow and edged nearer to make a suspicious inspection of the canine stranger. The dog sprang to the end of the leash and barked fiercely. His barks were shrill and penetrating and as loud and sharp as pistol shots. One of the cows lowered her head. He leaped back to the safety of Ken's arms.

Ken drove the cows away with clods and, suddenly inspired, took the dog into the hollow sycamore. Here, after replacing the bars, he could experiment safely. He untied the leash. The dog rolled over on his back, paws in air, and squirmed about in the most abject submission. Ken moved away. He scrambled to his feet and followed. Ken ran from side to side of the hollow tree. He kept so closely under foot that Ken fell over him. His heart beating faster, Ken lowered the bars. The dog sat, tongue out, watching him. He stepped into the open, putting all to the test. The dog was still at his feet. He ran toward the pond—the dog kept at his heels. Whichever way he turned his faithful follower was with him. He sat down and gathered the dog happily in his arms.

"Ken," called Eric from the slope of the mound.

Ken ran to meet him. The dog began to bark at Eric.

"Look at my new dog," exulted Ken.

"I see him," said Eric. He regarded the capering, yipping little animal without favor. "What's his name?"

"Rupert," said Ken.

He had not until that instant given any thought to a name.

"Rupert? That's a funny name. Why Rupert?"

"Because that's his name."

"Well, Mother said to tell you dinner's ready."

They ran up the slope, Rupert still barking. At the kitchen door Rupert darted between their legs and into the room. His earlier efforts had been but a weak preface to the clamor that burst from him upon being confronted by the number of people assembled here. He raced about the room, barking with new excitement at each new figure he encountered. His performance culminated in his appearing to recognize in Agatha a principal enemy. He planted himself before her, his barks sharpening with ever more frenzied hostility.

"Take him outside," she directed Ken. "Take him out this minute."

Rupert had not yet identified his name. He was deaf to Ken's desperate whistles and supplications. Ken was obliged to pursue him under table and benches and at length suffer the ignominy of its having been Eric who brought the chase to an end by one swooping dexterous grab. Clasping the struggling and still barking dog in his arms, Ken faced his unsympathetic audience.

"It isn't his fault. He doesn't know any of you yet."

"You heard your mother," said his father.

Sadly Ken went to the door, dropped Rupert outside, and closed it. Immediately Rupert began to scratch on the door and then mournfully to howl. His howling voice was as big as that of a hound but lacked any bell-like quality.

"It won't take him long to get used to us," argued Ken.

"There's still the question of how long it may take us to get used to him," said Garett.

"Take your plate and eat outside," said Agatha. "And do something to keep him quiet."

Ken went out, was immediately rewarded by Rupert's overwhelmingly affectionate greeting, and ran down the slope, laughing at the dog's excited leaps upward toward the plate of buffalo stew. Duncan, coming out to watch, noted the day's first signs of life around the Slover cabin. Polly was in the yard chopping wood. She had a blackened eye and a split lip but, between her grunts as she swung the axe, was humming contentedly. He strolled over to her. She wagged her head in pleasant reminiscence.

"We-uns had us a right good time to yer place last night."

"I trust all continued to go as well after you got home."

She looked up suspiciously, saw the twinkle in his eye, and grinned broadly.

"I made out," she confessed.

"And Olen?"

"He simmered down along toward daylight. He gits him a sight o' good out'n his likker, Olen does."

"After you left last night we had some Indian callers."

He made the announcement casually but expected her to be thunderstruck by the revelation. The Slovers were perpetually conscious of the Indian threat that had tormented every year of their frontier lives. But she only nodded.

"Caleb he told us he'd be a-fetchin' some around one day," she said.

"I thought all of you were so convinced that the only good Indian was a dead Indian?"

"Not these here pet Injuns o' Caleb's. They'll never do us no dirt. Not whilst Caleb's around."

Duncan tried another stab at her complacence. The Slovers were inordinately proud of the sagacity of their dogs.

"Five Indians you could smell a half mile off trailed right past your door last night and your dogs didn't so much as growl."

Polly nodded. "These here winter nights when they's in there along with us they never fool none when they's no call fer it. They got better sense than to git theyselves throwed out in the cold."

Duncan made one more try before giving up this last of his recurrent attempts to explore the Slover mentality.

"General Clark was here this morning." He paused for effect but the great name seemed to mean little to Polly. "He's not sure the peace will last."

"Caleb he ain't neither."

"General Clark thinks we need a stockade."

Again Polly nodded. "Caleb he says 'twould look some better was we-uns to have us one." She gestured toward the cabin. "Soon's they's done sleepin' it off they'll go to fetchin' yuh poles."

Rupert's afternoon was a greater social success than had been his morning. Led about on his leash and required to make the acquaintance in turn of every inhabitant, he eventually ceased barking at any of them. After a couple of exasperated nips from the Slover dogs he ceased also barking at them. Only the cows remained his enemies.

"You can see how smart he is," said Ken. "Look how fast he learns."

All that evening, his belly distended with the amount Ken had fed him, Rupert slept peacefully and silently on the hearth. But after the candles had been extinguished and all had retired, he quickly squandered the favor he had so far painfully gained. Ken's proposal that Rupert sleep with him in the loft had been vetoed. Left alone in the vast dark kitchen Rupert was stirred to excessive vigilance. The slightest whisper of wind at a loophole or the crackling of an ember in a fireplace excited in him a spasm of frenetic barking. Intervals of complete silence in the world about him were equally as suspect and demanded as resolute a challenge.

Duncan, stumbling about with a candle, found pursuit hopeless. To Rupert his nightshirted figure was obviously a specter of nightmare proportions. Ken was summoned from the loft to effect the capture. But, forcefully exiled to the yard, Rupert, as before, clawed at the door and filled the night air with his despairing howls.

"Eric," called Duncan, "go with Ken and see that that dog is tied up down in the hollow sycamore."

"But the cows are there," remonstrated Ken. "Rupert hates them. He'll just bark and bark, way down there by himself."

"Good. Maybe he'll get hoarse."

The next day, however, Rupert proved able to render his first service to the community. Jarot and Jacob had emerged and, axes on shoulder, had plodded dejectedly off to the wood lot to cut palisade poles. Betsey and Lina, too, had come out to assist their mother in cleaning the four rabbits and three partridges she had caught in the snares she kept set in the edge of the woods. But Olen clung stubbornly to his bed. He asserted he was of a mind possibly never to get up again. The smell from the cooking pot had no effect upon him. He professed not to be hungry and doubted he ever again would be. Finally even Polly's patience was exhausted. She beckoned to Ken.

"Let's have us the loan o' thet pup o' yourn."

"What for?"

"I'll show yuh."

Polly scooped up Rupert, thrust him into the Slover cabin, and shut the door. Instantly Rupert began furiously to bark. The staccato din continued, interspersed with intermittent roars of indignation from Olen. Polly nodded complacently.

"No," protested Ken. "Let Rupert out. Olen will kill him."

"Olen?" Polly shook her head. "Olen he hollers big but he wouldn't no more hit a dog'n he would a day-old baby."

The unequal contest went on and on and became the center of station attention. Olen's swearing dwindled in volume but Rupert was tireless. After half an hour Olen surrendered. He emerged, glowered at the onlookers, shouldered his rifle and set off across the meadow and into the soothing quiet of the woods.

At dusk he had not returned. An hour after dark Polly called on Daisy to make sure he was not sulking in Caleb's cabin. She came back genuinely disturbed, having for the first time learned of Caleb's absence. Two hours after dark Jarot and Jacob made a wide circle in the woods, pausing at intervals to listen for a call or shot of distress. At midnight Duncan and Garett were still sitting by the fire waiting for word.

"There's nothing we can do until daylight," said Duncan. "Jat and Jake can't see to track him until then."

"There's one thing we can do," said Garett, yawning. "We can get some sleep. Ten to one that's what Olen's doing. With his bump of caution he's not likely to have let anything happen to him."

The door flew open. Polly, disheveled and panting, stood in it.

"Injuns," she gasped.

Duncan twisted in his chair and gaped at her, unable for the moment to accept the reality of her terror.

"But I thought with Caleb here you'd stopped worrying about visiting Indians."

Polly delivered the gist of her warning while turning to bolt out again.

"Caleb ain't here. And these Injuns ain't visitin'. Olen seen 'em. We-uns ain't squattin' here right where they know where to reach for us. You-uns best clear out, too."

Duncan pursued her into the yard. The Slovers, clutching their rifles, axes and sack of seed corn, were already moving around the corner of the house, keeping close to the wall. Olen turned to shush the low whine of one of his dogs. Duncan seized his arm.

"Where you going?"

"We aim to hide out," whispered Olen hoarsely. "But ain't no use our hidin' if'n the rest of yuh fool around so long the Injuns foller yuh to whereat we be."

Duncan shook him impatiently. "Tell me," he insisted. "We'll either join you right away or not at all."

"Yuh mind thet patch o' swamp along the bank—'bout two mile upriver? We-uns is a-wadin' crost thet and holin' up in them willows on thet little island out'n the edge o' the river."

Olen pulled away from Duncan.

"I'll show 'em, Paw," said Lina.

The Slovers, except for Lina, faded off into the darkness down the slope of the mound. Duncan beat on their doors to arouse the Lymans and the Negroes and returned to the kitchen. Garett had roused the women. All of them from indoors and out, wrapped in hastily caught-up dressing gowns or oddments of bedclothing, came swarming in, betraying their instinctive alarm by the urgency of their demands to know what was causing it.

"Will everybody be silent," ordered Duncan. "I can't tell you what's happened because I'm not yet sure myself. Now,

Lina, will you tell us—and slowly, please—what exactly did your father see?"

"A pack o' Shawnee," said Lina. She was sufficiently composed to be studying the night attire of the Jordan women while she spoke. " 'Bout three mile t'other side the falls where thet old Injun trail crosses the crik. Paw he figgers they was mebbe forty—all bucks—and all painted. They come on him so sudden like Paw had no time fer nuthin but jam hisself into a hole under a log. It was fetchin' on toward dark and they camped right there by the crik. They was so close Paw he never dast crawl off till 'bout an hour ago. Paw he figgers they's fixin' to jump the station come daylight."

"You all heard her," said Duncan. "The Slovers feel they're better off hiding in the woods than waiting here. They've already gone."

He looked around at the others with the speculative eye of the beleaguered commander whose decisions must wait upon his estimate of the temper of his garrison. Frank threw back the blanket draped about him and thrust his head out of the folds like an old turtle.

"Olen can't count past ten even when he ain't scared out of his wits. But if he did see a parcel of Indians and they are coming at us we're better able to stand 'em off here behind these walls than skitterin' around through the brush."

"I'm inclined to agree with Frank," said Garett, "but I don't like this division of forces. The diffident Slovers will fight if they have to and they're better shots than any of us. I'd say catch 'em and make 'em come back to help us hold this place."

"Think of the children," begged Agatha. "We can't go creeping off into the swamps in this kind of weather."

"This would scarcely seem the moment to hold a town meeting," said Louisa. "It's for you to decide, Duncan. Whatever you say—that's what we will do."

Duncan's nostrils were pinched and the muscles of his jaw working. "There is no getting away from the facts," he said huskily. He cleared his throat and continued in a harsher voice. "It's one fact that the Slovers are fully convinced that we are about to be attacked and equally convinced they can save their lives only by running into hiding. Nothing we can say or do will persuade them to come back. It is another fact that if we are seriously attacked we cannot hold this place with six rifles and no stockade to keep the attackers from rushing us. You and Frank, Garett, have soldiered enough to know that as well as I do. But the principal fact is that in this instance the Slover judgment is better than ours.

They have been through this kind of Indian situation many times before and we never have. Polly has witnessed the murder of three of her children on her own doorstep and Olen the butchery of both his parents. They know precisely and in detail that what they have to dread is worse than the hardship of crawling through a swamp or the shame of running when threatened. These are facts we cannot sidestep. We have to run, too. Dress warmly. Everybody take a blanket."

Announcement of the decision to flee brought with it the first chilling realization of the enormity of the threat from which they were fleeing. Frank, jerking open the door, flinched and peered into the dark yard before running across to his own door. Agatha paused to listen before running to the ladder leading into the loft where her children still slept. Olivia wrapped her arms around Garett as though reaching out to welcome, in the trial that was upon them, the need to share with him her young strength. The Negroes huddled together, their eyes rolling, their lips moving in supplication.

Duncan brought from the storeroom a bale of pemmican, tore it open and dumped out on the table the five-pound elkskin sacks of mixed corn meal and tallow. When he had procured this supply of the standard frontier emergency ration it had seemed an insurance for which there was not one chance in a thousand they would ever have need.

"Everybody take one," he directed.

He counted his reassembling company. Ken was missing.

"That miserable dog," gasped Agatha. "Ken's gone down to the hollow sycamore to get him."

Before Duncan had reached the door to start after him Ken appeared in it, towing Rupert at the end of his leash. The congregation of so many people, together with the general atmosphere of excitement, was immediately too much for Rupert. He began to bark. Ken's desperate efforts to silence him only aroused him the more.

"I've always wondered about the stories of fugitive settlers leaving their dogs shut up in their cabins behind them," remarked Garett.

"No," cried Ken. "No. No."

"He'll have to stay," ruled Duncan.

Frank snatched the leash and tied it to a table leg.

"Eric," said Agatha. "You keep hold of Ken—hang on to him every minute we're off wherever this is we're going."

"Blow out the candles," said Duncan. "I'll take the lead with Lina. The rest of you follow in single file. And keep close to whoever's in front of you. Garett, you bring up the rear."

The door was closed. In the house behind them Rupert ceased to bark and began to howl dismally. Duncan and Lina started off down the dark slope toward the path that led along the stream to the river. The others, clinging nervously to one another, groped into line to follow.

Tracy had run out into the yard before the candles were blown out. She could no longer endure the pain of watching Duncan's pain. She knew so well his every smile, his every frown. She always knew what he was thinking, more clearly, more sympathetically, more understandingly, she was sure, than Agatha could ever know. She remembered the light in his eyes that day of their arrival when they had stood side by side on this very spot where she was standing now. He had planned for so many months, had invested in the undertaking so much of what he owned and of what he was, that to be able at last to stand here and look about him had been a great experience for him, one she had been able to share. He could see spread out before him his whole future and his children's future. She alone knew how much it was costing him tonight to be giving it all up, to be running away without a battle—he, a soldier. She alone knew that.

She leaned against the great oak and, made weak by her anguish for him, sank to the ground, burying her face in her arms. The others were moving away, unaware in the darkness that she was not with them. Her heart went out to them, too. They were his people. She could even love Agatha, because he did, and because, as his wife and the mother of his children, Agatha, too, was a part of him. A frantic longing came upon her to be possessed of the power to shield them from every danger, since if they were lost then he, too, was lost. But at this moment they were creeping off away from her through this wintry darkness, pursued by unspeakable horrors, while she was too weak to do more than lie here dissolved in helpless compassion for them and for him and for herself.

Suddenly a thought struck her. She sprang up, her weakness falling away. It was not a great service but it was something tangible that she could do for them and the personal risk to her gave it meaning. She ran down to the hollow sycamore and lowered the bars. If nothing else could be saved she might still save milk for the children. The cows were reluctant to leave their warm shelter. She belabored them with a stick, drove them into the forest as far as the wood lot, and tied them to trees. There was the chance that here they would fall prey to wolves before the night was over, or that the Indians might still find them in the morning, but no such certainty of loss as had they been left in plain sight of the station.

The preoccupation with her task ended, there swooped upon her a consciousness of the darkness of the night forest and of her loneliness in it. Indians contemplating an attack at dawn might already have crept this near their goal, might already be crouched in the deeper shadows of any thicket about her. She ran along the wood lot trail, over the top of the mound, and along the path toward the point which the others had taken. The act of running away imposed its immediate penalty. She was beset by fears she had not imagined when running toward the sycamore and the wood lot. Shadowed terrors filled the darkness on every hand waiting to spring out upon her. She clenched her teeth against the hammering impulse to scream. As she neared the point, in her blind panic she strayed from the path. Suddenly her foot was seized. She fell headlong.

The metallic rasp had told her what it was that had so savagely gripped her even before she had recovered enough to run her hands down her leg to the steel jaws. She had stepped into one of the Slover wolf traps which with typical Slover heedlessness they had set so near the path. The toothed jaws had not quite cut through the stout leather of her hunting boots but were inexorably fastened upon her foot just below the ankle. The springs of the trap were too strong for her to loosen and the log to which the chain was stapled too heavy for her to drag. She was caught like any wild animal, condemned to lie here at the mercy of whatever the dangers of the night until the light of day exposed her to yet more fearful dangers.

A shadow appeared against the night sky. She tried to scream but could only whimper.

"Tracy," called the shadow, low-voiced. "Tracy."

With a sudden great throb of incredulous and shamed delight, she realized that it was Duncan, that Duncan, himself, had come back to look for her.

"Duncan," she whispered.

He could not see her on the ground in the darkness.

"Tracy," he repeated. "Tracy."

"I'm here," she gasped. "I can't get up."

He was kneeling beside her, gripping her arms, touching her face, running his hands over her to discover her affliction.

"My dear, my dear," he said. His hands found the trap. "Those Goddamned Slovers."

She had never before heard him swear. His rage seemed to make his nearness to her even more real, more personal.

"Can you stand up?"

"Yes. I'm not hurt much. Just caught."

He took her by the shoulders and lifted her to her feet. "Now hang on to me."

He held her upright against him, felt with his toes for the hinges of the trap, and, pressing against her, thrust his full weight on them. The jaws fell open. She was free.

"I'm sure nothing's broken," she said, the tumult within her making her frantically anxious to seem calm. She stood on one leg and tried the toe of her cramped foot against the ground. "I can walk."

"Nonsense," he said.

He slung the strap of his rifle over his shoulder and picked her up in his arms.

"Hang on tight," he advised her.

Her arms were wound around him to ease the labor of his carrying her and her face was pressed in the hollow of his shoulder against his neck to escape the scrape of branches. His physical presence, like his gust of rage, was real. He was sweating and he had not shaved since the day before. The masculine smell and roughness of him were real. The straining, convulsive embrace in which they were clasped was real. The excitement and terror and pain of the last hour had made her seem able to think with a sudden extraordinary clarity. He must sense the half-terrified, half-shamed, but wholly enchanted bliss that suffused her. If he had not long since, he must in this moment be guessing. He must know by the quivering of her flesh, the warmth of her body, the beating of her heart, that she loved him. But she was safe with him. Not tomorrow, or the day after, or ever, would he let her see that he knew. Tomorrow their eyes could meet as naturally and candidly as yesterday.

"When you first stepped in the trap," he said, holding her closer as he stepped over a log, "why in the world didn't you call out?"

"There was no use. I was so far behind the rest of you no one could have heard."

"Why were you so far behind?"

"I'd remembered the cows. I took them out of the hollow tree and tied them up in the woods where they'd be more out of sight."

"You didn't! What an absurdly gallant gesture. And what a damned-fool one. The next time you get any such preposterous idea as that will you tell me about it first?"

"Yes, Duncan."

There was a sudden sharp rustle in a nearby thicket. It was

no more than a wood mouse, in its frantic flight setting up a commotion out of all proportion to its size. But Tracy had raised her head from Duncan's shoulder to listen and he at the same time had turned his to peer toward the sound. Their faces came together, his mouth brushing the corner of hers. His breath caught, his lips strayed across her cheek, and returned to find hers. The sudden kiss seemed less the venture of a suitor than the unthinking impulse of a man conditioned to the habitual caresses of an affectionate family. But her surprise that it had occurred at all released the storm of her pent-up emotion. Her arms tightened about him, her moan was a welcome. In the ecstasy of her surrender it was she who prolonged the moment. And it was he who recoiled. His start of dismay filled her with a greater dismay. She could not in the darkness see his expression clearly but she could sense with what consternation he was scrambling to safety.

"I didn't mean that," he stammered. "I don't know what I could have been thinking of. Least of all at a time like this, with the chance of an Indian in the next thicket, and you scared out of your wits and not even able to walk."

"Put me down," she whispered. He let her slip from his arms. "See. I can stand alone. Quite well." Her fingers, still holding to his sleeve to steady herself, sank into his arm. "Anyway, we both know the truth—now."

"You can't realize what you're saying. This horrible night—your running around alone in the woods—getting caught in that trap—it's been like a nightmare."

"I know very well. I've known for years. But don't be too shocked. It need make no difference, to anyone."

"You poor, blessed, crazy child. What can I say that makes any real sense?"

Tracy removed her hand from his arm and stood unassisted. "I can say all that need be said. I could have been much worse off. If I'd been left behind in Virginia, for instance. What I keep remembering is that we're not just two people. You're more than the head of a family. You're like one of those patriarchs in the Bible. You're the chieftain of a clan, of a tribe, almost. And I can be glad I have a place in it. Think of me as a kind of concubine. Not one who will ever be taken into your tent, naturally. But one who is always standing ready to serve you. That's an infinitely more tolerable role than not being here at all."

Duncan laughed unsteadily. "If you're trying to tempt me with this talk of tents and all, you're certainly succeeding. Concubine, indeed. If this were sixteen years ago I'd not be long making you repent that taunt."

"But it's not. It's sixteen years too late. I know that. Better than you do. Or even than Agatha does."

"I still can't believe any of this. I've been so used to seeing you around, always so busy and serene. Of course Agatha and Olivia have had their heads together off and on. Trust wives to sniff out anything the least bit difficult about another woman. But they'd decided it was Garett."

"There's one advantage in your knowing. I won't have to be so desperately on guard, because you, too, will be on guard. Now shouldn't we be getting on? Look. I can not only stand alone. I can walk alone. See."

On the island the main party of fugitives crouched in the darkness under the willows, shivering with cold, plucking at the frost particles forming on their wet garments, and nursing their general and special anxieties. All, except Louisa and the two younger children who had been carried, had become soaked to the waist in crossing the marsh, as again and again they had broken through the thin crusting of ice over the invisible pools.

"Anyway, Duncan's moving around," said Garett. "He's keeping warmer than we are."

"Whatever can be keeping him so long?" complained Agatha. "I told him it was useless to look for her in the dark."

"Duncan has long proved able to take care of himself," said Louisa. "But what can ever have happened to that poor girl?"

"You think more of her than of your own flesh and blood," said Agatha.

"No," said Louisa quietly, "but just next after them."

Eric, keeping a grip on Ken's belt, pushed to the edge of the willows and stared into the darkness across the marsh. He felt triply deprived. The two people who meant so much to him were out there. And his father had refused to take him along in his search. Betsey crawled to his feet and wriggled upright at his elbow. She peered out over the swamp toward the woods beyond which lay the station.

"No fire yet," she said.

"What fire?"

"First off, Injuns allus burns yuh out."

Ken started with an apprehension which had not previously occurred to him.

"You can't see the station from here," said Eric. "You're just talking."

"You'd see the fire agin the sky fast enough—oncet they set her off," said Betsey.

Lina touched Eric on the other side.

"That pine stub back there," she said. "Yuh climb thet yuh could see clean to the station."

Eric went with her. The stub, towering above the matted willows, was a dead pine, drowned when the river made one of its perpetual changes of course. It was too large, however, to reach around and the lowest branch was above Eric's reach. Lina leaned against the trunk and braced herself.

"Climb up on me," she said, "and yuh kin ketch hold thet branch."

Her body which he remembered as so soft and yielding now felt remarkably hard and firm. He stepped on her arched back, balancing himself by holding to her upraised arms, stepped to her shoulders, grasped the branch, and pulled himself up. Other branches were within reach. He climbed higher and presently, over the massed shadow of the woods, made out the faint gray blob of the pond. Of the mound or station he could see nothing but he could tell by the line of the stream exactly where the station was and that there was no spark of light about it. He tried to imagine the Indians crouched in that darkness shrouding the station, waiting for the first streak of daylight to make their screeching assault. They might already have taken Tracy, his father, too. He looked at the east. It seemed already to be paling. Hastily he slid down to the low branch and swung to the ground, catching hold of Lina to regain his balance. Again she felt soft and yielding. Then he remembered Ken and let go of her. He ran back to Betsey at the edge of the marsh.

"Where's Ken?"

"He tuk off."

"Why didn't you stop him?"

"Whut fer?" Betsey laughed. "He kept a-whinin' 'bout fire and thet pup o' his'n and then he tuk off."

"Which way?"

"End o' the island where we-uns come acrost."

Eric plunged through the willows and across the marsh to the firmer ground beyond. Rounding the upthrust root spread of a fallen poplar he came upon his father. Tracy was standing beside him. It was getting enough lighter for him to see how tired his father was.

"I keep telling you I can walk perfectly well," Tracy was saying.

"Eric," said his father, swinging around.

Eric's immense relief that they were safe became mingled with the shame of the confession he must make.

"Ken got away."

"But you were told to watch him."

"Betsey started talking about the Indians burning the station. I climbed a tree to look. And Ken got to thinking about his dog in the fire. Anyway, he got away."

His father no longer looked tired.

"He must have cut across through the woods or we would have run into him."

"I'm all right," said Tracy. "I can make it the rest of the way."

"The island's right over there," said his father. "Tell them to stay there until they hear from me. You come with me, Eric."

Eric sprang forward. His father set straight off along the bank toward the point. Eric kept at his heels. So many people had come and gone this way last night that it had become a trail anybody could follow, let alone an Indian. His not hanging on to Ken was a terrible thing. But it was almost worth it to have it lead to his being allowed to accompany his father to look for him. At the point his father stopped and grasped his arm.

"There's been enough foolishness for one night. So see that you do exactly what I say. Stay a good fifty yards behind me. Keep me in sight, though. Whatever I signal you to do—do it. If anything happens, no matter what, turn and run. I'm counting on you to take word back to our people on the island. Understand?"

Eric nodded. His father set off at a trot again along the path toward Revel Rock. As he neared the foot of the mound he left the path and crawled in the shadow of the brush alongside. Eric did likewise. It was getting definitely lighter now. The bushes and trees were beginning to take shape. He speculated on how you managed to see an Indian in the woods before he first saw you. He was relieved that he was not more scared than he seemed to be. He was scared some, of course. The trigger finger of his right hand kept trembling and the back of his neck felt hot and cold by turns. But he was not scared enough to wish he were somewhere else. He was glad he was here following his father and not still squatting back there under the willows on the island. His father was creeping up the side of the mound, keeping his head up to look around, and every few feet pausing to listen. It came over Eric that this was the hour the Indians were supposed to attack. They must be all around in the woods. Betsey and Lina could remember their cabin being burned three times and one other time when they did not run off soon enough when the Indians came at them when they were still in it and they were saved only because a company of rangers out scouting just happened to be near enough to hear the hullabaloo. Betsey said Indians when they first jumped out of the woods always whooped and yelled and made all the noise they could in order to get people so upset they had no idea what they were doing. Some such uproar as that might break out here any minute now. He controlled the impulse to run forward to join his father. If he could see him so clearly from this distance then the hidden Indians must also be able to see him. Then he saw something else. There were columns of smoke pouring from both the station's main chimneys. The fires they had left must long since have died down. Someone must have been in the kitchen to have got them going again. Suddenly his father got to his feet, ran upright to the station, and looked in at a loophole.

All Duncan could see through the loophole was the fireplace in the end of the kitchen toward the office. It had been heaped with logs and was burning with a warmth he could feel against his face at his distance. He moved to another loophole that gave him a view of the other fireplace in which also logs had been heaped. Ken was asleep on the hearth, his arms wrapped around the dog who was also asleep. In Louisa's armchair, drawn close to the fire, sat Caleb Lewis. He had removed his wet leggings and moccasins to dry them and sat with his bare legs stretched out toward the heat. Beside him on the floor was a plate with remnants of corn bread and ham he must have found in the larder. He was smoking one of Duncan's clay pipes and sipping from a bottle of Duncan's brandy. From time to time he looked about him contemplatively with the unmistakable air of a man able to take a proprietary satisfaction in his surroundings.

Duncan waved to Eric to come on and walked to the door. Caleb looked around at his entrance but did not get up.

"You appear to have got back early," said Duncan.

Caleb grinned. It was the first time Duncan had ever seen a change of expression cross his face.

"So do you."

"We've been hiding in the woods."

Caleb nodded. His grin had faded but his eyes remained amused. Duncan continued his uncomfortable explanation.

"Olen saw them—the Indians, I mean."

"So did I. About an hour before light. Just as they were breaking camp."

"What makes you so sure they weren't after us?"

"Because I know what they were after."

"Olen says they were some of your Shawnee—and painted for war."

"So they were. That was because they were on their way to Fort McIntosh to tell the Delaware and Wyandot they are fools to sign a treaty."

"Do I gather, then, that our only mistake was in taking alarm too soon? That we may still expect trouble from—your friends?"

"That is possible. But the time to hide in the woods is not yet. Before that time comes I will be able to tell you."

Eric came in. His mouth fell open when he saw Caleb and Ken, but when he saw the look on his father's face he instantly and silently closed it again.

"Go tell our people on the island it was a false alarm," said Duncan.

Eric ran out. Caleb rose and drew a folded bit of paper from a pouch at his belt.

"A letter for you from General Clark."

Duncan took the letter and broke the seals. Caleb began to draw on his leggings and moccasins. The letter read:

Dear Colonel Jordan:

I met Geo Morgan at the Muskingum he says the latest Word at Pitt is that the Delaware and Wyandot are coming in Caleb tells me the Shawnee are Divided some want war and Some want peace I told him to tell them they can have Whichever they want Geo Morgan knew Corbit Revel he tells me that Back about 1772 he saw Caleb Lewis in Corbit's camp on what is now your Creek Caleb was then a boy of maybe Seventeen Corbit had bought him off the Shawnee and later that year sent him to New Orleans to work for a trader and learn English Caleb was mighty close mouthed with me but he says he spent the next eight Years at Sea neither Geo or me ever heard of his being around this part of the Country during the War I think I would have heard about it if he had been and had Sided with the English or Indians I know about and Remember all of them Rascals My opinion after Watching him for a day and a night is that he is like a young Horse that has not yet been gentled he could turn out to be a real Good one or a real bad one he is still thick with the Shawnee but he has some hankering to be a White Man he can be some Good to you this winter and I will keep on asking about him at Pitt and Louisville and Vincennes and wherever I am at my advice is for the Present to keep an eye on him but to keep him around if you can put up with him.

Y'r ob'd't servant
G. R. Clark

Duncan looked up from the letter. Caleb had his rifle under his arm and was moving toward the door.

"Why haven't you told me that you knew Corbit Revel?"

"You did not ask me."

"Why should it have occurred to me to ask you? . . . I take it you on your side have had no idea I was his kinsman?"

"Yes. I knew that."

"Then when you came here you expected to find us here?"

"No. But I expected you to come sooner or later."

"Do you propose to continue to live here, on your side of the creek?"

"Yes."

"What led you to select this valley?"

"As a boy I camped here. Many times with the Shawnee and after that with Corbit. I have been many places. I like this one best."

"You speak of him as if you had been especially attached to him."

"I had reason to be."

"Aside from his ransoming you from captivity?"

"Yes. He treated me like a son."

"Yet in the one letter we ever had from him—written from Pittsburgh the year after he had sent you to New Orleans—he made no mention of you."

A shadow crossed Caleb's face.

"When a man is old and sick and alone and knows he is dying, he thinks first of his own family."

"We might as well come right out with it, Mr. Lewis. Do you feel we have usurped some claim you might have had here?"

"No. This place belonged to Corbit. The Shawnee gave it to him. He gave it to you. It now belongs to you."

"I am glad you can take so broad a view. Let us hope we may continue to prove good neighbors."

Caleb nodded, took another long look around the room, and opened the door. Duncan hesitated, smothered his irritation, and strode after him.

"Drop in on us any time you feel like it," he said, offering his hand.

Caleb's taking it was a purely formal gesture. In his eyes there was another faint glint of amusement. He nodded again and set off for his cabin. Duncan considered going to meet his returning people, realized how tired he was, and sat down on the doorstep to wait.

The others came streaming in, their return as noisy with relief as their departure had been silent with apprehension. Garett, staggering with fatigue but still grinning, patted the log wall.

"Nothing like a night in the swamps to make you realize what a palace we inhabit."

Agatha flew to Duncan. "We could imagine we were safe where we were but you never were. You were always off somewhere. Never has there been a night so long. Is Ken really quite all right?"

In the midst of the weary rejoicing, Frank remained dour. He waited until the Slovers straggled into the yard, at the end of the procession, to deliver his pronunciamento.

"The big reason you bundled them along with us," he said, pointing a stubby, accusing finger at Duncan, "was because you claimed they knowed so much about the woods and about Indians." The finger came around to stab at Olen. "What do they know? Nothin'. Last night showed that. They ain't up to telling an Indian from a tamarack. They keep Indians off our backs? They ain't men enough to scratch the lice off their own. All of 'em put together ain't half so much good to us as Ken's dog."

The Slovers listened attentively, as though they did not wish to miss one syllable of Frank's outburst. They were not offended. While he was speaking they kept nudging one another, and when he had finished they whooped with laughter. They were forever being seized by spasms of private amusement at moments suggesting to no one else anything but discomfort or dismay.

"One thing yuh'll larn, Frank," said Olen, sobering and giving Frank a kindly pat, "if'n yuh live long enough. Yuh'll larn that it's a sight smarter t'run forty time when there ain't no real reason to run than to set tight jest oncet when there be."

"All of you get some rest," said Duncan. "Because beginning this afternoon there's not going to be any rest for anybody until we've got a stockade up."

Louisa, leaning on Tracy's arm, turned in the middle of the kitchen to wait for Duncan.

"I must admit that for once I agree with Frank," she said. "The Slovers are lazy, dirty, mischievous, stupid, and cowardly. They even laugh at things only imbeciles could laugh at. They have no single redeeming feature."

That afternoon, however, the Slovers emerged from their cabin, axes in hand. They rushed to the task of cutting palisade poles with the excited urgency of farmers getting in hay when clouds threaten.

"The lesser of two evils," said Garett. "They fear Indians more than they hate work."

Duncan's satisfaction with the development was diminished by the explanation speedily volunteered by Betsey.

"Caleb he tol' em to git a-goin'. Whenever Caleb he jest gives 'em a look they jump right out'n their britches."

"Caleb is in a position to be very helpful to us," said Duncan.

"Thet's whut Paw says. Paw says it's mighty lucky fer us Caleb he come along."

"I'm sure it is—for all of us. We're all in this together."

Betsey eyed him sharply, trying to guess whether his cheerfulness was genuine or merely to cover up her success in baiting him.

"We-uns is all behind the same stockade—thet's fer sure."

The next night Caleb took advantage of Duncan's neighborly invitation to drop in. The Jordans were still at supper. He declined the suggestion that he join them at the table and took a seat beside the fireplace in the end of the kitchen toward the office. This was the hearth about which the family was accustomed to gather in the evening, leaving the other end of the room to the Negroes and their domestic duties. To all attempts to include him in the table conversation he replied with monosyllables or not at all. He seemed merely disposed to sit stolidly as an Indian in the warmth of the fire and from his post as bystander to listen intently to whatever was said and to watch even more intently the expression on the face of whoever was saying it.

"Notice his eyes," whispered Garett to Agatha. "Damme if they're not as yellow as a panther's. Fancy a panther choosing our company."

"They're more green than yellow," murmured Agatha. "But as unsociable as a cat's—you're right about that. He makes me as uncomfortable as I could wish we made him."

When the others gathered about him at the fireplace, Caleb remained as unresponsive but, at this so much closer range, continued to stare, first at one and then at another, as intently as before. His glance tended to pass over Duncan and Garett, as though he had by now come to some conclusion about them. It was the several women who absorbed him. The conversation flagged.

"Why don't you read to us, Tracy?" proposed Louisa.

This was an evening diversion to which they frequently turned. Among the few books brought with them was a volume of Shakespeare's tragedies. Tracy leaved through the pages reflectively.

"Othello," suggested Garett.

Tracy found the place and began to read. She had a clear

and spirited reading voice which, without overdramatizing, attached color and meaning to the lines. Caleb gave no indication that the words meant anything out of the ordinary to him. But during the whole of two acts he watched the play of expression over her face as she read, his eyes straying occasionally to her hair shimmering in the candlelight or to her hands as she turned a page. Then, as though some unspoken question had been answered for him, he turned his stare on Agatha and Olivia. Olivia appeared to take no notice, but Agatha frowned, fidgeted, kept changing her position, and finally rose.

"I'm sorry, Tracy. You know how much I ordinarily enjoy your reading. But tonight I'm very tired. Please keep on. Good night, Mother. Good night, all. Good night, Mr. Lewis."

She withdrew. Tracy looked around to estimate the wish of the others about her continuing to read. Caleb got up, crossed to the door to pick up his rifle leaning there against the wall, nodded an abrupt good evening to the company, and went out.

"Personally," said Garett, "I find his calls more tolerable when he brings his Indians."

Duncan joined Agatha in their room.

"I can't stand his looking at me that way," she said. "He keeps watching my face as though he was bound to know what I might be thinking. And not only that. Once in a while"—her hands fluttered in a swift protective gesture toward her bosom and thighs—"it's as though he were seeing right through my clothes."

As so often when she was serious Duncan took refuge in lightness.

"Who could blame him—with a figure like yours?"

"You're a man, Duncan—and my husband. Act like it. I am your wife, and your wife is not for him even to look at."

The next night, and the one after, Caleb returned to sit in the chimney corner, as silent and as observant as before. Each evening after an hour or so he rose and, still silent, withdrew. Tracy had not been asked to read on either of these following nights. Instead the Jordans resorted defensively to another of their evening diversions. They played cards. Caleb declined their perfunctory invitation that he take a hand or at any rate sit with them and look on. The sole purpose of his calls seemed to continue to be the opportunity to sit and study the women of the household. When the door had closed upon him the third time the Jordans laid down their cards and looked at each other.

"This just can't go on," said Olivia. "We've always had

such pleasant evenings together. He's ruined them for us." She looked resentfully at Garett. "When he's here even Garett —who usually welcomes anything that makes us uncomfortable—gets so annoyed he takes half a dozen extra drinks."

"Tonight only five and a half, my dear." Garett lifted his half glass of whisky, contemplated it, and tossed it down. "Six, only now. Seems to me I've heard something about Indian courtships. Doesn't the brave hang around the wigwam until the object of his affections takes some notice of him? I believe the next step is some sort of trial involving a blanket. Tracy?"

"If that's so," said Tracy calmly, "in this instance he will have rather a long wait."

"Actually," said Duncan, "the man's simply devoured by curiosity, just as the Indians were. He's never before been around people like us and everything about us is novel to him."

"What disturbs me more than his manners," said Tracy—"if you and Duncan will forgive my saying so, Agatha—is the way he has captivated Eric. Eric idolizes him because he knows the wilderness, how to hunt and track and all about Indians and everything else Eric is wild to know. Eric is over there with him every day."

"I don't like that either," said Agatha, "and I think it should be stopped. Though Duncan thinks those are things Eric should have a chance to learn. But what I really can't stand —and Duncan also refuses to see—is the way he's pushing in on us, as though he owned the place. The Slovers have done more work these last three days than the last three months. Why? He told them to. We seem reasonably safe from Indians. Why? He is their friend. No wonder he feels he's the same as commander here."

Garett put down his refilled glass. His voice was suddenly firm.

"That'll be his longest wait of all."

The brothers' eyes met with understanding. For a moment both their faces were as cold and expressionless as Caleb's could ever be.

"Now that we're getting down to fundamentals," said Duncan, "may I say this: Nothing's so important to me as to do whatever we can to hold this place until we're well enough established to be certain we can go on holding it. To do that I'll take any kind of help from anybody."

"Agatha's talking nonsense," said Louisa. "We all know who's in command here. And if that man has any doubts, either Duncan or Garett will be able to put him straight fast enough. But there *is* something, Duncan, to deal with now, before worse comes of it. He isn't sitting around here harboring some simple courting idea. Anybody can see that. He's after a woman, any woman. He has more eyes for Agatha and Olivia than he has for Tracy. He struts about like a dog in heat. That's what's got to stop without any wait whatever."

"We could most certainly do with less frequent calls," said Duncan. "I'll have a talk with him tomorrow."

The next day brought the first hard blizzard of the winter. Duncan, leaning into the blasts of driving snow, crossed the stream which, now frozen, could be crossed at any point, and struggled through the drifts toward Caleb's cabin. Taking no account of the weather, other than that the snow on the ground eased the task of dragging logs into piles for later burning, Caleb and Daisy were still at work enlarging his clearing. The howling of the wind made speech nearly impossible. Caleb led the way to his cabin.

Duncan was struck by the spare neatness and orderliness of the single room. Everything was scrubbed and scoured and in its place. Even the blankets on the pole-and-rawhide bed were stretched taut. He remembered Clark's report of the presumed years at sea. This cabin in the woods was as shipshape as one aboard a man-of-war. Caleb turned to face him and waited calmly. Duncan had been casting about for the precise words with which to make his announcement. The man's easy assurance, bordering on insolence, hardened his purpose.

"I came to say that it would seem to us more suitable if your visits were rather less frequent."

"You have some reason?"

"We have. To put it bluntly, our womenfolk have gained the uncomfortable impression that you are looking them over, as it were, to determine which one you prefer."

"That is so. It is not good for a man to live alone."

"You have a woman."

"Daisy? She is only for this winter. And she is an Indian. I plan to stay here, and next spring I will need a white woman."

"Then you will need to look more widely. The only one available in our household, Miss Carter, has taken a strong—possibly an unreasoning but nevertheless a strong—dislike to you."

"There are two others who are still young and who have learned what it is like to live with a man."

Duncan controlled his temper. In order to stress his innate superiority to this man who was so near a savage it was necessary that his own attitude remain undeviatingly civilized.

"Unhappily each is already supplied with a man."

There was again that glint of amusement in Caleb's eyes. "You have come to a country, Colonel Jordan, where men seldom die of old age. It is a country where young women may any day become young widows."

"If you mean that as some sort of a challenge, I accept it. Meanwhile, since we must continue to be neighbors, please feel free to call at the station whenever you have business there, but let us postpone further social calls until we are better acquainted."

Caleb accepted the ruling with the same impassive formality with which he had accepted Duncan's earlier handclasp.

"It is your house," he said.

There was for a second the same faint glint in his eyes. But Duncan was no longer so sure that this indicated a kind of unaccountable amusement. He was reminded of the alien inscrutability of the Indians about whose actual state of mind, as they had lined up inside his door that night, he had been able to make no slightest guess.

The blizzard continued into the second night. The next morning Eric was the first to venture out. He came floundering back frantic with excitement.

"They've gone," he exclaimed. "Caleb and Daisy have gone. The cabin's shut up and they took everything with them. You can see their tracks. They've gone."

"Thank heaven for that," breathed Agatha.

"Take heart, my young friend," said Garett. "Your paladin has doubtless but resorted for the winter to the more congenial precincts of his Shawnee kind. Spring may return him to us —worse luck."

"No," insisted Eric. "He planned to stay here all winter. I know he did. Something's happened."

"Let's hope," murmured Louisa, "to him."

January

The first blizzard was succeeded by another and then, after a week of intermittent heavy snow, by a third. When this one ceased to howl, it left in its wake the stillness of an intense cold. The timbers of the buildings groaned. Limbs snapped from trees. The snow underfoot creaked. The pond and the stream became one solid block of ice. The Ohio itself froze over, so changing the familiar landscape that to the people of the station it seemed that morning that they had awakened to a different world. They were more relieved than oppressed by this final weight of winter. The frozen river seemed no longer an avenue of easy approach for whoever might chance to be abroad and the snowbanked forest had again become their shield against the distant and the unknown. Behind these comforting barriers they could rest for a time in seclusion and peace. Encircled by their newly finished stockade and assured by the existence in the storeroom of ample food to supply them into midsummer, they settled by their firesides for a pleasant respite which they could feel they had earned by their recent labors and anxieties.

The one interference with their ease was Duncan's insistence on a regular guard mount. Every hour of the day or night, he was determined, there must be a man on watch at the gate. It was the usually apprehensive Olen who protested the most loudly against what he maintained was an altogether unnecessary precaution. He attempted to explain the facts of wilderness winter life to Duncan.

"Whilst there's snow on the ground we-uns got no call to fret about Injuns. They never lay up nuthin' fer winter so this time o' year they's all busy scratchin' around fer somethin' to eat. More'n thet they never like to hunt fer trouble nowhere's thet's way off from where they belong account yuh can't go nowheres in the snow without leavin' tracks. It goes agin' the grain with a Injun if'n other folks kin see right off where he's bin and whut he's bin up to. Injuns ain't a-goin' to bother us none till the snow goes off in the spring."

Nevertheless Duncan continued to insist and the regular guard was established. The man on the gate could always tell when his relief was due because he could hear the distant faint chime of Louisa's clock, and with four-hour watches divided among eleven men there was no great interruption of the station's indolence. But as the days crept the long hours of drowsy huddling about fires began to lose their first appeal. Minor bickerings broke out. The perpetual feud between Lymans and Slovers developed new edges. Meanwhile the continued cold had given their many fires an appetite for fuel that had much reduced the wood supply.

Appreciating the twin need for work and wood, Duncan organized a woodcutting project in which all were to participate. He had learned by now that the Slovers' congenital aversion to work was only to be counteracted by a suggestion of play. Therefore he termed the community effort a woodcutting bee. A fire was built in the wood lot. In the ashes edging the fire Geneva kept rows of sweetened corn pone toasting. Beside them simmered a kettle of pickled buffalo tongue. Another steaming pot of ginger-flavored water was laced at suitable intervals with a gurgling contribution from a demijohn of rum.

Frank had knocked together a stout sledge to haul the wood to the station. The incline to the mound was sprinkled with water which immediately froze into a smooth glaze. With the entire corps of women and children pulling on the ropes, enormous loads of wood were snaked with ease up to the growing pile in the stockade. Duncan and Luke and Ned and Clem formed teams on the two-man saws to cut the larger logs into lengths for splitting, but it was upon the Slover axemen that the chief burden fell. Laughing and yelling, they leaped to meet the challenge. With so many eyes observing their prowess they became engines of energy. Pausing only to snatch an occasional mouthful of corn pone and tongue or another dipperful of hot watered rum, they kept their axes flashing and whirling. Before the crash of a falling tree had ceased to echo, they had it trimmed and were beginning to cut it up. There was always a new load of split cordwood ready for each return of the sledge. By mid-afternoon the heap of wood in the station yard had reached the proportions of a two-month supply for all five fireplaces.

Meanwhile the team of women and children pulling the sledge under Frank's supervision had made a happy discovery. If, returning with the empty sledge, they climbed aboard at the top of the slope they were able to coast all the way back down to the wood lot. When Duncan announced a formal end to the woodcutting, the Slovers, Ned, Clem, and Luke immediately seized upon the sledge to take their turn. Their excited yells matched those the coasting had drawn from the women and children. After a second ride down this relatively modest incline the next step was a natural one. Beyond the wood lot there rose a considerable ridge. The snow was crusted hard enough and the trees sufficiently widely spaced to make this a slide with a much more interesting appeal. Here a far greater velocity was to be gained, there was the advantage that during its rapid descent the sledge must be guided in and out among the trees, and the final zest in that when at length it came hurtling out into the cleared area of the wood lot there were brush piles to be avoided and a studding of stumps bound sooner or later to overturn it. In the event so it proved. Every flight ended at some stage with the sledge's upset, throwing its passengers sprawling into snowbanks when they were lucky and into thickets or against trees when they were not. The forest rang with their whoops of delight.

At his mother's insistence that she be given another turn on the sledge now that its career had become so much more exciting, Jarot relinquished his place to her. As he stood by the fire, laughing at the next descent of the sledge, his fingers presently began to pluck at the empty air in the curve of his arm. His laugh stiffened into a grin and then into the brooding, trancelike mask that always accompanied his desperate fumbling with his mandiddle. Garett watched fascinated.

"What can he be trying to get at?" he asked Lina.

"He's jest a-hankerin'."

"Hankering for what?"

"Nobody knows fer sure. Could be he don't hisself. It's allus jest like he was a-tryin' to ketch somethin' only he never kin figger jest whut it is and so he never ketches up with it."

Mark, on duty at the gate, came out to the corner of the stockade and began calling that his time was up. Jacob, whose next watch it was, was extracted from the sledding party and dispatched to relieve him.

"Get Jat's mandiddle," said Garett, "and have Mark bring it down with him."

Jacob picked up his rifle from the stack leaning against a tree and plodded up to the gate. Mark, eager to have his turn on the sledge, came running down with the mandiddle. Garett thrust the instrument into Jarot's hands. His fingers closed upon it but, plucking now at the strings instead of empty air, plucked so gently that no more than the faintest whisper of sound was drawn forth while he seemed to sink more deeply than ever into his trance.

"I want to try something," said Garett. "Hey, you, Clem, Ned—let someone else ride in your place. You and Hebe and Geneva come over here. Now sing something—something loud and lively—and old."

There was a slight delay while Ned and Clem got their wind and the quartet conferred. Then they launched into "Clinch Mountain."

"Louder," demanded Garett.

For a time Jarot seemed unaware of the four Negroes singing lustily immediately in front of him, then suddenly he appeared to take notice of them. He cocked his head to listen, grinned, and at once began to play the air, very briskly and decisively.

"Why, he can play," exclaimed Garett.

"Fer sure he kin play," said Lina. "Now and then back home when folks craved to dance, he uster play fer 'em most the night."

During several verses Jarot appeared pleased and interested in the Negroes' vocal performance and his own share in it; then suddenly he ceased to accompany the quartet and relapsed into his strange, inward struggle.

"I believe I've got it," said Garett to Duncan. "The man's a thwarted genius. That's his trouble. He has in him strains of music which he can't quite capture. Or maybe it's lines of poetry. The birth pangs of creation—they're what he's grappling with."

"You may be right," said Duncan. "Though so far it seems an unrewarding quest. Meanwhile, it's getting late and I think Mother's beginning to get cold. We'll be moving along."

Picking up his rifle from the array against the tree, Duncan instructed the elder children to come in when they had watched one more descent of the sledge and started up toward the station with Louisa, Agatha, Tracy, Susie, and Chris. The sun was dipping behind the western woods. The short winter day was coming to an end. As the path veered past the corner of the stockage he saw that the gate was standing open. Impatient to reprimand Jacob, he strode on ahead of the others. As his view of the open gateway widened his anger mounted. Jacob was sitting in the snow banked against the Lyman cabin, his head back against the wall, his mouth hanging open. His reaction to his arduous day had been promptly to seize a first opportunity to take a nap.

Duncan was still a step away from the gateway when he

heard a call from Agatha. He turned to look back. All four of the Slover dogs were racing up the slope. They swept on past him, whining with vicious eagerness. Duncan leaped after them and came to another stop in the gateway. The twilight was rapidly darkening but there was still light enough to reveal with terrifying clarity what was happening.

Three Indians, who must just have emerged into the yard from the kitchen, were recoiling from the charging dogs. One was John Turtle but both of the others were younger men than any of that original five who had called with Caleb. John Turtle sprang to the safety of the top of the woodpile. One of the others kicked off the nearest dog and dove into the Lyman cabin, slamming the door behind him. The third, now beset by all four dogs, caught up a stick of wood with which to ward them off and set his back against the wall of the Negroes' cabin. The dogs were hardened killers, accustomed to coping with wounded bears or packs of wolves and trained especially to abominate Indians. They easily avoided the swinging club and gathered themselves for the concerted lunge which must bring down their prey. Duncan, still disagreeably surprised by the presence of the Indians, was nevertheless moved to run to the savages' assistance. But John Turtle acted more quickly.

Expertly whipping arrows from the quiver on his back, he shot four with such incredible rapidity that all seemed in flight at once. Each transfixed one of the dogs. With his stick of wood their intended victim began methodically to bash in their heads as they writhed in agony about his feet. John Turtle sprang down from the woodpile and advanced on Duncan, grinning happily, his hand outstretched.

Jacob had been sighing and grunting as he passed through the protracted throes that marked one of his awakenings. His eyes opened in time to fall upon John Turtle's advance and his hand reached out to grasp the rifle which he had left leaning against the wall beside him when he had sat down. It was not there. With the celerity of a jack coming out of its box he shot upright, dove into the Lyman cabin, and slammed the door behind him. It was the same door through which the second Indian had darted, but after one muffled curse from Jacob no further sound came from within.

John Turtle gripped Duncan's hand with his own right and with his left tapped himself on the chest. "Friend," he said. He tapped Duncan's chest. "Friend," he repeated. The other Indian, still clutching his bloody club, moved forward to join them.

Duncan permitted John Turtle to continue to shake his hand

and essayed an approximation of the Indian's infinitely cordial grin. He was acutely conscious of the presence of Agatha and the others, now clustered about him, staring in consternation at their unexpected guests and at the dead dogs.

"Go into the house," said Duncan quietly to Agatha. "Don't run. Just keep moving. And when you're inside bar the door. I'll keep these two talking. Everybody else will be here any minute."

In the shadows of the woods it was getting almost too dark to see, except near the fire. Cam watched the last careening descent of the sledge and its satisfying crash against a stump at the end of its run and turned back to the other tableau provided by Garett's still fascinated concentration on Jarot's creative torment. Suddenly her shrill voice rang clearly above the laughter of the sprawling tobogganers.

"Look, Uncle Garry. Look. An Indian just took all our rifles."

Everyone looked in the direction she was pointing. The Indian was no longer to be seen. But in the flickering shadows at the outer edges of the light cast by the fire the tree against which their rifles had been stacked was now bare. The response was unanimous. All began at once to run toward the station. From the woods behind them squealed three short sharp blasts of an Indian war whistle.

The fading light from without failed to penetrate the loopholes or the small windows in the wall on the side toward the yard so that it was dark as night in the kitchen. Louisa released Tracy's arm as they crossed the threshold.

"Good heavens," she sniffed. "They've been in here. A marvel that two Indians just being in a room should leave so strong a smell."

The others groped in after Louisa and Tracy and closed the door. Tracy felt her way along the table, took a candle from the basket on the shelf over the fireplace, and lighted it at one of the smoldering coals on the hearth. As she straightened she heard Agatha gasp. She spun around, holding up the candle. Ranged motionless as statues around the walls, their eyes catching and reflecting the dim glow of the candle, were the dark, bulky, fur-shrouded figures of twenty or more Indians.

In the yard Duncan could hear the pounding of feet as the party from the wood lot ran for the gate. He prolonged the ceremony of shaking hands with the second Indian. The fugitives came floundering through the gateway.

"Father," panted Eric. "An Indian stole all our rifles."

"Shut the gate," said Duncan, taking care to keep his

voice steady and calm. "We've got three of them here. We'll hang on to them until our rifles are returned to us."

Eric swung the gate shut.

"Friend," said John Turtle. He tapped his chest and pointed to the new arrivals. "Friend," he repeated. It was now so dark that his face was indistinct except for the whites of his eyes and the whiteness of his teeth as he continued to grin. From his parted lips came then the low coo of a dove.

Every door within the stockade opened and some thirty-five or forty Indians emerged into the yard. A half dozen of those from the Lyman and Slover cabins carried pine-knot torches which cast a lurid glow over the array of dark faces and dark figures. None was painted and only three carried rifles. But from the fact that only a few were equipped with bows and arrows Duncan judged that most had firearms that had been laid aside somewhere close at hand.

"Hold it," he said to his people. "Don't make a move."

He glanced around at them, apprehensive lest one of them make some useless and merely provocative gesture of belligerence. He need not have feared. Garett, his arm around Olivia, was, of course, as steady as a rock. Eric merely gaped, as though at some preternaturally theatrical performance. Ken was holding Rupert clasped in his arms, his fingers tightly closed over his snout to keep him from barking. Cam edged forward, trustingly, toward her father. The Lymans, as though unable to believe what they were seeing, had been shocked into total inertia. The Slovers, who understood all too well what they were seeing, had become immediately as dispirited as though already they were captives. Jacob, apparently none the worse for his brief sojourn among the savages with whom he had shared his refuge, stumbled from the Lyman cabin and edged along the wall to join the group of whites.

The Indians swarmed forward but after some elbowing for points of vantage in the front rank did not press too closely in upon the conference between John Turtle and Duncan.

"Friend—friend—friend," John Turtle was chanting loudly while continually pointing in vigorous and alternate succession at various members of his company and at individuals among the whites grouped behind Duncan.

"Friend," agreed Duncan.

John Turtle snatched a bow from a youth beside him and extended it to Duncan. "Friend," he said, reaching for Duncan's rifle. "Swap? Swap, no?"

It was not a situation in which a single rifle was of much use. Duncan released his to John Turtle's grasp. The bow he received in exchange had no string. He held it up to indicate this deficiency. John Turtle laughed merrily and discharged Duncan's rifle into the air. By cheerful gestures he indicated that they were now equally unarmed as was the only right and proper case with such good friends.

"Friend," he said, clapping Duncan heartily on the shoulder. "Eat, no?"

"We'll just have to put up with this as best we can," said Duncan to his people. "I suggest going to your houses and mixing with them as little as you can manage."

"Eat," he said, nodding to John Turtle.

Pushing through the circle of Indians he strode to the kitchen. Tracy had lighted a dozen candles, filling the room with a blaze of illumination. Garett, Olivia, Eric, Cam, and Ken were able to follow him without being deterred by the Indians.

"What are they going to do to us?" asked Louisa.

"Nothing for the moment, except probably steal us blind," said Duncan. "All of you go with Agatha to our room. That is the most out of the way. Stay there and stay together. If any of them insist upon coming in give them anything they seem to want."

Snatching one of the candles he ran through the office and unlocked the door to the storeroom. With one of the spare axes there he began to break up the three remaining kegs of spirits—two of whisky and one of brandy. The liquor gushing out of the floor sent up choking fumes. Before he had swung his axe at the brandy keg John Turtle ran in and caught his arm.

"No. No. No," he expostulated. "Friend."

He was heart stricken. He could not find gestures sufficiently eloquent to express his disappointment and surprise and dismay that Duncan had so soon betrayed the bond of good-fellowship which had been established between them. Other Indians crowded in. The sight and smell of so much good whisky wasted brought the first dark scowls to mar the pleasure all had so far taken in the occasion. Duncan cast one last look around at the well-stocked storeroom and forced a hospitable grin. He indicated for them to help themselves.

Pushing through the press of Indians crowding the doorway, he returned to the kitchen, into which more of the Indians from the yard were rushing. They were muttering excitedly but their complacency was restored by the discovery that there remained an unbroken keg of brandy. There soon developed a boisterous procession to and from the storeroom from which each emerged clutching a ham, a side of bacon, a sack of corn meal, a crock of honey, or a string of buffalo jerky. Geneva plucked at Duncan's sleeve. The four Negroes were huddled in a corner.

"They won't let us into our place," she reported.

Evidently it was there the Indians' missing rifles had been deposited.

"Then you'll just have to get along with them in here," said Duncan. "Show them how to cook whatever they want. Cook it for them if they want you to."

The Negroes nodded. Their first panic was beginning to pass. They had already sensed that the Indians recognized in them a certain kinship of color, that for them the Indian protestations of friendliness were possibly genuine. Duncan went out into the yard. Beside the doorstep an Indian was expertly cutting up the carcasses of the dogs. A large fire, fed by logs from the new woodpile, brightly lighted the whole interior of the stockade. As evidence that John Turtle, in the midst of all the wild hubbub, was still keeping some sort of order, two Indians with rifles were standing before the door of the Negroes' quarters and there were two others on guard at the gate.

Duncan gathered up an armful of wood to account for his moving across the yard toward the Slover cabin. The Indian sentries merely watched him. The Slovers had not troubled to build up their fire. They were crouched shivering on the cold floor, too dejected even to try to keep watch through their loopholes. Duncan threw a few sticks on the coals.

"I tried to spill all the hard liquor," he said. "But they got a half barrel of brandy. That's more than enough to get the whole pack of them blind drunk. If we watch our chance we may be able to make a break for the woods before the night's over."

"No use," said Olen heavily.

"We've got to do something. We can't just sit here while they work themselves up to the pitch of knocking us all in the head."

"No use to run," said Olen. "Not with the tracks we'd leave in this snow. Nuthin' they'd like better'n the fun o' runnin' us down."

Duncan rubbed the back of his neck thoughtfully as he considered the pointedness of this observation.

"Then maybe we're wrong to try to stay clear of them. Maybe we should mix with them instead. They keep claiming they're our friends. Maybe if we did they'd get to feeling that they actually are."

Olen brightened a trifle.

"I'd surely crave to git me one last dipper o' likker whilst I still got me a neck to pour it down."

"Olen," remonstrated Polly. "Mebbe yer a-goin' to die but it ain't fittin' to die dead drunk."

The Lymans refused to budge from the refuge of their cabin.

"The end which is coming to us this night," said Frank, "is the end I foretold when we came to this accursed place. But we will not forgather with the heathen. We will spend our last hours preparing ourselves by meditation and prayer."

Duncan led his own family out into the kitchen. The entrance of the Jordan and Slover women and children upon the scene of festivity stirred the Indians to new and more exuberant manifestations of friendliness. They singled out the two youngest, Chris and little Susie, for special attention, petting and patting them and forcing on them offerings of food.

"They're said to dote on children," said Garett. "Maybe they really do."

"They're obviously still trying to seem friendly," said Duncan, "in their own benighted way."

One minor incident threatened for a moment this agreeable atmosphere of tumultuous amity. An Indian who had taken it upon himself to preside over the cooking preparations sighted the fat little dog in Ken's arms and snatched it from him. Ken burst into immediate wild protest. He pursued the kidnaper, pummeling him with his fists. His counterattack attracted general Indian attention. There were roars of laughter which presently were mingled with cries of encouragement. The tide of opinion turned entirely in Ken's favor. The dog was restored to him, his assailant reproved, and, amidst many congratulations for his temerity, he was assured that his pet would not again be molested.

The interminable handshakings of which the Indians seemed never to tire went on and on. The keg of brandy, its top knocked out, had been brought out and set up on the table where it might be dipped into the more conveniently. Many of the Indians were already beginning to show the effects, though so far it was only making them more merry and more amiable. The outside kitchen door had been propped open and there was much traffic to and from the three centers of food preparation, the two kitchen fireplaces and the big fire in the yard.

"Look, Duncan," moaned Agatha. "Look. Our cows."

A number of Indians were coming through the gateway with dismembered quarters of the two milk cows. One of them was holding a set of cow's horns to his head and greatly amusing his fellows by bawling as though to call a calf. Another had wrapped himself in one of the cow's bloody hides. The advent of the butchering party was welcomed with yells of approbation by the Indians about the fire.

"Perhaps the time will come when we can even a few scores," said Duncan. "But that time is not tonight."

After her first panic had subsided, Geneva had begun to take an interest in the cooking arrangements at her fireplace. A lifetime of purveying to her masters had taught her that there was no more certain road to approval. The establishment's largest pot, which she had slung on its crane over the fire, had clearly become the one to which the Indians were looking with the greatest anticipation. Every Indian was attending to the grilling on sticks and forks and ramrods of his own selections of ordinary meat, but it was this great kettle of boiling water which it was, appropriately, her good fortune to tend, for which the most desirable delicacies were being assembled. She accepted and dumped into it with nods of slightly surprised endorsement a sack of corn meal, a sack of dried peas, a basket of pounded pecans, and a whole ham for flavoring. On her own initiative she surreptitiously added a handful of kitchen herbs and a heaping spoonful of her precious pepper. But she clung at the mantel for support, her co-operative mood totally disrupted, when she saw that the principal ingredients for this culinary masterpiece were to be the heads of the four Slover dogs and the cows' entire intestines complete with natural contents.

Betsey squatted in a corner, her arms wrapped around her knees, watching the room with bright, sharp eyes. No ill fortune she had in all her bitterness wished these people could have equaled what now had come to them. And it was getting worse by the minute. The Indians, after all their early preparations to feast upon the station's bounty, had developed a so much greater interest in drinking that they had little left in eating. They had discovered the barrel of cider in the storeroom and were using that instead of water as a thinner for the brandy. They were drinking the mixture not in sips or swallows but in gulps. She had often heard that Indians never drank to feel pleasant or to be sociable. They knew no other aim than to get drunk as fast as they could. And when they got drunk they got crazier drunk than any white man ever could. Already they were yelling, singing, dancing, pushing one another over tables and benches, pouring drinks over each other. Soon they would be quarreling and then fighting among themselves. It would not be long after they had reached that pitch of excitement before their knives and hatchets would be red with other blood than their own.

She took particular satisfaction in watching the pale, strained faces of the Jordan women. They liked to keep their house so clean. Now it was filthier than any pigsty. They liked to stand off from common folks. Now they were jammed tight in the middle of a pack of stinking Indians. They liked to think nothing was good enough for them. Now they were having it as bad as anybody on this earth could ever have it. They were beginning to guess that what was coming to them was just getting started. But they had not yet begun to guess how very much worse it was going to get. So far the Indians were still feeling playful. But even when they were just fooling there was no telling what to expect. Their sense of humor was tickled by things nobody else in the world would think of laughing at. A sample of this was going on now. A fat, middle-aged Indian, weaving with drunkenness, his face smeared with grease from a beef rib he had been gnawing, had pulled down his breach clout and was looking around for a spot upon which to relieve himself. Suddenly inspired, he made for the fire in which he produced a great hissing and sputtering. Geneva jumped back just in time. Her scream of horrified disbelief attracted general attention, which turned at once into a general roar of laughter. The next minute a dozen other Indians were imitating the first one, against table legs, against the wall, against each other or whoever chanced to be within reach. Betsey began to laugh hysterically. It would not be much longer before it would take actions far more outrageous than these to keep them entertained. She was resigned to the certainty that she herself would not live through the night. Meanwhile she could watch the Jordans, as she was watching Duncan now. He was white-faced, shaking with rage.

Then, as suddenly, she sobered. There was something oddly out of key in the performance. It was like watching somebody gathering himself to take a jump and then seeing him slowly sit down instead. Duncan was shepherding his women and children toward the door beside the kitchen fireplace that led to his and Agatha's bedroom. Instead of blocking his way the Indians were standing aside. Now he had his family safely through the doorway. Still the Indians had made no objection. John Turtle was even nodding his approval. When Duncan closed the door and set his back against it a still sober brave took station beside him. Betsey saw then that there were six or eight other young warriors who had not been drinking and who were moving about quietly through the crowd. She had heard of the Indian custom of selecting policemen whose duty it was to stay sober during a drinking bout in order to make sure that their drunken companions did not do one another too much harm. Tonight they had taken the trouble to appoint such policemen. A drunken Indian snatched a stick from the fire and began to run about the room waving the blazing end. Two of the sober ones at once took it away from him and threw it back in the fire.

Betsey looked around anxiously to locate her father, and when she saw him her new suspicions were confirmed. He was only pretending to drink. He was still cold sober. All his life he had known a deathly fear of what Indians can do to a man. Earlier in the evening he had had no other idea than to prepare for it by drinking himself into a senseless stupor. But he knew Indians and something since then had made him change his mind. He had decided there was a chance of living and he was staying sober to take advantage of it. Betsey began to consider the possibilities. She had never heard of Indians planning an attack that they had to travel through snow to make. Yet they had planned their coming here. It had cost them a hard two-day journey from their nearest town. It could be then, after all, that their visit was exactly what they had so loudly announced it to be, a sociable call on their new neighbors. That they were so wildly wasting the station's winter food supply was nothing strange. They would have done the same at home. Indians were always as ready to waste whatever they happened to get their hands on when it belonged to themselves or their friends as when it belonged to their enemies.

There crept over her a colder apprehension than when she had taken it for granted that she was soon to die. The threat that now appeared was more real because it was more familiar. She could not remember a winter when the Slovers had not begun to get hungry before March. Here it would be worse, because there were so many people in the station and it was a harder winter than usual. The Indians might as well have left them dead as to leave them so little that they were bound to starve before spring. On the floor at her feet was a half-gnawed rib with a hunk of dripping meat still clinging to it. She picked it up, slipped it under her shawl, and sided toward the door. The rest of the night she spent flitting like a ghost among the stumbling and lurching Indian merrymakers to snatch up scraps of food. These she hid in the snow on the yard, back of the woodpile, under beds in the Slover cabin.

It was the very quantity of brandy available that provided an antidote to the excesses it had excited. Indian after Indian passed from the stage of falling down to the stage of being unable to get up again. Toward morning only John Turtle and his sharp-eyed young policemen were still up and around. They remained as watchful as they had been throughout the night. Shortly after dawn John Turtle blew a number of shrill blasts on his command whistle. Most of the sprawled and sodden sleepers rose like men from the dead. They sat up, stared blearily, shuddered, and staggered to their feet. The policemen roamed about, kicking those who were slow to awaken. Those few for whom this was insufficient were rolled in snowbanks. No one laughed or so much as grinned. All was in grim earnest. The frivolity of the night before had passed. In the cold light of morning the whooping, floundering revelers of the night before had been transposed into the silent, attentive members of a military organization. Each knew what was expected of him. There was the orderly bustle of imminent departure.

Duncan's satisfaction that they were clearing out so much sooner than he had dared hope was short-lived. In the edge of the woods across the stream appeared two Indian youths leading a long string of pack horses. The train was brought into the stockade where the full enormity of the Indians' intentions was revealed. For all their gluttony and wastefulness they had not the night before made a fatal inroad upon the station's winter stores. The staple bulk of the food supply, the tiers of sacked corn, peas, and beans, had scarcely been touched. But now they were carrying out these sacks, together with the remaining hams, sides of bacon, festoons of jerky, and everything else that had not previously been eaten, burned, or spoiled, and loading it all on the horses. Duncan began violently to protest. John Turtle no longer grinned. His eyes were like stone.

"Friend?" he asked. "Friend eat, no?"

Other Indians crowded nearer, scowling, appearing to welcome the possibility of resistance. All now carried the rifles which formerly had been kept out of sight. Their raw temper was a natural aftermath of their indulgence. It was a more critical moment than any of the night before. Duncan shrugged, acknowledging the uselessness of protest.

"At least give us back our rifles," he said. "You don't want your good friends to starve, do you?"

John Turtle was carrying Duncan's rifle. None of the others, either Jacob's or any of those taken from the tree in the wood lot, was in evidence. He pretended to understand that only Duncan's was in question.

"Friend," he said, almost genial again. He patted the rifle

and settled it the more snugly under his arm. "Friend swap, no?"

Duncan stood with Garett in the gateway watching the Indian column parade off over the now well-trampled trail through the snow.

"They planned it from start to finish," he said bitterly. "Before they left their town they knew just what they were after. One way or another they'd have got in on us, but we made it easy. I was up on the roof just now looking off at their tracks. All they had to do was nose around until they knew just where we were. Then they came up the stream side of the mound. They knew we couldn't see the gate from the wood lot. They could just walk in."

"I'd say we had good neighbor Caleb to thank," said Garett.

"That's possible, of course. John Turtle certainly got his chance to look us over the night Caleb brought him to call. Still, nobody had to give him the idea. Indians are always hungry in winter. He didn't have to be prodded to see a chance to feed his whole village at our expense. So I don't think we have to take it for granted Caleb put them up to it. I got the very strong impression that Caleb really wants to settle here, and I think there's no question he wants to stand well with white people—particularly important ones, like Clark, for example. Actually, he may still have been saving us, perhaps inadvertently. It could have been to save face with him that his Indian cronies stopped short of cutting all our throats last night."

"Instead of just leaving us to starve," said Garett.

In the kitchen Duncan found the women already engaged in a frantic assault, with shovels, brooms, mops, kettles of boiling water, and the aid of Clem, Ned, and the children, upon the indescribable mess left by their recent guests.

"We'll never get it clean again," said Agatha. "Never in this world. All we can do is keep at it until it begins to look clean."

Duncan walked on to the storeroom. Aside from a broken sack of corn and another of beans upon which an Indian had defecated, literally nothing was left. In the loft were two sacks of seed corn which had been stored separately to make more certain that the grain would not get mixed with the ordinary corn. These now constituted the bulk of the station's food stock.

He crossed the yard to the Slover cabin. There was a delay before the door was unbarred, during which he could hear much whispering and rustling within. When they did open the door they regarded him uneasily. But he had no time to speculate upon what might account for their nervousness.

"They stripped us bare," he said.

"They done thet," agreed Olen.

"Do you think your friend Caleb set them on us?"

"He could of," said Olen, nodding his head judicially. "In one way, thet is. Them Shawnee they was nuthin' they craved more'n to axe the lot of us. Could be whut saved us was Caleb his steerin' 'em to jest grabbin' all our grub—makin' out like it was a big joke. Injuns is right partial to jokes."

"They surely laughed themselves silly," said Polly. "But more'n likely they was more to it than jest a joke. Ain't no question them Shawnee they don't want us here. Like's not they figger thet now with nuthin to eat we'll be bound to take ourselves off and they'll be shet of us."

"How can we take ourselves off—with the river frozen and the snow as deep as it is and the nearest stations in either Kentucky or Virginia as far off as they are?"

"Ain't no way we kin, thet's fer sure," said Olen, again nodding his head judicially. He seemed to be taking a kind of bitter satisfaction in the inspection of each new facet of their helplessness.

"There are twenty-four of us. Twenty-four mouths to feed. From what I can see left in our house there's not enough, even with the strictest sort of rationing, to keep us more than two weeks."

"They stripped us clean's they did you," said Polly hastily. Her eyes wandered to a rafter from which hung a row of smoked venison strips. " 'Cept fer thet mite o' jerky up there."

Duncan made an impatient gesture. The Slovers were as simple-minded as children. It was a task to catch and to hold their attention.

"We have to think of more than a mouthful here and there. We have to think of the months to come. Our only hope is what we can get in the woods. That's something you understand better than I do. Just what are our chances to get game?"

Olen blinked his mild surprise at so ignorant a question being posed by a man of Duncan's intelligence.

"We-uns got us no guns, so we got us no chance a-tall."

"How about bows and arrows?"

"The Injuns they got good ones and they know how to use 'em. Most o' them got rifles besides. All the same, come a winter like this, they go so hungry a parcel o' them allus dies off."

"You keep telling me what we can't do. We have to think

of something we can do. Seems to me I've heard of hard winters when the elk collect in yards they've trampled in the snow. With the snow so deep they can't get away and people come on snowshoes and kill them with axes."

Olen chuckled. "Oncet I come on a old bull buffalo thet had his back busted when a tree hit by lightnin' had fell on him."

Polly did not grin at her husband's wit. "They's one thing fer sure I know about huntin'. When yuh take to huntin' 'cause yuh got to knock down something or yuh ain't a-goin' to eat, thet's the time yuh never have no luck."

"What about your snares?"

"A partridge or a rabbit now and then ain't goin' to count fer much. Snarin' ain't good when the snow's deep. Besides we-uns bin here long enough so's most the game—the little as well's the big—has moved off a ways."

"Fishing?"

"The crik's froze solid."

"So what it all adds up to," said Duncan, exasperated by their unshaken pessimism, "in the light of your years of experience, is that we're sure to starve."

Polly shrugged wearily. "We're sure to git so hungry we'll go to chewin' bark and old moccasins and to grubbin' down through the snow a lookin' fer mouses' nests. But somehow or other we'll hang on till spring. We-uns allus have."

In the kitchen the wave of housecleaning had receded from one small island about a fireplace, where Garett had found refuge. Duncan came in and squatted beside him.

"There's only one answer," he said. "I'll have to get to Kentucky and get back with something to keep us the rest of the winter."

"How do you plan to manage that?"

"Somehow I can make it overland. The river's never been known to stay frozen too long. By the time I get a cargo scraped together I can bring it back by boat."

Garett nodded soberly. "It would not appear that we have much choice. If I were only the half of a man, I'd be the one to go. Then you could be the one to stay here where you're needed and where you belong."

"I can go," Duncan reminded him, "only because I can know that you will be here."

Agatha stood over them. The flush of resolution that had enlivened her scrubbing had drained away, leaving her face pale and smudged. "I could tell the minute you came in that door." She was stricken by a sudden rush of comprehension of how much was about to be demanded of her. "When are you going?"

Duncan straightened to face her. "The sooner the better. First, because it'll be too long in any event before I can get back with what we need—with what we have to have. Second, because it'll be so much easier to get across the river while the ice still holds."

"Not today. Not now. Surely not this minute."

"No," he said gently. "It's already too late in the day. The first thing in the morning."

But in the morning the ice had already started to move. Somewhere farther upstream there had been a change in the weather. The river had risen and, in rising, had burst its frozen crust. Again its flow was in the open as it swept past with its new burden of tossing, clashing, grinding cakes of ice.

"Can you build a raft strong enough to stand that kind of pounding?" Duncan asked Frank.

"Yes," said Frank. He was always confident of his ability to build anything.

"It'll only have to last long enough to get me over to the other bank."

Olen, Jarot, and Jacob, their apathy dispelled by this sudden new interest, ran to cut logs. Frank, Mark, and Luke set to work on the lee shore of the point. Experiment soon demonstrated that a raft heavy enough to withstand the bombardment of the careening ice cakes must be too large for one man to handle. A crew of at least three would be required to get Duncan across.

"We can angle with the current over to the other bank," proposed Duncan. "Soon's I've jumped off, the three men with the raft can angle back to this side and walk back up the river to the station."

There then loomed the problem of selecting the men who were to be subjected to the risk of making the double crossing. Duncan drew Garett aside.

"I'd ask for volunteers if I thought it was any use. Should we draw lots?"

"No," said Garett. "I'm being left in command here so it's something for me to decide. We can't mix Slovers and Lymans so the crew will have to be all one or all the other. Useless as they are, we can count on the Slovers to scratch around in the woods and find something now and then to piece out what we have in the station to eat. So it'll have to be the Lymans."

Frank demurred, not, it became apparent, because he and his sons dreaded the danger but because he was opposed to the Slovers being arbitrarily excused. Garett settled the issue.

"The next bite you get to eat," he said, "will be after you've put Duncan on the other side."

The next morning all assembled at the point for the raft's launching. It was a cold, blowy day with occasional flurries of snow. The floating ice in the river kept up a perpetual grinding rumble that was like the mutter of distant thunder. Duncan had paid his farewells to his family during the intimacy of their early rising. Without further ceremony he and the Lymans jumped on the raft and it was shoved from the shelf of creek ice into the swirling water of the river.

For a time, while their poles could still reach bottom, they were able to maintain some headway toward mid-river. Their progress slowed when the water got deeper and they could only shove against adjacent bobbing cakes of ice. Then they were able to reach bottom again where there was a mid-channel sandbar, and began once more to make progress toward the farther bank. The raft was lurching and tipping under the impact of caroming ice cakes but continuing to right itself and showing no visible signs of breaking up. Suddenly a snow squall dropped a curtain, cutting off completely the view of those watching from shore. No matter how desperately they strained to see, they caught no later glimpse of the raft. When the squall passed the river was empty. Garett explained hurriedly to Agatha that at the rate the raft was drifting with the current it must have been swept around the bend, only a couple of miles away, during the squall.

From noon on they began anxiously to watch for the reappearance of the Lymans as they walked back along the nearer bank. It should not have taken them more than an hour to get across and another hour to get back. The current could have carried them a number of miles downstream during the two crossings but at worst they should have been able to wade back through the snow in another two or three hours. But the afternoon wore on and night fell and still they did not appear. A great fire was built on the point to guide their approach if they came during the night.

The next morning Eric and Jarot set off downriver along the bank. They returned just before dark to report that they had found easier going than they had expected, since in many places the snow was packed so hard they had not had to flounder through it. They estimated that they had traveled at least nine or ten miles but had found no spot where the raft could have landed or its crew disembarked. Not until the next day did Eric steel himself to tell Garett alone the rest of the story. Before they had turned back they had come to a straight reach of the river where by climbing a tree they had been able to survey another six miles of the snow-covered bank beyond.

Cam knew it was useless to attempt to question Eric, Garett, or Tracy. She could not bear even to look at her mother's drawn, white face. She went to Olen.

"You think my father's drowned, don't you?" she demanded.

Olen looked down from his shaggy height to meet the child's piercing eyes.

"No," he said carefully. "Nobody yit's got ary call fer figgerin' thet."

"Then what have you got reason to think?"

"We kin be middlin' sure the raft she never got back to this side."

"Then it went down."

"She could o' fetched the t'other bank first."

"But that isn't what you really think."

"The last look we-uns got at thet raft they was a-polin' her along like they might sure enough make it," said Olen doggedly.

Cam turned and began to run. She dared lose no time finding a place where she could surely stay safely out of sight until she was able to stop crying.

February

The extreme cold passed. A fitful wind sprang up, veered to the south, and died away. For three days it snowed, gently, steadily, heavily. Layer on layer was spread over as much of the world as was visible from the station. The two slides, the blackened embers of the fire in the wood lot, the tracks of the Indians and their horses, the reddened blotches where the cows and dogs had been butchered, the filth strewn across the snow of the yard, the frantic trampling along the river bank where the raft had been built and launched—all these reminders of disaster were mercifully covered. Winter seemed to have advanced a kind of idiotic suggestion that such things could only have happened at some other place or in some other year. Not only was the past buried but there was as yet no present to succeed it. No new tracks took the place of the old. To get so far as from the door to the woodpile involved floundering through breast-high drifts. Even the creatures of the wild seemed to have lost the will to move about. No delicate tracery of mouse trails, no bolder imprint of rabbit, marten or fox, no wallowing, lunging course of deer, elk, or buffalo, was visible anywhere across the smooth white expanse of meadow and pond.

Dark days followed, with noons as dim as twilight. A freezing gray mist hung over the snow. The leaden overcast seemed, in having banished the sun and the stars, to have obscured the distinction between minutes and hours and days. The members of the Jordan household rose reluctantly, moved about slowly and stiffly, addressed one another in low voices. Only the harsh, inexorable tick of Louisa's clock was a signal that time had not lost all meaning.

Each day centered about the morning and evening meals. The necessity of formal rationing had not been openly admitted. By common consent all referred to their situation as one of waiting for Duncan's return, which could not be delayed beyond two or three more weeks at the latest. But when Geneva ladled out the thin corn gruel to which their every repast was limited, all, by the same sort of unspoken common consent, took a very little and, as they grew hungrier, each day accepted less.

The Slovers had adapted themselves to their plight by lingering longer each morning in bed until for them time stood so nearly still that their domestic routine took no account of any difference between day and night. There had been one brief flurry of activity immediately after the heavy snowfall when the entire family had collaborated in the digging of a tunnel through the enormous drift between their door and the door of their outhouse. But thereafter only Polly ever emerged in the open, on occasional dashes to the woodpile for wood or more hesitant advances to the Jordan kitchen to "trade," as she termed it, a twist of their remaining jerky for a cup of corn meal.

"Best fer folks to take it real easy," she explained, defensively, "when they ain't got enough to eat. The easier they take it the longer the little they got to eat will do 'em."

The Jordans were convinced of the existence of a secret hoard of food which the Slovers had had the primitive foresight to lay away during the earlier days of plenty but Louisa vetoed any move toward searching the Slover cabin.

"We're not yet so put to it," she said, "that we must sink to the level of squabbling with their kind of trash."

"I absolutely agree," said Garett. "Especially when I reflect that they have three very large men while we have only Eric."

Within the week two-thirds of the Jordans were as immobilized as the Slovers. An epidemic of uncommonly severe colds swept through the household. First Garett was afflicted, then the Negroes, then Eric, then the younger children.

"I've always heard people never caught colds," protested Garett, "When they're as much off by themselves as we are here."

"We weren't so much by ourselves," said Tracy, "when the Indians were here."

Louisa insisted upon all taking to their beds.

"No doctor I ever saw," she said, "could do as much for a cold as a person can do for himself by getting into a good warm bed and staying in it."

Agatha moved her two youngest down from the children's sleeping quarters in the loft and into her room.

"Mother's been crying all night," Cam explained to Tracy. "Every night. She hates herself for doing that because it's the same as admitting something's happened to Father. But she can't help it. That's why she has Chris and Susie sleeping with her. She won't dare cry with them right there beside her."

After another endless night, Agatha sank toward morning into an exhausted sleep. When she awoke, Chris and Susie were whispering. Their faces were still flushed but they looked much improved and they were playing a game which involved counting on their fingers.

"A big bowl of pea soup," said Chris, "with globs of melted butter floating on it."

"Mush with butter," said Susie. "And sugar, too."

"We've already got mush. It's all we have, every day."

"We have not. We just have corn soup. I meant fried mush, with lots of butter and sugar on it."

"All right. You can have mush. I'll have a thick slice of ham, with honey poured over it."

"Bifkits with honey."

"You always just say what I say."

"I do not. I like honey. And I like bifkits. But if you took all the honey I'll have bifkits with maple syrup."

"Biscuits."

"I said bifkits."

"Anyway, what I'll have next is a whole buffalo hump with the fat burned black and the juice running out of it."

"That's not fair. We can only wish for what Papa will bring. He's coming in a boat."

"You can shoot a buffalo from a boat."

"He hasn't got a gun."

"He'll get guns in Kentucky."

"Is he coming today?"

"Uncle Garry says maybe."

"Every day Uncle Garry says that."

"He's bound to come pretty soon."

"Then why did Eric have to go hunting with his new bow and arrow?"

"He didn't. He hasn't got it made yet."

"He has so. Cam told me. He finished it yesterday."

Agatha sprang from bed, caught up a robe, and ran to the kitchen. The Negroes, clinging to the privileges of their ills, were still in their quarters. Only Olivia was in sight. She stood by the fire stirring the boiling corn in the pot.

"Where's Eric?" demanded Agatha.

"Hunting. Trying out that bow he made. He was off at daylight."

"But he shouldn't even be out of bed. He's not well yet."

"There was no stopping him. Though he still looked weak as a cat. I told him he ought to take at least a swallow of this but he said Indian hunters always hunt hungry. Gives them luck, they think. It likely does make them more anxious to shoot something." Olivia lifted a spoonful of the gruel and eyed it resentfully. "If you don't stir it, it burns. If you do, it turns to slime. Still, I suppose we have to be thankful we've had it. But this is the last. I thought there might be less wasted if we cooked it all in one batch." She plopped the spoonful back into the pot. "Tracy went with him."

Agatha ran to the nearest loophole and drew aside the block. Through the opening came a gust of cold air. All that she could see was a narrowed glimpse of a lifeless white slope merging with a lifeless black forest under a lifeless gray sky.

"My turn to break trail," said Tracy.

Eric shook his head and continued to flounder on through the snow. Tracy caught at his belt and forced him to pause.

"You have to take care of yourself." She grinned cheerfully. "Remember, you're the tribe's only hunter."

She pulled him back to a sitting position against a drift. He resisted for a moment, then sank down. She drew off one mitten, reached into the pocket of her blanket coat, and extended her hand toward him. In the palm was a tablespoon-sized heap of pounded corn mixed with maple sugar.

"Eat it," she said. "You'll need it to keep going."

He recoiled.

"Where'd that come from?"

"Your grandmother bought a small sack of it in Pittsburgh. It's been in her trunk. She'd forgotten about it."

Eric pushed her hand away. "Save it for Susie and Chris—and Cam—and maybe Uncle Garry. He's beginning to look like a ghost."

"I have been saving it—for times we might need it most. This is one. You can't wade miles through snow on what you've been eating. I've been watching you. You eat less than anybody, even your mother."

"It chokes me. We've got so little left and I'm the one who should be getting more."

"That's why you must eat this. Else where will you get the strength to hunt. Eat it, I say."

She caught his chin in her mittened hand and clapped the bare one to his mouth. He began to chew, without relish. There were tears in his eyes. He looked disgustedly about at the wintry forest.

"Hunt? You can hardly call it hunting. We've been plowing

around for hours and so far we haven't seen so much as a single track."

"Probably it's too soon after the big snow. In another day or two it may be different."

His thin, white face set stubbornly.

"The Slovers say the game has all pulled out. They say that sometimes happens in a hard winter. But that doesn't stand to reason. Where would it go?"

"It does seem odd. But you hear all the time about whole villages of Indians starving in the winter. They're experienced hunters and still they starve."

"The Slovers just want an excuse for staying by their fire." He stared at her accusingly. "You don't think I'll be able to kill anything with this bow and arrow, do you? You just came along to look after me."

"I came along to help, if I could. I do think that before you try to hunt in snow as deep as this you should have snowshoes."

"Who knows how to make snowshoes?" He regarded his bow critically. "I had to go by guess even to make this." He got to his feet. "You're just talking so we'll rest longer."

They plowed on. He was aware that he was tiring faster than Tracy and this made him the more determined to keep going. Getting up angrily after having fallen, suddenly he stiffened and pointed.

"Tracks," he whispered. "Just the other side that log."

They floundered ahead and climbed up on the trunk of the fallen tree. On the other side were the fresh tracks of an animal heavy enough to have broken through the thin crust at every step. It had been making its way by short hops, from the tangle of dried vines about the tree's outflung upper branches to the similar tangle about its upturned roots, and then on into a copse of scrub cedar. The imprint of its belly showed between each of the hops. It had not been in a hurry. After every three or four hops it had lain down, resting at one point long enough to have left behind a thin glaze where its body heat had briefly melted a film of snow.

"A bear?" suggested Tracy.

"A bear?" Eric was dismayed by her ignorance. "Not a quarter as big as even a small bear. A lynx. See how much the tracks look like a cat's?"

"Is a lynx good to eat?"

"Indians think so. *Look*. There he is. Right over there."

The lynx had come out of the cedars, less than a hundred yards away. He came to a stop and looked at them over his shoulder. There was gray on his tufted ears and about his muzzle. He looked old and gaunt and worn. Eric whipped out one of his arrows but did not fit it to the string.

"It's too long a shot," he whispered.

They jumped from the log and plunged forward through the snow. The lynx took several unhurried hops. He appeared to regard their approach with more unsociable distaste than actual concern. No matter how desperately they struggled toward him he continued to keep his original distance. Each time they paused for breath he ceased his weary hopping and lay down. He, too, was panting.

"It's always too long a shot," complained Eric, between long shuddering breaths.

"You must hold up for just a minute," protested Tracy. "You'll kill yourself."

"But we've got to get him. He's the only game we've seen."

"We'll never get him this way." She grabbed his belt and held him back. "Wait. You squat over there back in that thicket. I'll circle around and get on the other side of him. Maybe he'll forget about you and come back this way, close enongh for you to get a shot at him."

"Try it and see," he wheezed.

Tracy took several deep breaths and set out. Eric crawled to the shelter of the thicket, knelt, and waited. She kept on, breaking her laborious way through the crusted snow and with each step the more painfully repenting her suggestion. She was much weaker than she had thought. Each onward lunge required a renewed and separate effort. Eventually she began to realize that, in her anxiety to describe a sufficiently wide circle, she could have lost her bearings. She had long since returned to what she conceived to be the area where the lynx last had lain down, but had not sighted either the animal or its tracks. The occasion for her exhaustion began to seem as nonsensical as a child's game of make-believe. Eric's determination to hunt with his makeshift weapon was absurd and her lending herself to the farce was more absurd. The bleak sky, the somber forest, the deep snow, were so many outward reminders that her struggle was senseless. Since Duncan had gone nothing had had real meaning, no effort genuine value. She could no longer help him. Now she had set out to help his son and had managed only to get lost in the woods, leaving the boy to freeze while waiting for her.

"Eric," she called, surrendering.

Eric's reply came from no great distance. Then she saw the lynx, not twenty paces away. He was reclining in the snow, watching her with yellow, expressionless eyes. This so much nearer view revealed how thin he was. He looked sick as well as starved. She pushed toward him. He did not move. She broke the tip from the dead branch and tossed it at him. Still he did not stir. Eric was wallowing forward through an intervening drift.

"Look out," called Tracy. "He's right here."

The lynx turned his head toward Eric, gathered his paws under him, and began taking short hops off to the side. Eric straightened and fitted an arrow to his bowstring. His shivering made his movements slow and fumbling. But when at last he bent his bow the arrow's flight was straight. Its iron-tipped head struck the lynx in the shoulder. The beast snarled, clawed at the arrow, and then, animated at last, began to take long leaps, leaving the arrow behind him in the snow. His third bound carried him out of sight in a patch of undergrowth. Eric plunged forward, picked up his arrow, and stared at it.

"It was a beautiful shot," said Tracy. She was too weary to put spirit into her attempt to console him. "Just back of the shoulder."

"What difference—when you've got a bow that doesn't shoot hard enough to knock down a fly?"

Eric broke the arrow and threw down the bow. He was as tall as a man, which made it seem the more incongruous that his face should be working with the rebellious anger of a child. She tried to remember with what resolution he had sat up in bed to work on that bow and arrow between spasms of coughing.

"These days are so short," she said. "Don't you think perhaps we should be starting home?"

"Might as well," he agreed sullenly. "We're not doing any good out here."

He set off, his angry disgust giving him for the moment the appearance of new vigor. Tracy picked up the bow and followed. Then, as he kept steadily on, gasping, grunting, getting up each time he fell, she began to feel remorse that she had not taken more care to conceal her own depression.

"Eric, did you notice John Turtle's bow?"

"What about it? Indians know how to make bows."

"At the hand grasp in the middle and at the two principal curves it was bound with what looked like deer sinew. Do you think that could have been to make it stronger?"

"Deer sinew. We might as well wish for a rifle. Where we going to get a deer?"

"I've got a ball of very strong waxed thread."

He swung around to face her. His eyes had brightened. He took the bow from her and bent it experimentally.

"It migh help," he said. "It certainly might."

He went on, his stride longer and firmer. They came out into Caleb's clearing. Both stopped and stared. In a dozen places about the cabin and along the edges of the woods, holes had been dug down through the snow and into the frozen earth beneath. Eric began to laugh.

"The Slovers," he exclaimed. "They must have got hungry enough to get themselves all out of bed at once. They've been digging for Caleb's caches." He chuckled at Tracy's continued mystification. "Can't you see? All of a sudden they remembered how busy Daisy was last fall. She was always gathering nuts and dried berries and smoking ducks and fish. Indians bury food for the winter. The Slovers have been trying to guess where she buried Caleb's."

"Do you think they found anything?"

"No sign of it," said Eric, after inspecting each of the holes. "Chances are Caleb and Daisy took it with them when they went back to winter with the Shawnee."

"Let's see if they broke into his cabin."

Eric hesitated, momentarily, to commit this trespass. Tracy lifted the bar and quickly pushed the door open. In the failing light the cabin looked as neat and orderly as when Caleb had occupied it.

"The most likely place would be under the floor," observed Eric, "but doesn't look like they lifted the floorboards. They're really afraid of Caleb. If only he had stayed here this winter . . . He'd have kept them out of bed."

"If only he had never come at all," said Tracy.

"He didn't steal our food."

"His Indians did."

"They're not his Indians. And you started hating him even before that."

"How can you defend him? He's the kind of man who never thinks of anyone else. No more than does an animal."

Eric nodded, casually accepting the indictment. "That's the kind of man you have to be to get along out here."

"No, Eric, no. Don't ever joke about trying to be like him."

"It's no joke. There's not much chance of my being like him, as you saw today. As everybody will see when we run out of corn meal tomorrow. We've been the same as starving but then we'll really starve—for all the good I'll be."

He stalked away from her. She followed him up the slope along the trail through the snow beaten down by the Slovers in their sudden sorties. It was dark by the time they reached the gate. Olivia met them at the kitchen door. Her voice was strained.

"Where have you been?"

"Here. There." Eric sagged against the door frame. "Making tracks in the snow. Millions of tracks in the snow."

"Wherever you made them, did you see anything of Garett?' '

"No, we didn't."

"Could he have gone over to Caleb's with the Slovers?" asked Tracy.

"I don't know where he could have gone." Olivia's tone indicated this had been another of the days she and Garett had not been speaking. "All I know is that he's not in the house now."

Eric pushed himself away from the door frame. "I'll see if the Slovers saw anything of him."

He plodded across the yard, knocked on their door, and pushed it open. The single room was hot and close, smelled of unwashed bedding and clothing and people. Polly and Lina were crouched on stools by the fire over which was slung an iron pot from which came a more agreeable smell of simmering broth. On the hearth was a wooden platter upon which rested a beef bone, with the tines of the fork with which it had evidently just been lifted from the pot still fixed in the knob of gristle adhering to one end of the bone. Polly hastily shifted her position on the stool so that the overhang of her dress shut off Eric's view of the platter. The three Slover men, looking oddly like overgrown, bearded children as they lay side by side and turned their heads in unison to stare silently at the visitor, were in one bed. Betsey, her dull eyes suddenly sharpening with interest, peered from the tangled nest of blankets in the other.

"I came over to ask," said Eric, "if you'd seen anything of Garett this afternoon."

Lina sprang up and took an eager step toward him.

"No, Eric. We never seen nuthin' of him."

"When we come in jest afore dark," said Polly, "there was smoke a-comin' from the Lyman cabin and I heared somebody bangin' on the anvil in there. Could thet o' bin him?"

"Thanks," said Eric, backing out.

He had taken no more than two or three stumbling steps away when the door opened behind him. Lina ran to him and grasped one of his hands. He felt the greasiness and the warmth before he realized that what she was pressing upon him was the beef bone.

"Fer you," she whispered. "Take yerself a chaw on thet. It ain't meat but it's bin boiled so long thet gristle is real tasty."

He jerked his hand away. The bone fell to the snow between them. She picked it up and put an arm around him to support him.

"Yuh got yerself so hungry and so tuckered thet yuh can't even hang on to it. Here, I'll hold it fer yuh."

He pushed her away.

"Gnaw on it yourself. You may not gag on it, but I would."

"We-uns never stole it," she said. "Betsey jest picked up some bones thet the Injuns throwed down." She tried again to press the bone into his hand. "Take it," she begged. "It's mine to give and whutever is mine is right fer you to have."

"Can't you get it through your head?" he gasped. "I don't want it, or anything else of yours."

He stumbled on to the door of the Lyman cabin. There were coals still glowing in the forge. Various Lyman tools, formerly hung on the wall in a neat row, were scattered about the anvil. He went on to the kitchen.

"The Slovers haven't seen him," he reported. "But some-one has been working in the Lyman shop."

Cam's voice floated down from her bed in the loft.

"I know what he was working on in there. I could see from the loophole up here when he brought it to the door to look at it in the daylight. It was a fish spear."

"A fish spear," exclaimed Olivia. "The river. That's the only open water around. That's where he went. The fool. He didn't have the strength to walk across this room. He could have fallen in, or just fallen down and not been able to get up."

She ran for her cloak.

"No, not the river," said Louisa. "The edge of a river is no place to spear fish. Garett knows that. But I *can* guess where he is. When he and Duncan were boys they used to spear fish at night by torchlight. In the pool at the foot of the spillway below the mill dam. He's up at the falls."

"But he's sick," cried Olivia. "It'll be the death of him. We've got to go bring him back."

"Leave him alone," said Louisa. "I know he's sick. But he's also a man. He knows the state we're in. If we don't let him at least try to do something it *will* be the death of him."

"He's my husband," shouted Olivia. "I'm not going to let anything take him away from me. Nor any of you. Not all of you. No matter if you all die. I'm not going to let him die."

She rushed out. Agatha rose and took her cloak from its peg.

"He might have told her what he was up to. The chances are he's fallen down in the snow before he got halfway to the falls. Olivia may not be able to get him back alone."

Tracy and Eric struggled up from their chairs.

"Sit down," commanded Agatha. "Or, better yet, go to bed. You two have tried to do too much already today. Olivia and I will have trouble enough with Garett without having to carry you back, too."

She went out. It was a dark night but there was light enough reflected from the whiteness of the snow to enable her to follow Olivia's tracks down the slope toward the pond. There Olivia had come upon Garett's tracks where he had left the Slover trail to Caleb's cabin and had started up the frozen, snow-covered stream. She had begun to run. Agatha could see how often Garett, the first of the three of them to force his way through these drifts, had fallen, and with what desperate haste Olivia had struggled on to overtake him. Her own passage was easier in the trail that they had broken, but she soon began to realize how weak she had been left by her days of fasting. She kept expecting momentarily to come upon them but the tracks led on and on until she, too, in her weariness, was staggering and falling. At last she caught a glimpse of the water of the falls, gushing from its ice-capped ledge, shimmering faintly in the dying light of the pine-knot torch. Garett, the invalid, had made it all the way to his goal.

He was stretched out on the bank above the black, ice-rimmed pool, the unused fish spear beside him. He had had the resolution to strike flint and steel, light the torch, stick it up in the snow, and then, as he reached for his spear, had collapsed. His face looked like a dead man's but from his lips was coming a weakening babble of meaningless words. Olivia sat beside him, rocking back and forth, moaning, her face covered by her hands.

"He's not dead yet," gasped Agatha. "His fever's come back on him. He's out of his mind."

Olivia dropped her hands and looked at him. Her face was livid, not with grief but with rage.

"He's worse than out of his mind. He didn't know me. He kept calling me Tracy. He kept reaching for me and trying to pull me down beside him. He kept on and on calling me Tracy and mumbling about how glad he was she'd come to him."

"You can see he's delirious," said Agatha sternly. "Get up

and help me. We've got to get him back and get him warm. He'll die here."

"Let him die. I hope he does. That miserable slut. She's as cold as this snow. That's why she has eyes only for Duncan. Because she knows there's no chance of her ever having him—of her ever having to give a man anything."

Agatha bent down and slapped Olivia hard across the face. "Get up," she commanded.

Olivia's hysteria passed. She rose remorsefully.

"Duncan has never so much as given her a second look," she said, gripping Agatha's arm. "You know that, don't you?"

"Yes, I know that. But Garett's the one that concerns us now. We've got to get him home."

They soon discovered that they had not between them the strength to lift him. Their tugging at him seemed to catch, vaguely, at his far-wandering attention. Each time he slipped from their grasp he laughed.

"Will you shut up?" panted Olivia. "Will you, for God's sake, shut up?"

"You, too," said Agatha. "If we can't carry him, we'll have to pull him."

Each took hold of one of his feet and they began to drag him through the snow. The movement served again to rouse him slightly from the stupor into which he had been sinking. He began to sing, feebly but with a kind of ghastly gusto, snatches of "The Darby Ram."

"and you'll see the same as I . . .
and you'll see the same as I . . .
and when they took its measure . . .
the devil cut it off, sir . . ."

Their agonizing progress was not so much eased as confused when they reached the pond. There they encountered Eric and Tracy, who had struggled out to look for them despite Agatha's injunction. All four were so exhausted that they were nearly as helpless as the sick man. Somehow they made it up the slope, through the gate, and into the kitchen.

Louisa had dragged the mattress from Garett's and Olivia's bed out to the family fireplace and had stretched the blankets over chair backs to warm. Wrapped in the heated blankets, Garett drifted off into a sleep so deep that Louisa hastily thrust her hand under his shirt.

"His heart's still beating," she reported.

The rescue party staggered to chairs and benches.

"Mother," called Cam from the loft. "Ken's gone outside.

And he took Rupert with him." There was a strange emphasis on the last phrase.

"Ken?" said Agatha. "He went outside? Whatever for?"

She gathered herself to get up from the bench at the table. The door opened. Ken came in. His face was white and tear-stained but he was calm, almost as abstracted as though he were walking in his sleep. He was holding Rupert in his arms. The dog was limp, his legs and tail dangling. Ken walked steadily to the table and laid his burden before his mother. Only then did Agatha see the knot in the leather leash. It had been drawn hard about Rupert's neck. The dog was dead.

"Indians eat dogs," said Ken, speaking in an odd singsong, as though reciting something he had learned but that had for him no meaning. "And you'll all die if you don't have something to eat."

"Ken," cried Agatha. "You couldn't have done this? You didn't do this yourself, did you? Not to Rupert."

"Yes," said Ken. "Nobody else would have. Besides, it was better for me to do it. Rupert wasn't afraid of me."

Ken made a break for the ladder and scrambled up to the refuge of his bed in the loft. Agatha spread her arms on the table and dropped her head into them. Her weeping was weak and silent and yet shook her whole body. One of her outflung hands touched one of Rupert's paws.

"Somebody," she moaned, "somebody take the poor little thing away."

"No," said Louisa. "we've got to go through with it now. After what Ken has tried to do for us we absolutely must do that much for him."

Eric struggled to get up out of his chair. Agatha rose and shoved him back. She picked up the dog's body, carried it to the chopping block before the cooking fireplace, and drew a knife from the rack beside the block. Deliberately she began to skin, clean, and dismember the carcass. Her face was ashen, her eyes glittered, but her voice was soft, musing, hardly audible to the others in the room, watching horrified.

"So much energy in so small a body. Such a bundle of wriggling, and tail wagging, and barking. You were so full of life, Rupert. Enough to divide among all of us and give each of us life for another day or two. Ken saved you from the Indians who were such beasts that they wanted you. Now he has given you instead to us. And even I myself will accept—for I must go on trying to live, for the sake of my children. We all must go on trying to live—for the sake of one another." Suddenly her voice rose to a scream. "You all know Duncan is dead. But you won't admit it—won't even mention it. For fear of robbing poor, sad, demented Agatha of the chance to keep on hoping. But I know he is dead. I know it better than any of you. Because I knew him better. If he were alive he'd have found some way to get word to us. Even if he couldn't get back himself, he would have done that. He wouldn't have let us go on grieving and suffering. Duncan is dead. We have to face it—and go on, if we can."

Tracy crept from her bed at dawn. She was stiff and sore and so weak that she was obliged to grasp at chair backs to get as far as the kitchen door. Outside she pulled herself up to the ladder to the stockade fire step. Her first impulse every morning was to climb up here where she could see downriver. But this morning, like all the others, the gray river flowed on in sullen emptiness. No distant dark dot marked the conceivable approach of canoe or bateau.

With painful care she descended, crossed the yard to the Lyman cabin, and found a shovel. Sooner or later the Slovers would become so hard pressed that they would bring themselves to invade Caleb's cabin. She proposed to be the first to explore beneath those floor boards. Plodding through the gate and down the slope along the trail broken through the snow the day before, she walked like one carrying a crushing weight, bent over, head down, her dulled attention fixed on the path immediately before her. Not until she had almost reached the cabin's doorstep did she look up. She came, then, to an abrupt stop. An Indian toboggan leaned, upended, alongside the door, and beside it a pair of snowshoes. A curl of smoke came from the chimney. The door opened and Caleb stood in it.

Her gasp of surprise became a gasp of rage as his first glance flicked from the shovel in her hands to the holes in the snow, to her suddenly flaming face.

"Of course I came to dig for whatever I could find," she declared. "Your Indians took everything we had."

"It is common for hungry people to steal," he said. "But today you do not need to steal. I will give you something to eat."

He stood aside for her to enter. She drew in her breath, casting about unsuccessfully for words to frame a sufficiently scathing retort. But she hit upon none that seemed adequate. Swinging around, still speechless, she started back toward the station. As soon as she was certain that she was out of his sight, she began to run.

But at the foot of the slope she came to a stop. Caleb Lewis had come back. What had brought him back? Was his return a threat of some new danger? How was his coming likely to affect them? She foresaw the torrent of such questions with which she would be deluged the moment she had announced her encounter with him. To be forced to admit that she had seen and spoken to the man and yet had gained no slightest idea of his attitude or intentions was too wildly and impossibly irrational. She had to go back.

Again, as she approached the cabin, the door opened and he stood in it. When she continued to approach he stood aside. She went in. As the day before when she had noted the orderliness of his cabin, she was struck by the uncomfortable suggestion that he was a man who kept even inanimate things in total subjection. She felt the start of a new surprise before she had clearly realized the occasion for it. Hastily she looked about her again. They were alone in the cabin.

"Where's Daisy?"

She instantly regretted the personal inquiry and, before he could reply, if he had intended to reply, added: "I've often heard it's a sign that Indians are bent on mischief—when they leave their women behind, I mean."

Nothing about him was more exasperating than his habit of appearing not to have heard what had been said to him. On a flat stone by the fire rested an iron skillet with pemmican warming in it. He divided the pemmican in equal portions, shoveled one to a bark tray, stuck a horn spoon in it, and handed the tray to her. He squatted and began to eat from the skillet. The rich, sweet odor of the chopped venison mixed with dried huckleberries and goose fat made Tracy faint with hunger. She set the tray down.

"Are you truly so insensible? Or are you only trying to pretend you do not know what has bene done to us? We are starving, and we are not only men but children and women —one of them a child of four and another a grandmother. And four of our men are lost, trying to go for help."

He looked up from his eating.

"How were they lost?"

"We can't even be sure. They tried to cross the river on a raft. Three of them were to come back the same day. But that was three weeks ago and we have seen or heard nothing of any of them. You will undoubtedly be glad to know that one of the three was Colonel Jordan."

He resumed eating. Yet for once he had seemed to be giving consideration to something that she had said to him. And it had made a sufficient impression presently to call forth a far longer speech than she had ever heard from him.

"For people who have come out here there is no use to cry for help. There is no use to run for help. In this country there are very many things which the people who come to it must know how to do and which nobody can do for them." He looked up at her over his last spoonful of pemmican. "You are very hungry. It is better for you to eat."

"I can see it is useless to try to talk to you. Words seem to have a different meaning for you. And words like 'good' or 'evil' no meaning at all."

He set down the skillet and rose.

"All your people are very hungry, too."

"They certainly are. We have been living on one spoonful of corn meal a day and tomorrow we will not have even that. Can you possibly be trying to indicate you are sorry?"

"Sorry. What use is sorry?"

"What use is anything? And what is the least of all is imagining that you can begin to understand the way ordinary civilized people think and feel."

Tracy had started for the door but his next words brought her up as short as though he had cast a rawhide noose over her head.

"Maybe your people are so hungry that they would be glad to have a bear to eat."

She whirled to stare at him.

"A bear? You have killed a bear? Did you run across one on your way here?"

"No. In winter bears hide and sleep."

"I know that. But do you think you know where to find such a den?"

"Yes. That is what I think."

"You do? Then by all means go for it now."

He had scarcely so much as glanced at her since she had come into the cabin. Even when he had looked up at her news of Duncan's fate it had been past her, as though out over the icebound river. But now he gave her a sudden appraising scrutiny. "Always it is more easy to say hunt than to go hunt."

"You want me to go with you? Then I will. I can't think of anything I'd rather watch. If there is a bear, I should be so relieved to see game that somebody is able to take. There is also the chance that you may get clawed and I should not want to miss that."

"First you will need to eat. There will be work for you to do."

She picked up the tray. The pemmican had chilled and the fat turned to grease, but never had she tasted anything so delicious.

He gathered up his axe and rifle and her shovel. At the door he paused to toss his snowshoes back into the cabin.

"Won't you need them?"

He paid no attention.

"Listen to me," he insisted. "If you've any idea that I'm going to break trail for you—as you'd probably make Daisy do——"

He righted the toboggan and set off into the woods, pulling it after him.The track behind the toboggan was a firm path in which she could walk with ease. Then she saw that this was so because he was taking the trail that he had made on his way toward his cabin with the toboggan loaded. It was a route that from time to time intersected the one she and Eric had taken as they had approached the clearing. She could see in the snow, now to one side, now to the other, the marks of their sprawling lunges as they had veered and wandered. Caleb, his direction chancing to correspond with theirs, must have arrived some time last night, perhaps just after she and Eric had left the clearing. His trail, however, ran straight as a line drawn between two points. This same straight course seemed to serve him as well now, as though his destination were as predetermined as it had been then.

"You are very sure about your bear," she said.

"Today you will have better luck than yesterday."

"You spied on us yesterday?"

He shrugged. "Who can walk in the snow without making tracks?"

She thought of Eric crouched shivering in the thicket, her laborious meandering circle, the sick lynx bounding away. Contrasting his assurance now with their pitiful flounderings then, her exasperation with him reached a new pitch.

He came to a stop beside the stub of a dead sycamore. She could see in the drift at its base where she and Eric had lain back briefly to rest in one of their many pauses for breath on their homeward course yesterday. Then he saw that Caleb was turning the toboggan around so that its rolled-up prow pointed back down the trail. She realized that this must be the spot that he had had in mind and regarded the sycamore stub with sudden attention.

It was twelve or fourteen feet in diameter and was presumably hollow, though its outer surface, blackened by some ancient fire, was still hard and unbroken. The stub was not much higher than it was wide, the main column of the original tree having been snapped off at some earlier time by storm or lightning bolt. A vigorous sumac vine had taken possession of the top and its overhanging mat of branches was covered by as thick a platform of snow as might be the roof of a house. She could see nothing about the snow-banked stub to distinguish it from the next drift or the one beyond that one or any one of a thousand others.

"You actually think there's a bear in there?" she asked, challengingly.

He examined the priming of his rifle and handed it to her. "Be ready to give it to me," he directed.

With the shovel he cleared the drifted snow away from one side of the stub. Next he broke and assembled a pile of sticks a few feet away, got out his flint and steel, and started a small fire. She understood that this was in preparation for smoking out the bear which he continued to assume was ensconced somewhere in the recesses of the hollow stub.

"Tell me," she demanded. "You've just got to tell me why you're so absolutely certain there's a bear in there."

He glanced up at the snow-covered crown of sumac branches at the top of the stub. She looked more closely and noticed that in one fold of the branches there was a small dark hole in the snow. It was no larger than a teacup but, once she began to observe it, it looked oddly unnatural and the edges of the snow about the tiny opening drooped inward. Some slightly warmer current of air from within the stub had, in rising and escaping, melted the snow, and, she was forced to admit, the most likely source of the warmer air must be the breath and body heat of some fairly large animal.

"So you just happened to see that little hole on your way past? Are you trying to tell me that you never go anywhere without constantly looking up and around—in this case it must have been up and behind, after you had passed—for things as small as that?"

Her question drew from him the unexpected acknowledgment of a brief chuckle. It was the first audible sign of amusement she had ever heard from him. He picked up the axe and began to cut a notch in the base of the stub. The outer dried shell of the sycamore was as hard as iron but, swinging from his heels, he made each easy, graceful arc of the whirling axe so swift and powerful on its downward swoop that it ended with the blade sinking deeply into the flinty wood. The stub shuddered. At each alternate thud a great square chip flew away. Any lingering doubt that there might be a hibernating bear inside came to an abrupt end. The bank of snow behind the axeman began suddenly to stir and then to heave upward. The creature had been sufficiently aroused by the crashing axe to make unnecessary any final resort to smoke, and the entrance to its den proved not to be by way of the crown of sumac leaves, but at some lower point hidden by the drift, and well away from the base of the stub.

"Look out," yelled Tracy.

The upheaval in the snow became an explosion. The bear, rearing upward on his hind legs, was made to seem the more enormous by the shower of snow flying from his shaggy coat. A rumbling, infuriated roar burst from his gaping mouth and his huge forepaws reached out for the disturber of his winter peace.

Tracy sprang forward to hand Caleb his rifle. But, pivoting without stepping back, he did not so much as interrupt the swing of his axe. He merely altered its direction as he turned and, with the same force with which he had been driving it into the stub, brought the glittering blade down upon the bear's head. The monster, his skull split, dropped to all fours, lurched forward, and sagged, legs spraddled, until he was prone. Caleb, jerking the axe free, stepped lightly aside to avoid the gush of blood.

The approach of Tracy and Caleb was not observed until they had pulled the laden toboggan into the center of the station yard. Eric was just coming out of the kitchen door on his way to look for her. His wild yell was the trigger of a sensation that developed like the eruption of a succession of bombshells. Caleb's reappearance, the tobogganload of meat, Tracy's participation in the bear hunt—each phase of the miracle struck the onlookers as in itself spectacular beyond belief. In combination they were astounding beyond comprehension. Louisa, Olivia, Cam, and Ken came running out. The Negroes, their ills forgotten, bolted from their sickbeds. The Slovers could not have boiled from their cabin with more expedition had a hornet's nest been tossed in at a window.

"Mr. Lewis," said Louisa, "I could not conceivably have imagined that I should ever be glad to see you. I do not know that I am now. But I most assuredly am glad to see what you have brought with you."

Caleb did not reply. He was looking past her at Agatha, standing in the doorway. The others ceased their excited gabble and also turned to look.

"The Lord of the backwoods," she said bitterly. "He giveth —after he hath taken away."

Caleb bent, took hold of the side of the toboggan, dumped the bear's carcass out in the snow, and strode out the gate, dragging the toboggan behind him. Olivia ran to Agatha.

"Have you completely lost your wits? Why drive him away? He was helping us, and he just might have been willing to go on helping us. God knows we need help so much we can forget a little."

"He is worse than a robber," said Agatha. "He is a murderer. Are you asking me to forget that?"

Chris and Susie, still in their woolen night clothes, pushed into the doorway beside her. She dropped to her knees and with a groan drew each of them convulsively against her. The Slovers' interest had already returned to the bear. Jacob and Jarot rolled the carcass over. Olen squatted to prod it with his fingers.

"Fat," he announced. "Might run to more'n four hunert pounds."

Agatha shoved Chris and Susie back into the warmth of the house and came forward.

"Haul it into the kitchen," she directed.

"You-uns figger to take it all?" remonstrated Polly. "Don't we-uns git us no share?"

"So long as it lasts," said Agatha, "you'll eat with us. That way we'll all get our share, our exact share."

Polly, instantly intrigued by the social aspects of the proposal, began to beam her agreement. The Slover men dragged the carcass within and embarked eagerly upon its butchering. Expertly they skinned, drew, and quartered it. No portion was wasted. The entrails were emptied and laid aside, the thick sheath of fat under the skin placed in a pot for rendering. All watched the process with breathless attention. Both fires were built up. Every kettle was got ready. The children were allowed to stay up and to dress. Garett's mattress was brought out into the kitchen. He was too weak to sit up, but pillows were piled behind him so that he could watch.

"Less you-uns wants to git yerselves real sick," advised Polly, "you'll take nuthin at first but a spoonful o' soup. And arter a spell mebbe another. Hold off on yer real eatin' 'til arter yer innards has tuk to workin' agin."

The agreement to abide by this counsel was unhesitating and cheerful.

"Put the four paws in the brass kettle," directed Polly, luxuriating in the privilege of ordering the Jordan servants about. "They make the richest broth there is."

Geneva and her helpers, frantically anxious to get on with the project, took over the actual cooking operations, under Polly's increasingly relaxed supervision and with Agatha perpetually on watch to make sure no one snatched a premature morsel. Waves of warmth from the two great fireplaces rippled across the room. These pleasant currents and eddies began to convoy whiffs from the brass kettle, an aroma of simmering meat which was faint at first but soon stronger and impregnated with tantalizing promise. The children crouched on the floor almost under Geneva's feet, their eyes sharp and intent on her every move and Polly's every gesture. They kept wrinkling their noses and from time to time they wet their lips or tried to swallow. Suddenly Ken ran to his mother and buried his head in her lap.

"I didn't have to do it to him so quick," he whimpered. "I could have waited just another day—and then I wouldn't have had to do it at all."

"No, Ken," said Agatha, silently and desperately praying for guidance. "What you did was good and fine. You must never feel sorry for having done something like that."

"What was so fine about it? What good did it do? Nobody touched it. Cam told me. It's still in that pot in the back of the fireplace."

"Last night we all felt so bad we just couldn't. But we saved it, and it may still save us, just as you wanted it to." Ken was beginning to tremble and when she drew him closer he tried to pull away. "What you did wasn't wrong darling. It wasn't wasted. We'll none of us ever, ever forget what you did for us. Love is never wasted."

"Rupert's was. I wish he was alive, or I was dead. That's what I wish."

"But don't you see, Ken?" urged Agatha, suddenly inspired. "It was you and Rupert that brought us all we have today. You know how the Indians sacrifice something before they go out to hunt because that brings them luck. Eric and Tracy missed that lynx yesterday, but after what you gave us last night, today we have a bear. And it isn't only Indian magic that works that way. It's one of our beliefs, too, that the Lord helps those who help themselves."

Ken did not reply but he had ceased to tremble. Agatha breathed a sigh of thanksgiving.

"It's still a mite weak," announced Polly, dripping a spoonful of the bear paw broth back into the pot, "but it's best thet way, fer a starter. The more watery she is, the more apt to stay down."

The company lent itself to the ensuing ceremony with solemn fidelity. First a sip, then a wait, then half a spoonful, then a wait, then a whole spoonful, then, finally, half a cupful. As Polly had forecast, gradually their digestive processes began to revive and their shrunken stomachs to expand. They became more ravenously hungry than at any time during their days of starvation. Meanwhile, joints of meat had been put to turning on spits and racks of ribs set on edge to grill. The fat sputtered and crisped, the lean browned and oozed. The smells became unbearably inviting. Anticipation became an ecstasy.

"Look at that chunk," whispered Chris. "Turning black and the juice running out—just like I wished for."

"You wished for buffalo," objected Susie, "and this is bear."

"Bear's better than buffalo."

Polly looked about her, scrutinizing each face, appraising individually the degree of impatience each was betraying, savoring and prolonging her moment of dramatic decision. She nodded judiciously.

"Time's come fer takin' one solid bite," she announced.

A roast was swung to the chopping block. Polly held thumb and forefinger to illustrate the precise size. Geneva cut off a slice and then divided it into pieces half the size of a walnut. The bits of meat were arranged on a tray.

"You pass her around," said Polly, shoving the platter at Tracy. "She was partly yer bear."

Tracy passed the tray. Each took his portion in his fingers, popped it into his mouth, and rolled it blissfully over his tongue.

"Chaw her up good," advised Polly.

At intervals, each of which seemed longer than the one before it, the tray went around again with slightly larger pieces, until the morsels had reached two-bite proportions.

"Give 'em a good hunk this time," Polly instructed Geneva, when the empty tray again had come back. "Some o' them will likely still git sick by now it won't do 'em no hurt if they do."

So far the quiet and decorum which might have marked a religious rite had been maintained. The only words spoken aloud had been Polly's in the course of her officiating. People waited patiently, accepted their portions humbly, smiled faintly as they chewed, often with their eyes closed. Their entire attention was turned inward upon themselves, as though only by such self-absorption could they adequately relish the amazing new sensation of tasting and swallowing. But now the mood of solemnity began to pass. They began to look around at each other, to realize that they had companions in their good fortune. They began to talk and to laugh. The occasion was no longer a rite. It had become a feast. Even Agatha's wan face glowed as she observed her children.

"After today," she ruled, "we'll start in making what is left last. But today, just for this once, we'll eat all we want."

The warmth in her voice, even more than the welcome sentiment she had expressed, brought cries of approval from mouths not too full for response. The Slovers, the Negroes, and the children were tearing at their meat with the avidity of hungry animals. Olivia laid aside the plate from which she had been endeavoring to persuade Garett to eat.

"You wouldn't have to worry so much about how long it may last," she said, "if you weren't so set on keeping Caleb at a distance. He would bring us more."

Eric sprang up.

"He'd ought to be here eating with us," he declared. "After all, it's his bear. May I go ask him, Mother?"

"May I go with Eric?" cried Cam. "May I, Mother?"

"No," said Agatha. Her face was white again. "If you're all bound to have him here I will try to endure it. But I will not send my children to fetch him."

"A nice point," said Garett. "And one which I, for one, can understand. But the fact remains—we need the scoundrel. Tracy. It would appear you were indicated. You've had remarkable luck with him. First you made him produce the lost Eric, now this second miracle. Go summon him to our festive board."

"No," said Tracy. "Obviously we need his help. Obviously that means our trying to be civil to him. But, speaking for myself only, I'd rather starve."

"Polly," said Louisa. "Why not you? You consider him a distant relative of sorts, do you not?"

"He's my own sister's husband's third cousin's oldest boy," said Polly, "even if he don't know it. And if he was the devil's uncle I'd crawl four mile on my knees jest to pat the stock o' thet rifle o' his'n."

She wrapped her ragged blanket cloak about her, selected a rib to solace her en route, and went out. Once more silence fell upon the company. Again there was the strain of expectation, but this time it was an uneasy silence. Only Olen and Geneva were still eating. The others had discovered that, hungry as they had imagined themselves to be, they had not been able to eat a quarter of the amount they had anticipated.

"When you've gone without fer a spell," said Jacob, making one of his rare remarks, "yer gut gits so puckered up she won't hold nuthin'."

He leaned back and fell asleep. Eric got up and went to a loophole, as though to observe Polly's progress across the stream. Under cover of fumbling with the block he stole a look at Lina. She had grown thinner, as had they all, but this had in her case merely made the softly pleasing contours of her face seem more childlike, even angelic. She looked as placid as though her mind, if active at all, were chiefly preoccupied with a kind of brooding contentment. Nothing about her expression suggested that she might have a care in the world. Slowly as she had turned to look at him, he was even slower in turning away. Their eyes met. She smiled gently.

Garett pushed against his pillows and looked scowlingly about him with the irascibility of the invalid.

"Great God, is this a wake? Either the wretch will join us or he won't. Anyway, for the moment our bellies are full. Jat, where's your mandiddle?"

"I'll git it," said Lina, springing up.

Eric peered from the loophole, replaced the block, and crossed to inspect the nearest fire.

"Need more wood," he muttered.

At the woodpile he straightened as Lina returned across the yard. Again she looked smilingly at him. Her smile was not reproachful or forgiving. It was pleased and friendly. He caught her arm.

"Are you really that silly?" he demanded harshly. "I've been mean to you. I've treated you like dirt. And all you do is simper and grin. Does nothing make any difference to you? What can be on your mind, or don't you think at all?"

"Yes, I think. All the time."

"What?"

"I think," she said mildly, "that most any day now you will git to be a man."

She went on.

Jarot seized upon the mandiddle. But its introduction into the circle promoted no lifting of the company's spirits. He became even more absorbed in the instrument than was his custom. He bent over it. He squirmed and writhed. At times he surveyed each of the others in the room with bright, curiously understanding eyes. At other times his eyes were blank or tightly closed as though he were struggling desperately to listen. Perpetually his lips moved and his fingers plucked at the strings. But no whisper of sound came forth.

Olivia rose and began to pace restlessly.

"He's likely already on his way back to the Shawnee. If he had any idea of staying on here he'd have brought his Daisy with him."

Jarot looked up. He had heard something. The door opened and Polly came in. She was alone. There was an elkskin sack on her shoulder. She crossed to the table, set it down, and jerked open the mouth to show that it was filled with pecans and hickory nuts.

"Daisy's cache was under the floor of his cabin." Polly

glared at Olen. "Jest where I tol' yuh it would be. Only ye never had the gumption to dig it up whilst we had us the chance." She slapped the elkskin sack. "This is the end o' whut we'll git from Caleb this winter. He's takin' the rest with him."

"With him?" gasped Agatha. "Back to the Shawnee?"

Polly dropped wearily into a chair.

"Nope. He's goin' a sight further'n thet. He only stopped off here because this was on his way to the river. He's headed fer Redstone, the tother side o' Pittsburgh."

"Surely he might spare us more than this one sack of nuts," said Louisa. "We would pay him well."

"Nope," said Polly. "He's real sure he needs the rest for hisself. When a man's in a hurry and got a good way to go and it's the dead o' winter he wants to take along enough so's he won't have to stop off to hunt."

"What we'd really pay him well for," said Garett, "is his rifle."

"Might's well ask him to leave us one of his legs."

"But he can't abandon us like this," said Olivia. "He just can't."

"He's set on goin'," said Polly. "And when thet Caleb is set on somethin' yuh got no more chance to change him than yuh got to push yer hand through thet wall there."

"When is he going?" asked Agatha weakly.

"Soon's he gits hisself a canoe made. He's started in a-workin' on it now."

March

The winter, which had already seemed so harsh, took yet another turn for the worse. The drift of warmer air from the south came so slowly that the change was at first barely perceptible. The gray overcast thickened and lowered, enveloping the tops of the taller trees and settling to the very roof of the station on its mound. The next day a drizzling rain set in and persisted through the night and the day after. The drifts, without changing shape, gradually and sullenly shrank in size. The air remained as raw and penetrating as before. Only in the footpaths about the station was there visible thawing. These became rivulets of slush.

During the third night the drizzle ceased. A wind began to whisper about the corners of the station, soon began to whine, and then rose to the pitch of a screaming northwest gale. The clouds were swept away. The stars became icily brilliant. Before morning the temperature had dropped below zero. The sun, so long unseen, rose to cast a blinding glare upon a land that sparkled and glittered with insensate menace. The shrunken drifts were glazed with ice, the slushy paths frozen into innumerable points of needle-like sharpness. Every step in the open became a feat. Wood was to be hacked from the dwindling woodpile only by more arduous axe work than had been required for its original cutting. Any renewed attempt to hunt or fish had become unthinkable. The outlook in every direction, into the recesses of the wood lot, across the icy meadow, pond, and stream, along the frozen edge of the forest and bank of the river, was hopelessly forbidding.

The chill without pursued the people within. No matter how closely they huddled over their fires they remained aware of that grim sheath of ice that stretched from the doorstep across the whole compass of their desolate world. For the inhabitants of the wilderness, human or animal. March was traditionally the month of starvation. This legend which they had so often heard had taken on a sudden immediate reality.

To their hunger today was added a sharper fear of a greater hunger tomorrow. They repented having feasted so heartily upon the bear. What was left but served to postpone and make more threatening the swiftly approaching day when they would again have nothing. In the earlier days of their hunger they had sought to cheer one another by pretending to ignore their plight. Now they sought as diligently to share their worst premonitions. They talked of nothing but their extremity, examined it, dissected it, magnified it. Spring, they reminded each other, was still many weeks away, and even the prospect of spring offered few new hopes. The eventual reappearance of game and migrating waterfowl signified little to people without firearms. Even the chance of catching fish in the pond, once the ice had gone out, was clouded by the likelihood that by then no one of them would have the strength left to make the effort.

The cold however, had brought them one faint consolation. The sudden freeze in the night had postponed Caleb's departure. He, too, had been taken by surprise. He had left his nearly finished canoe uncovered in the open. The fresh, unseasoned bark had split in freezing and he had been required to start over again. There was at least a grain of comfort in his continued presence. So long as he was still here there was the possibility that he might after all relent and do something more for them before he left.

For all his grim application to the task, his work on this second canoe was marked by none of the ease and celerity with which he had shaped the first. On account of the continuing cold he was unable to strip the bark directly from a standing tree. Instead he was obliged to fell the tree, to build a long fire, and to roll the trunk near the fire to thaw, in order to remove the bark in the one unbroken strip that he required. This was a slow and tedious process, involving much rotating of the log and infinite care in handling the brittle bark. Since it was taking place on the bank of the stream, his every move was watched with the closest attention from the loopholes of the station.

The cold hung on as though it were still midwinter, but by the dawn of the fifth morning the second canoe appeared so near completion that the anxious watchers realized his departure might be near. The Slovers had as usual thronged into the kitchen shortly after daylight. Agatha had cut the community meals to one in mid-morning and another in late afternoon, but the Slovers so much enjoyed company that they always turned up hours in advance. Polly joined Tracy at the loophole and squinted through it.

"Gawd pickle us all," she exclaimed, leaning her head against the wall, "he's so near done with it he could be a-pushin' off afore noon."

Tracy bent to peer over Polly's shoulder through the loop-hole. "Why did he need so large a canoe? Did he tell you?"

"He never tells nobody nuthin'. Mebbe he's a figgerin' on luggin' him some truck back from Pitt."

Tracy gave a start of chagrined surprise. She turned to face Agatha and Olivia. "It just this minute came back to me. When I was in his cabin that morning there were a dozen buckskin sacks standing against the wall. They were tight and round, like sacks of corn. Or maybe it was pemmican—he was eating pemmican. Anyway, it must have been some kind of food. What else could he have taken the trouble to drag through the snow all the way from the Shawnee country? So he's not only got what Daisy buried under his floor last fall but this whole toboggan load besides. That's why he's built so big a canoe. He's got all that to take away with him."

"Seed corn, most likely," said Polly.

"But why take corn to Pittsburgh? If he wants to sell any, it would be worth much more in Kentucky."

"He ain't no hand to be sellin' nuthin'. Whut he's more likely doin' is jest takin' it upriver a ways to bury out'n our reach. Then he'll dig it up agin on his way back."

"Enough to keep us all," said Agatha, "for weeks and weeks."

Louisa rose from her chair and took Polly by the arm. Motioning to the three other women to follow, she led the way to her room. When all had entered she closed the door and confronted them. There was a feverish flush of color on her wasted, pale face.

"We are five women," she said. "Five women responsible for a family of twenty. You, Polly, have children. And you, Agatha. And so have I. Olivia, you have a sick husband. Now tell me this. Are we five women going to just sit here sniffling and moaning while one ignorant, stubborn clod of a man makes off with a canoe-load of food which could keep all twenty of us alive?"

Polly blinked. "It don't stand to reason. It don't, fer a fact. But how yuh goin' to stop him?"

"I'll tell you how. You've got three men, Polly. Give them no rest. Scream until they listen. Make them see what they have to do. Clem and Ned are big and strong. They'll do what I tell them. Eric will help. That's six men. Six men to go down there and take what we have to have."

Polly continued to blink. "Six to one ain't so much, not when the one is the only one thet's got him a rifle."

"Surely six men with their wits about them could hit upon some way to get his rifle away from him."

Polly began to shake her head.

"Thet Caleb ain't so easy to sneak up on. But supposin' they managed to git his rifle away from him and his corn and whut all else he's got—all he'd do is take off back to the Shawnee. How long d'ye think it'd be afore they was on us? Me—I'd ruther have me an empty belly than no belly at all."

"I've never known people to equal you Slovers," said Louisa, "for finding so many good reasons for doing nothing."

" 'Taint so hard to find good reasons, not when they stick out at yuh plainer'n the nose on yer face."

"Suppose," said Olivia deliberately, "suppose he wasn't able to run back to the Shawnee?"

The others, startled, regarded Olivia with widening eyes. Polly, however, began to nod understandingly.

"Yuh mean if'n he got hisself knocked in the head?" She considered the possibilities and then again voted no. "Mebbe yer Niggers or yer Eric is up to tacklin' thet. But there ain't one o' my men thet's got it in him. Was they in tight enough corner thy might shoot him from in back of a tree, but they'd never go at him with no axe. Anyways, was he somohow to git done in no good'd come of it. We'd be in the same fix. Long afore spring the Shawnee'd find out. Yuh mind whut it was like when they come down on us afore. Thet time they was feelin' as friendly as they knowed how. So mebbe yuh kin fetch yuh some idee how they'd take on oncet they started in to feelin' *on*friendly. 'Twould be we-uns—not the cows—that'd wind up skinned and on the fire."

"It's just not conceivable," said Louisa, sinking down on her bed, "that there actually is nothing we can do to help ourselves."

"There's one thing we can do," said Agatha, spacing her words as though each had a separate bad taste. "We can all go down there together. We can beg, implore, get down on our knees. It might be awkward for even as hardened a brute as he to refuse five despairing women."

Polly sat down beside Louisa, once again shaking her head gloomly.

"Not fer him it wouldn't. He's set on goin', and goin' quick."

"What can this business be," asked Tracy, "that's so all-important?"

"I ain't told yuh," said Polly, " 'cause I knowed 'twould only fret yuh more'n yuh bin a-frettin'. He's made up his mind he wants him a woman and he's in a tearin' hurry to git him one so's he kin git back fer his spring plantin'."

"But that's ridiculous," said Tracy. "I mean, ridiculous that he should go along until this late in the winter and then all of a sudden be in such a hurry."

"A man can't git in no bigger hurry. And it's worse when he's bin off by hisself in the woods fer a good long spell. I mind oncet when Olen—he was some younger then—one winter he was mindin' a trap line over on the Little Kanawha. After mebbe two months out there by hisself, all on a sudden he jumped up and run home over the mountain through snow most as deep as we've had this year. I was over to a neighbor's and they was nobody in the cabin but my Aunt Reba. She was near seventy, cross-eyed, and bent up with the rheumatiz crookeder'n a knotty rail. But Olen he was so upsot when I wasn't there a-waitin' fer him thet Aunt Reba she had all she could do to fight him off."

"No doubt Mr. Lewis may be equally impulsive," said Tracy. "But if so, why didn't he keep his Daisy within reach?"

"He's aimin' to settle here like a white man, so he don't want no squaw no more."

Polly's hearers were beginning to take a slightly less hostile interest in the several aspects of Caleb's predicament.

"Has he some special woman in mind," inquired Agatha, "back there in Redstone?"

"Naw. He's headin' fer Pennsylvany 'stead o' Kentuck' 'cause the further east yuh go the more women there is to pick from."

"Wait," said Olivia. "What about your Betsey or Lina? Why wouldn't they do him as well as anybody he'd be likely to find at Pittsburgh or Redstone?"

"Nuthin'd suit me better," said Polly, "than to see either o' them git theyselves so good a man. But Betsey she's still got the miseries in her innards."

"And Lina?" asked Agatha.

"She's in a family way, so she'd be no good to him."

"When will she—when will she——?"

"Come fall, and we're all still a-livin', you'll be a grandmother."

"Grandmother!" said Olivia, her eyes sparkling. "I must say, Agatha, you most certainly don't look it. Starving agrees with you. The thinner you get the more becoming it is. I swear you're a more fetching woman this minute than you were ten years ago."

The two women's glances locked.

"Even ten years ago, my dear, I was not so young as you are today."

Olivia laughed. "There's few signs of your great age. Certainly not one to put a man off. Take even this dolt, Caleb Lewis. Remember his sitting those nights by our fire? He couldn't take his eyes off you. You got so flustered you had to leave the room. Remember?"

"I remember that when he looked at me his face was completely blank. No wonder. I wasn't so different from what he was used to. I am nearly as dark as his Daisy. You were the novelty. You, with your yellow hair and blue eyes."

"Agatha!" said Louisa. "Olivia! Will the both of you—and at once, please—stop this unspeakably distasteful joking."

"It ain't no joke," said Polly, jumping up. "Ain't no manner o' doubt whut could come o' Caleb findin' hisself a mite o' company, off and on, down there in thet cabin o' his'n. With any kind o' luck he might put off leavin' till it was too late fer him to go at all afore plantin' time." She turned at the door. " 'Course, could be yer jest wastin' yer time squabblin' over which one o' yuh it's to be. Could be he figgers yuh ain't his kind and he don't want no part o' none o' yuh. So save yer sweatin', whilst I find out."

"Polly," commanded Louisa. "Stop. Come back here." The door slammed. "Agatha, call her back. Make her come back. Olivia. Tracy."

No one of the three seemed to hear her. Agatha and Olivia continued to stare at each other. Tracy watched them. She was as taut and strained as they.

"I am not forgetting you have children," said Olivia. "We are never allowed to forget that. But doesn't that give you all the more reason? You would not be the first mother who has ever taken to the streets to get bread for her children."

"You have a reason as strong. At least, for you it is as strong. In fact, you have two. You have a sick husband who is so weak he will be the first of us to die. The only thing you wish more than to keep him alive is to keep him miserable. See how at one happy stroke you can gain both comforts."

"The complete madonna. Always you think first of others."

"Will you both be silent," said Louisa. "I will not listen to such idiocies."

The attention of the two women remained fixed on each other.

"I don't need you to goad me," said Agatha. "But I have no wish to be doubly shamed. He is a young man. What interest could he be expected to take in a mother of five?"

"I'll tell you what interest. Your fertility. The man has a special regard for any sort of increase. The first thing he asked me was how many children I had. When I said none, he went back to his eating."

Agatha's mocking smile became more venomous. "You tremble. You breathe hard. Just talking about this excites you. Doesn't it?"

"Ask yourself that. There is not so great a distinction between our situations. You are apparently a widow and I am the same as one. A familiar picture. Both of us starved in more ways than one. Is that the notion you keep circling around?"

"Stop it, for heaven's sake, stop it," said Louisa. The new note of weary reason in her voice captured their attention. "Stop teasing each other, or yourselves, whichever you are doing. You are quite right. Somehow we have to deal with that man. If I were younger I'd go down there myself. I'd have dreaded it more then, of course. I've had to grow old to understand how strong a woman is. In so many ways she's stronger than any man. She can stand hunger, cold—any number of things—better than a man. You, Agatha, or you, Olivia, could go down to that cabin—that is, if you were able to do it without any one else knowing—and be able to come away again without having suffered anything you couldn't get over. Your reason for going would be sufficient to save you. But under our circumstances you cannot do that. You could not take ten steps down that slope, Agatha, without everyone here, down to little Susie, knowing immediately where you were going, why you were going, and, when you came back, what had happened to you. You might get over it, but your children never could. And as for you, Olivia, you know Garett would get straight up out of his sickbed and try to kill Caleb Lewis. It would be the death of him. It is impossible for either of you. You just cannot do it."

"But I can," said Tracy. "I have no children. I have no husband. I can."

"Tracy," cried Louisa. She sprang up, livid, shaking. "It's the most impossible of all for you. It is altogether impossible."

"So I would have thought until ten minutes ago. But we've all begun to realize that we have to do something. It follows just as clearly that I am the one to do it."

"I forbid it," said Louisa, her voice breaking. "Do you understand? I forbid it."

"Maybe you can tell us," said Olivia, "why you're so much more tender of her than of Agatha or me. Is her precious virginity more important to you than the honor of your own sons' wives?"

"Certainly I can tell you," said Louisa. "You're both married women. You have been for years. The animal part of a man is no mystery to you. She has no such defense. We've already agreed neither of you can go down there, so we can speak plainly. For a girl like Tracy it would be an infinitely more devastating experience than for either of you."

"A girl like Tracy," said Olivia. "She's a year older than I am. If she's been just dreaming all this time, then it's high time she waked up. It might do her a world of good—not to speak of the rest of us."

"Especially Garett, you mean," said Agatha.

"Or Duncan," said Olivia.

The door flew open. Polly, panting and even more disheveled than when she had left, staggered in and collapsed on the bed.

"Thet goddam' ice," she groaned, pulling up her dress and rubbing her knees. "I fell down so many times, could be I'll never walk again."

"Well, did you talk to him?" demanded Agatha.

"I surely done jest thet. Real plain talk. When he knowed whut I'd come fer he spoke right out."

"What did he say?" demanded Olivia.

"I'm a-comin' to it," said Polly. "Soon's I kin git my wind. First off—he don't want to go to Redstone if'n there's any way he kin git out'n it. He don't want to lose all thet time. He'd ruther stay here and git on with his clearin'."

Louisa, Agatha, and Olivia looked at one another, appalled by the sudden necessity of facing an actual decision. Only Tracy remained outwardly calm.

"That would seem to settle it," she said.

"It don't settle nuthin'," said Polly. "He said more'n thet. He said he don't want none o' yuh a-crawlin' in and outer his bed. Whut he's a-lookin' for is a woman he kin keep. One thet kin work fer him and cook fer him, as well as sleep with him. He wants him a wife."

"But that's even more impossible," gasped Louisa. "It's so impossible it's—it's ludicrous."

"He can't be serious," said Olivia.

"Yuh kin figger thet fer yerselves," said Polly. "He knows

Garett was a magistrate back in Virginny. He wants first off to stand up in front o' Garett and have Garett read the marriage lines."

Louisa moaned and sank down on the bed, covering her face with her hands.

"That would most certainly seem to settle it," said Tracy. "Neither you, Agatha, nor you, Olivia, can do that."

"No more can you," said Olivia, stiffening with sudden fury. "Garett would never marry you to Caleb Lewis—or any other man."

"No one," said Tracy, "can manage to be more mistaken more often than you can, Olivia."

"Go ask him, Olivia," said Agatha. "We must know instantly what he really does think."

Olivia's flare of anger passed. She clutched at a chair back for support.

"I couldn't," she whispered. "I just couldn't."

"Then I will," said Agatha.

"Tell him we ain't got no time to do much thinkin'," Polly called after her. "Caleb he's a-waitin' right out there at the gate. His canoe's done and if there's goin' to be any balkin' he wants to start right in gittin' her out to the river and gettin' her packed." She struggled up from the bed and looked back from the doorway. "I'll tell Caleb the answer ain't yes and it ain't no—but if'n he'll hang on to hisself fer another couple o' jerks he'll git him one or t'other."

Louisa lifted her grief-ravaged face and looked at Tracy as accusingly as though she had brought this on herself.

"He knew when he sent that absurd message by Polly," she said, "that it could only have meant you."

"So it would seem," said Tracy.

"What does every man see in you?" cried Olivia. "That's what I can't understand."

She turned and ran out, past the silent, puzzled, staring people in the kitchen and on into her room. Garett was sitting up in bed. His face was gray-white, he looked more dead than alive, but he was grinning up at Agatha.

"So Tracy's to be our Judith?" he was saying. "Or rather, to be somewhat more apt, our Delilah—since we seem to be the Philistines in the case. Who maneuvered her into the breach?"

"No one," said Agatha. "It was her own idea. She insisted on it when she realized—when we all realized—that there was no other way."

"How true. We Jordans must eat." Garett looked around

at Olivia. "Why so distressed, my sweet? I would have thought our dilemma would strike you as the fulfillment of one of your fondest dreams."

"Don't chatter," snapped Olivia. "We haven't time. Caleb Lewis is out there waiting. You have to speak right out, and right now."

"You seem to find my decision more dramatic than—than even poor Tracy's, let us say."

"It is to me."

"Then I shall make you happy. Call in the bride and groom."

Olivia's bitterness sharpened.

"Tricks won't save you. You're caught, for once. You've got to be the one to hand Tracy over to him, to take down to that cabin of his. Tracy—do you understand? *Tracy*."

"Yes. I'm very much afraid I do." Garett was no longer grinning. "And, since it is I who must choose, my choice is a simple one. I much prefer that we all continue to live. Apparently, if we are to live we must pay the man's price. It's as simple as that. The one question, then, is who shall pay it? I likewise can think of but one answer to that. You, Agatha, and you, Olivia, are Jordans. Neither of you can be considered a candidate. Which leaves us Tracy. As fond as we all are of her, if there must be a bait thrown to the bear she would seem to be elected."

Olivia threw herself on the bed beside him and dissolved into a spasm of weeping. Garett leaned over and stroked her hair. She fumbled blindly for his hand, drew it against her face, kissed it over and over again. Agatha regarded the reconciliation impatiently.

"First off, Garett," she said, "he has to agree to move those stores of his up here. You must be sure to come to a clear understanding with him on that."

"A waste of breath, my dear," said Garett. "He appreciates our situation even more clearly than we do. Meanwhile, wouldn't you be more usefully concerned with—ah—decking out the bride, or holding her hand or something of that sort?"

"You are such a heartless dog," said Agatha. "I don't wonder Olivia is always in such a state."

She ran out and across the kitchen to Louisa's door. It was barred from within.

In the room Tracy was standing against the wall, her eyes closed. Louisa got up from the bed, crossed to her and gripped her by the shoulders.

"Now. For the last time. Will you listen to me?"

Tracy's eyes opened. They were calm and distant. She might have been miles away from the distracted old woman who was clutching at her.

"I am listening."

"Mother," prompted Louisa.

"I am listening, Mother."

"I have had five sons. Three of them were killed in the war. I have two left. I am proud that they are my sons. But I have always wanted a daughter. You have become that daughter. Does that mean nothing to you?"

"You know how much it does."

"Then how can you do this dreadful—this bestial thing?"

"How can I do anything else? All these years I have been a part of your family. Now you are in the most desperate danger and perhaps I can save you. How could I endure myself if I did not try?"

Louisa took Tracy's face in her hands. "What makes you so sure Duncan is dead?"

"I am not sure. I—I could not be."

"You are in love with him, aren't you?"

"Yes. I have always been."

"Then, when he returns how can you face him?"

"I have thought of that, too. But it has only made everything even more clear. There has never before been anything I could do for him. Now I can."

Polly began to beat on the door.

"We-uns can't wait no longer," she called. "One way or t'other—it's got to be now."

Louisa sank face downward on the bed. Tracy unbarred the door and went out into the kitchen. She was conscious of the pitch of excitement kindled by her entrance in a company which had only in the last minutes begun to realize the significance of what was transpiring. She saw the Slover men getting to their feet with foolish, elated grins, the wide-eyed, half-frightened stares of the younger children, the open-mouthed bewilderment of the Negroes, the incredulous, numbed horror on Eric's face, Agatha, bracing herself, agonized by her apprehension that even at this last moment some unforeseen complication might intervene to strike down her rising hopes. Then she saw Caleb, standing in the open doorway. He stood there, motionless, poised, waiting, as though expecting some imminent, sudden occurrence, such as a gunshot or a buck plunging from a thicket. The rifle in his hands, the powder horn, bullet pouch, tomahawk, and knife at his waist, his tightly belted buckskins, gave him the air of a man already embarked on a journey and for whom this might as well be a moment of departure as of arrival. His expression was cold, composed, yet oddly alert. His eyes met hers. That strangely direct gaze, which had disturbed her before, seemed to pierce into the secret recesses of her mind. She shuddered, gripped by a terrifying sensation that he understood her better than she understood herself and that it was the unsympathetic understanding of an antagonist.

"I am ready," she said.

Garett threw back the covers and sat on the edge of his bed. Olivia hastily draped his uniform greatcoat over his shoulders and knelt to wrap a blanket about his legs. Caleb and Tracy stood facing him, flanked on either side by Agatha and Polly. Betsey and Lina stood by the door. Betsey's grin spiteful and derisive, Lina's warm and pleased. The Slover men peered with unabashed, leering curiosity from the doorway. Eric, in a frenzy, had driven the Negroes and the children to the farther end of the kitchen.

"Unhappily, I have no prayer book at hand," said Garett, "unless we wait while ours is fetched from my mother's trunk. However, I take it that it is the basic, legal essentials with which we are primarily concerned."

"Yes," said Caleb.

"I must ask a preliminary question." He looked at Tracy. "Are you entering into this contract of your own free will?"

"I am," Tracy said distinctly.

"And you?"

"Yes," said Caleb.

"Then we will proceed. Take her hand, please."

Without looking at her, Caleb reached for Tracy's hand. His fingers closed over hers.

"Do you, Thryza Carter, take this man for your lawfully wedded husband?"

"I do," said Tracy.

"Do you, Caleb Lewis, take this woman for your lawfully wedded wife?"

"I do."

"Then, by virtue of the authority vested in me by the sovereign state of Virginia, I hereby pronounce you man and wife. God help you both—and God help us all." Garett's gray face became still grayer. He slumped sidewise against the pillows. "You must excuse me," he whispered. "I find I must rest."

Olivia lifted his legs into the bed, pulled the greatcoat away, and solicitously tucked the bedclothes about him. Caleb released Tracy's hand, stepped around her, and pushed through the doorway into the kitchen.

"Come," he directed Olen and his sons.

His gesture of command included Ned and Clem, as well. The five followed him out.

"Whatever can he be up to now?" Agatha asked anxiously of Tracy. "Where's he taking them?"

"I haven't the faintest idea," said Tracy. Spots of color had appeared on her pale cheeks. "The only words I've heard out of him since he came in have been two 'yesses' and one 'I do.' "

She went on into Louisa's room. Agatha and Polly ran to a loophole. The men following Caleb were slipping and sliding down the icy slope. They went on across the frozen stream, past the canoe, and disappeared in the woods in the direction of Caleb's cabin. Agatha and Polly were not kept long in suspense. The men reappeared, each with a sack or a basket on his shoulder. They began toiling back up the slope, scrambling to their feet when they fell and, when they fell again, crawling eagerly upward on their knees. The two women ran to the door. Jarot was the first one in. He deposited the elkskin sack on the table. Polly tore at the leather drawstring.

"Smoked turkey," she cried. "Jam pack full o' smoked turkey."

Jacob stumbled over the threshold, dropping the basket he had balanced on his shoulder. It burst, scattering a bushel and a half of dried serviceberries across the floor.

"Pick them up," Agatha directed the children. "Every last one."

Polly kept Clem and Ned by the door to prevent their stepping on the berries but immediately inspected their loads.

"A sack o' deer jerky," she announced. "And another o' smoked catfish. Thet Daisy, she was busier'n any squirrel."

Olen, the last of the burden bearers, set his sack against the wall. Polly gave it a kick.

"Corn meal," she marveled.

Olen straightened and regarded her coldly. Ordinarily when he came into the Jordan kitchen he snatched off his moth-eaten fur cap and sidled sheepishly into a corner. But now his bearings was clothed with all of the calm authority befitting the head of a family. After one startled glance at him Polly began to bristle.

"Yuh mind them wool socks yuh got put away somewheres," he said. "Go fetch 'em to me."

"So yer feet got cold thet quick," said Polly. "Yuh bin squattin' indoors so long it's a wonder they ain't dropped off."

"Go git me them socks," repeated Olen.

"Yuh must o' walked most a mile. Yuh jest rest yerself fer a spell and mebbe yuh'll git the strength back to go git 'em yerself."

"I'm aimin' to go a sight further'n any mile."

"Where?" scoffed Polly.

"Huntin'."

"How kin you hunt? Yuh got no rifle."

"Caleb he'll do the shootin'. We-uns,"—he nodded importantly at his sons and the Negroes—"is goin' along to pack in the meat."

"With the footin' bad's it is yuh'll never git far."

"We tie bresh to our feet, we kin make out. Now don't give me no more o' yer lip, woman. Go git me them socks."

Polly gaped at him, then, suddenly and happily submissive, she scurried out.

"Geneva," directed Agatha, "see to it that Clem and Ned are warmly dressed before they start. They're worse than children when it comes to looking after themselves."

Caleb came in. He looked about the kitchen. Agatha's glance went to the door of Louisa's room. Caleb crossed to it.

Tracy was seated on the bed, her arms about Louisa.

"It's too late now," moaned Louisa. "I realize that. We'll just have to put up with it, if we can. I know that."

Nevertheless, she sprang up in a fury when Caleb entered.

"I trust you realize," she cried, "that you are doing the same as taking her by force? Even in this benighted country violence to a woman is regarded as the most unforgiveable of all crimes."

Caleb continued to look reflectively down at Tracy. Louisa turned her back and leaned against the bedpost.

"I will be in the woods for some days," he said. "Maybe a week. There is not enough to eat to keep so many until spring. Since I must hunt I want to lay up enough meat now so that when I come back I can stay with my clearing."

"Thank you for coming to tell me," said Tracy.

He opened the game sack in his hand and displayed a dozen skeins of linen thread.

"I will need shirts for summer. When I get back you will be helping me clear. So while I am away"—he nodded toward the small loom in the corner—"you can be weaving cloth for the shirts."

Tracy rose and accepted the skeins of thread which he was extending toward her.

"Should I say, Yes, Mr. Lewis?" she inquired. "Or, Yes, Caleb? Or, perhaps, Yes, sir?"

"It does not matter what you say. Only what you do."

He turned and went out. Louisa embraced Tracy.

"How utterly amazing," she gasped, "But what a Godsend. A reprieve, if only for a few days. And we can hope, we can pray, that something just might happen to him before he can get back."

"He does not permit things to happen to him," said Tracy. "That is, not in the woods."

Agatha ran in.

"Whatever could have possessed him to take himself off hunting?" she demanded. "This afternoon, I mean, instead of —tomorrow morning, say. Do you think he wanted to give you a little time to get used to the idea of being married to him? Could he possibly have that much sense?"

"His explanation," said Tracy, "was simple enough. He wants to get his necessary hunting over with so that he can get at his clearing. Meanwhile he assigns me something with which to busy myself." She indicated the skeins of thread in her arms. "I'm to devote my time to making him shirts."

Agatha's laugh verged on hysteria.

"Maybe we've been taking all this too seriously? Maybe, Tracy, you have merely entered into a business arrangement?"

Tracy climbed to the fire step. One way she could see Caleb and his five followers beginning to mount the rise beyond the wood lot. The other way she could see off down the river. Suddenly she gripped the palisade. The dark dot for which she had so often looked in vain came into view around the distant bend. She watched, shaking, scarcely breathing, while the dot became larger. It became a four-oared barge, beating steadily against the current, the first craft of any description that had appeared on the river since Duncan's raft had faded from view. But as it came on and on the chill of the evening entered into her. For the barge kept to the shadows of the farther shore and kept on past upriver and on out of her sight. The travelers were no more than passing strangers who had no idea that the station existed. Her momentary excitement had but made the more crushing the sense of desolation creeping upon her.

April

March, after having exceeded the rigors of mid-winter, came forth with other excesses before ushering in April. The third day after the hunters had left the weather turned warm. The snow began to melt so rapidly that in another three days there were widening patches of bare ground. The earth, which had been soaked by the earlier, lesser thaw, could hold no more. Water oozed from the spongy soil, trickled, collected, flowed down every slope, filled every hollow. The stream rose, bursting its shell of ice. The pond expanded and spread into the meadow. Other dark pools gleamed in every flat of the woods beyond.

"Tain't no kind o' weather fer huntin,' " pronounced Polly. "They might's well wade home and dry off."

The unseasonable mildness continued. Spring came like a wave. Buds swelled. Willows flaunted their fluffy plumes. Serviceberry bushes paled, then whitened with blossoms. Frog choruses shrilled in the night. Flights of waterfowl appeared in the southern sky, circled, wheeled, and dropped with much boisterous splashing to the meadow's placid surface. The air was vibrant with the urgent honking of wild geese, the petulant squawking of ducks, the hoarse, thundering calls of the trumpeter swan. One morning came a flock of robins, and that afternoon another of mocking birds swooped into the station yard.

Caleb had set his return at within a week at the longest, but the seventh day passed like the others.

"Could it be that he's not omnipotent after all?" said Garett. "That he could get stuck in the mud like any ordinary mortal?"

"Let's trust he stays with the mud until he gets something," said Agatha. "The cupboard is going to be bare again in another week."

Polly and Agatha began openly and anxiously to watch. Whenever either was in the yard she kept going to the gate to look toward the eastern ridge over which the hunters had disappeared. But when on the tenth day Jarot returned, he came out of the woods on the west side of the stream and no one realized he was there until his axe began to ring. He had discovered the crossing log had been carried away by the rising water, had turned back to Caleb's cabin for the axe, and was felling a greater tree on a higher point on the west bank to serve as a new crossing.

"Do you really think something could have happened to the others?" asked Louisa.

Polly dispelled her not entirely disguised hope. "Was somethin' wrong with Olen or Jake, Jat he'd never be struttin' around like a turkey cock the way he is."

The pine cracked, leaned, and crashed, stretching, when the thunder of its fall had ceased to echo, from the knoll on the other bank to the flat rock at the base of the mound. Working his way across this new bridge, his axe swinging expertly as he came, Jarot notched the trunk for firmer footing and left of some of the branches, as he lopped them off, four-foot stubs to serve as hand grips on either side. It was in every respect a great improvement upon the earlier crossing.

"The whole winter you couldn't get those Slovers so much as to sit up straight," grumbled Agatha, watching. "Now they fly around like the devil was after them."

Jarot came in, wet to the waist and caked with mud but jaunty and cheerful. The load on his back turned out to be a hundredweight of fresh buffalo meat. Polly sniffed at it judiciously.

"Ain't bin kilt but two days," said Jarot. "Took me a extry day to git here 'count I had to circle so far to git around the high water."

"Take the six o' yuh all this time to git yuh one buffler?"

"Nope. Took us no time a-tall fer thet part. Caleb he knowed right where to go. Thet next crik east o' the ridge comes out'n a marsh mebbe thirty mile upcountry. In the middle o' the marsh they's a patch o'higher ground with a salt lick and a lavish o' young sycamore. A middlin' herd o' buffler bin winterin' there, lickin' salt and livin' off'n the sycamore bark. Caleb he knocked down fifteen the fattest the first day. Reason we ain't bin back long afore now was she turned so warm the meat started to go bad. We-uns had to camp and take to smokin' it."

Jarot lingered only to snatch at the platter Polly set before him.

"Who'd ever o' thunk dried catfish'd taste better'n fresh buffler," he marveled. "But fer more'n a week I bin eatin' all the fresh buffler I could push down." He backed toward the door. "Caleb's makin' him a raft. He'll have her done by the time I kin git back to camp. Then we kin float our jerky down thet east crik no matter how high she floods. Oncet we git her t'other side the ridge we kin pack her right in."

The next day it began to rain, and with only an occasional brief pause it continued to rain for eleven days. The flooded meadow became a lake which extended into the wood lot and finally all the way around the mound to rejoin the swollen stream below the flat rock. The station had become an island. Polly regarded the rain and the rising water with increasing pessimism.

"There ain't nuthin tricker'n smokin' jerky," she observed, " 'cept it's smokin' it in the rain. Thet buffler meat o' Caleb's likely ain't goin' to be worth packin' nowheres."

"Let it rain," said Louisa. "I hope the flood lasts all summer. The longer it lasts the longer before that man is back."

Tracy sat at the loom. She was not accustomed to weaving. Louisa had urged her to permit Hebe to weave the cloth, but Tracy had kept at it until she was now on the last skein of thread.

"You couldn't be making a sadder mistake," said Olivia. "That was the first thing he told you to do. The time to stand up to him was right at the start."

"You talk about Tracy's putting up with him," protested Louisa, "as though it were something that was all settled."

"Well, isn't it?" asked Olivia.

The long rain ended. There came one hard frost and then a week of conventional April weather. Clouds raced across the sky, gathering, breaking, clearing, with each day's sunshine interspersed with passing showers and occasional brief thunderstorms. The flood waters began to recede. Moss brightened on the black trunks of trees. The new leaves began their magic unfolding, bathing the forest in the pale green of their wreathing mist. A flight of passenger pigeons, so immense that the cloud of wings shadowed the sky, hovered, settled almost to the treetops, and then flew on to the north. Polly patrolled the edges of the stream, watching for the moment its waters might have cleared for fishing.

"Seen me one sturgeon today," she announced. " 'Nother week they'll be spawnin' and we kin go to spearin' 'em up by the falls." She sat down and blinked gloomily. "Ain't no question somethin's happened to 'em. Thet Caleb he ain't no hand to set on his bottom a-waitin' out no weather."

But the next day there came at last a second report from the hunters. Jarot and Caleb, himself, appeared on the west bank of the stream. Caleb dropped his pack on the ground and at once turned back into the woods. Jarot, carrying both packs, came across and trudged into the station. He did not look so well kept and well-fed as on his first visit. His buckskins were in tatters and he was reeling with fatigue. In the two packs were two hundred and fifty pounds of buffalo jerky.

"We brung this lot in first off," he explained, " 'cause it was some the rain got at. You'd best stew her up 'fore she spoils."

This time he had brought more than news. He was able to announce instructions that directly concerned his listeners.

"We wasn't up to workin' thet raft all the way down the crik like Caleb aimed to. The flood fetched so many trees down they was a log jam every forty rod. So we got to pack in near a ton o' jerky from mebbe fifteen mile up thet east crick. Caleb he wants to git it in right quick. If'n it rains hard again and the jerky gits wet the whole mess of it will go bad. So he wants all of you able to git around to come out and help pack."

At dawn the next morning the packing party set forth. Louisa, Garett, Betsey, Lina, and the younger children were left behind, but the other six women and Eric followed Jarot's lead, taking in single file the circuitous route that Caleb had selected the day before. It was a route that meandered from one patch of higher and drier ground to the next, skirting the ponds, swamps, and bogs that dotted the still flooded wilderness, crossed back to the east side of the stream above the falls, followed the old Indian trail for two miles, then angled to the northeast to climb the ridge and drop down to the camp on the east creek at the point where transportation by raft had been finally blocked.

Here were the scaffolds upon which the jerkey had been heaped and covered with hides, with low fires burning beneath the racks to prevent any accumulation of moisture. And here, too, the travelers from the station began to gain some idea of the extraordinary exertions to which the hunters had been committed. Their torn buckskins had rotted from continual wetting until they were all but naked. They were scratched, begrimed with soot, more drawn and gaunt than during their midwinter hunger.

"Ain't nobody," pronounced Polly, after a brief interrogation of Olen, "not nobody never—made theyselves jerky in such weather. Jerky don't stand wet no better'n sugar nor salt. But Caleb he made her, come hell nor high water. And when they figgered they was done with buildin' fires o' wet wood, and new racks every time they moved camp, and pushin' rafts around, and choppin' log jams, they wasn't done with nuthin'. No matter how wore out they got by day, come night he put 'em to work curin' the hides 'stead o' sleepin'. And buffler hides wasn't enough fer him. He'd brung him along a couple o' traps and he ketched hisself thirty beaver 'tween times." She wagged her head delightedly. "Thet Olen, he's done more real work this one month than all the rest of his life put together."

Caleb, in issuing instructions to his new helpers, addressed himself directly to Tracy, as though he considered her a natural extension of his authority.

"As good a day as we may get," he said, taking a last look at the scattered clouds in the sky. "Be sure that everybody takes all they can carry. But not too much. Because they'll all have to move fast with whatever they take. Once it is off these racks it must be under a roof before it rains again."

His month-old beard was red as copper, except where the ends were singed. His eyes were bloodshot; he was as ragged and worn and gaunt as the others. But his manner was as certain as when he had left the station.

"Try to take a half of it," he continued. "Then you can get the rest in one more trip. You will have everybody with you but Olen. He is going with me to raft down the last load from the lick. Tomorrow leave two of your people at the station. Have them look closely at every piece before they hang it in the storeroom. Have them hang the best and driest in the back where it will be used last. But the rest of you come back tomorrow no matter if it rains. You can wait here ready to make another run for it when the rain stops. Is everything that I have said clear to you?"

"Quite," said Tracy.

Caleb and Olen pushed off on their raft. The burden bearers began to assume their loads. In preparation for the earlier transportation by raft the long strands of dried, smoke-blackened meat had been arranged in bundles tied with buffalo-hide thongs. Each weighed forty to fifty pounds. The women took one, the men two. Jarot set off at a trot, the others, slipping and sliding on the muddy ground, trailing behind him. The first scramble up the ridge proved the most difficult lap of the entire race. The incline was steep and the mud was alternately like mortar and grease. When at last they reached the top, the sky was darkening. There was a rumble of thunder in the distance. Jarot lengthened his strides.

"Just like getting the hay in before a storm," gasped Agatha.

There came the first spats of rain as they crossed the stream above the falls.

"You don't have to stay in line," called out Tracy. "Everybody go as fast as he can."

Several of the men began crowding past and ran on. The intervals in the column widened until it had separated into groups, each of which was unable to hold to the pace of the one next ahead and which in turn dissolved as each individual discovered the final limit of his capacity to keep up. Jarot had reached the station while Geneva, puffing and wheezing at the end of the line, was still a mile from Caleb's cabin. After all their exertions the rain held off, and by the time the last of the procession was floundering up the slope to the gate, the sky was clearing again.

Louisa, clapping her handkerchief to her nose against the bitter, smoky smell that filled the kitchen, regarded the great bales of jerky dropped in disorderly heaps by the weary bearers.

"In this miserable country everything's absurd," she declared. "For months we have no meat at all and now enough for an army."

"This is only the half of it," said Olivia. "Tomorrow we go back for as much more." She sank to a bench. "That is—if any of us can walk."

"I think you should be the one to stay here tomorrow, Agatha," said Tracy. "You and Eric."

"Why me?" objected Eric. "Why not Olivia? I can carry two bales."

He looked around, hoping that it had not escaped general notice that he had been able to carry as heavy a load as any of the men and that only Jarot had beaten him to the station.

"Every one of these bales has to be lifted, moved to the storeroom, opened, sorted," said Tracy. "You'll be needed more here."

"And don't argue," said Olivia. "She speaks with the master's voice."

The next day at dawn, Eric, glancing from the loophole above his cot, saw the young buck nibbling at the new sprigs of green just across the pond that still stretched to the middle of the meadow. Grasping his reconstructed bow, he ran out. Circling through the muddy wood lot he crept back against the faint and fitful early morning wind. The buck's head came up as he caught the scent that he was unable for an instant to place. The bow bent. The arrow struck with an audible, vibrating thud. The gleam in Eric's eyes, as he sprang upon his prey with his knife jerking across its throat, was darker and wilder than the mere exultation of a successful hunter. He threw the carcass over his shoulder and strode up to the gate.

The day which had begun with so fortunate an omen continued to show promise. The bearers, who upon arising had groaned over their stiff points, gathered new courage from the amount of smoked turkey and dried serviceberry stew that they were able to consume at breakfast, and set off over the bridge in unforeseen good spirits. The sky was clear and the early sun warm. Garett, trying his unsteady legs, ventured out into the yard.

"The first real spring day," he said.

"The day he'll be coming back," said Louisa.

Garett eyed her reflectively.

"What do you do when you repent of a bargain? Just how do you get out of it?"

"It was no bargain of mine. I couldn't have been more against it."

"But you weren't able to prevent it."

"Everyone was terrified. We were starving."

"There's the rub. We were starving. Now he has heaped food upon us, a mountain of food. How do we tell him now that we will not pay for it?"

"I don't know. But we have to find some way."

Eric was moving the bales of jerky into the storeroom and helping Agatha sort and hang it. Ken and Cam were engaged in the cleaning and skinning of Eric's deer. Ken was biting his lips and trying not to look too closely at what he was doing.

"If you hate it so much," said Cam, "give me the knife."

"It's dead," said Ken, doggedly, "so what's the difference."

In the Slover cabin Lina was bathing. Betsey watched, her eyes smoldering with resentment as she contemplated the smoothly rounded body which was so much more pleasantly formed than her own. Lina passed her hands over her breasts and about her waist.

"Ain't no difference yit thet I kin feel," she sighed.

"Jest wait. 'Fore long yuh'll go to poddin' out like yuh'd swallered a punkin."

A pleased, faraway look came into Lina's eyes.

"D'ye see thet buck Eric got this mornin'? One shot was all it took. Jest as neat as any man could manage with a rifle."

Betsey smiled with a different kind of pleasure.

"Yuh know why he's bin workin' so hard with thet bow and arrer. Yuh know thet, don't you? Mebbe yuh ain't seen him down there in the wood lot shootin' over and over again at thet poplar stub. It's a stub 'bout the size of a man. He's got so's he kin hit the same spot every time, jest under the chin."

"Yer seein' things," said Lina. "Things thet ain't there."

"I bin seein' plenty o' things plainer'n you. He'll shoot Caleb 'fore he'll let Caleb have her. He'll drive an arrer into him jest as fur as he done into thet buck."

Lina placidly shook her head.

"Tain't only Tracy he's thinkin' about," persisted Betsey. "His father's dead. And Garett's sick. He figgers he's the man o' the family. He figgers thet whutever's got to be done he's the one thet's got to do it."

Lina, continuing to shake her head, began to draw on her clothes.

Chris and Susie were down on the flat rock, dangling one of Polly's fish lines in the water. A school of tiny perch, too small to take the hook, had congregated about the bit of red flannel. Suddenly there appeared another fish as much too large as the perch were too small. A five-foot sturgeon glided slowly in from the darker depths, rubbed against the rock, and came to rest on the bottom immeditely below the staring anglers. Chris lowered his hook and jerked it up and down before the armored snout. The sturgeon paid no heed. Chris handed the line to Susie and jumped to his feet.

"Watch him," he commanded. "Don't scare him off—just watch him."

He ran up to the shop, found Garett's fish spear, and ran back with it. The sturgeon still lay on the bottom beside the rock, his fins and gills barely moving. Chris poised the spear in both his hands. The two children were so intent that they were unaware of the barge that had turned from the river into the estuary. Chris plunged the spear downward with all of his strength. The previously somnolent fish was transposed instantly into an engine of energy. Surfacing with a tremendous splash, he circled and headed downstream, his great tail whipping a wake of froth, the spear sticking straight up out of his back like the mast of a ship. A loop of the line attached to the spearhead caught Chris' ankle and jerked him into the water.

Lina sauntered across the yard past Ken and Cam, preoccupied with their deer-skinning, smiled at Louisa and Garett on the bench beside the door, and slipped into the kitchen. She could hear Eric and Agatha in the storeroom. Eric's bow stood in a corner. She snatched it up and started back toward the door. The bow was too long to hide under her dress. Eric spoke from the office doorway.

"What are you doing with my bow?"

"I—I was only looking at it."

Eric advanced on her.

"Give it to me."

She ran behind the table to escape him. He stepped on a bench and vaulted over it. She twisted in his grasp and attempted to throw the bow into the fire. He caught her arm in time but she clung desperately to the bow. He was wrenching it from her by main force when both suddenly ceased to struggle as they heard Susie's first scream from the yard.

Susie, continuing to scream, came through the open doorway like a small cannon ball. She was in a state of excitement too intense for intelligible expression. "Oh—oh—oh," she kept crying. She cast one wild look around the kitchen and ran toward the storeroom. As she neared her mother her screams at last began to gain coherence.

"Mama—Papa's back. Mama—Papa's back. Mama—Papa's back."

Agatha dropped an armful of jerky and leaned weakly against the wall beside the nearest loophole. In the narrow opening to the outer world the incredible vision seemed to leap upon her. Duncan was at the top of the slope, scarcely a dozen feet away. He was wearing a new, snuff-colored serge suit and a new, ruffled shirt, but no hat. He looked strong and well. He was carrying Chris on his shoulder and both of them were laughing. Everything about the moment seemed to her incredible, including particularly the final circumstance that both Duncan and Chris were streaming wet and Duncan's free hand was dragging an enormous fish. Her knees buckled and she sank, fainting, to the floor.

Duncan came into the kitchen, still carrying Chris and dragging the sturgeon. Garett, Louisa, Ken, and Cam, exclaiming and gesticulating, trailed after him like a comet's tail. Lina stared and laid the bow in her hand carefully on the table. Eric came through the office doorway carrying his mother's limp body in his arms. Duncan put Chris down, let go of the fish, and took Agatha from Eric. Eric ran before him to open the door to their room. Duncan placed Agatha on their bed and knelt beside her.

"Duncan," she began to whisper. "Duncan."

Eric softly closed the door and turned to face the others.

"Let them alone for a minute," he advised earnestly, including Louisa and Garett in his admonition as though they were as much in need of it as the hysterical younger children.

The second day's packing party wound out of the woods into Caleb's clearing. The main procession kept on toward the bridge. Caleb and Tracy, whose loads were composed of the buffalo hides and beaver pelts, turned off to deposit these at his cabin. Betsey sprang up from the stump where she had been waiting and ran to intercept them at the door.

"The Kunnel's back," she announced.

Her sharp eyes studied their faces. But her planned sensation seemed a sad misfire. Each was motionless for a second, as though listening to something in the distance. That was all.

"He got in mebbe two hours ago," persisted Betsey. "He came up from Louisville. Bill Granger fetched him in one o' his barges. He brung hams and bacons and more'n a hunert sacks o' corn. They got plenty to eat now up at the station without yer jerky."

Caleb swung his huge bundle to the ground and, loosening Tracy's shoulder straps, tossed her pack of beaver pelts to the doorstep.

"He's alive," whispered Tracy, closing her eyes. "I was sure of it. No, I wasn't—quite."

"You had best go up and see him," said Caleb.

Tracy's eyes opened.

"You are giving me your permission to see him? Is that it?"

"No. I am telling you to see him. So that you can tell him that if you are not back here by dark I will be coming up to get you."

Betsey brightened.

"He brung new rifles fer everybody," she said. " 'Course Paw and Jat and Jake they'll stand off out'n yer way and the Lymans ain't with him. So you'll jest have the Jordans to handle. But all the same, Caleb, you'd best watch whut yer about. They don't aim to let yuh have her. Before his paw got back, Eric, he was figgerin' to shoot you with his bow and arrer. Now all three o' them got rifles and the Kunnel he's got him a new brace o' pistols."

Tracy's face was drawn but she was meeting Caleb's eyes steadily. "What I decide to do," she said, "will not depend on anything Colonel Jordan says or does, and even less on what you say or do. And when I have made up my mind I will come back to tell you what I have decided."

"You have had a month to make up your mind."

Caleb had spoken so quietly that Betsey's hopes sank again. She edged around until she could look up at Tracy.

"What he wants yuh fer is to work fer him like Daisy done," she said. "Thet's whut Maw says. Maw says was pleasure whut he had most on his mind he'd o' picked Agatha. He was most took with her. He liked Olivia next 'count o' her yaller hair. But when he thunk it over some he figgered thet he better have him a woman he could keep around all summer to help him with his clearin' and plantin'."

Caleb looked down at Betsey. She flinched, backed reluctantly away, and ran to overtake the others.

"There would be some relief," said Tracy, "if I could be certain that what she said was true."

"What is true," said Caleb, "is that I want a wife. And if you are lying about coming back, then I will still come up to look for you."

"I will come," said Tracy. "Because we are agreed on one thing. We are agreed that we will settle this between ourselves. We are, aren't we?"

"If," said Caleb, "no one stands in our way."

Tracy walked off toward the bridge, one second almost running, the next coming almost to a stop. At the top of the slope she found Garett sittting on a bench at the corner of the stockade.

"I am here soaking up this blessed sun," he said. "I am also here waiting to give you the gist of the news. Everyone inside is still too delirious to get out a single connected sentence on any subject, while you will be obliged to grasp our situation clearly—and quickly."

"How true," said Tracy, sitting beside him. "Is he—well?"

"Very. Overflowing with more energy than ever. His adventures were harrowing but simple. He got safely off the raft on the south bank. He could not see in the squall but he took it for granted the Lymans had succeeded in returning here. After two days of wallowing through the snow he saw a fire. Unfortunately it turned out to be a camp of snowbound Cherokee on their way south after paying a visit to their Shawnee cousins. They took him captive, estimating him to be worth a good solid ransom. But after they'd got him to their town down on the Tennessee he ran across Old Tassel, an elderly chief who used to be more friendly to whites than Indians are able to be in these land-grabbing days. Old Tassel happened once to have known Corbit Revel, and Duncan made such a play on being Corbit's kinsman that finally the Cherokee let him go on his promise to forward his ransom when and as he was able. He got back to Kentucky none the worse except for the delay of two months. There he learned that after he had left the raft, the estimable Lymans had floated on downriver to Louisville rather than returning to the station to share our poor fortunes. He had realized all along the desperate straits to which we must have been reduced and was every day in a greater frenzy to get back to us. He had little money and less credit, but Duncan can talk most anybody into most anything. With some help from Clark he got together a boatload of supplies and persuaded Bill Granger to ferry him up and here he is—late but, thank God, nevertheless here. So, all's well that end's well—so far, at least. Now, if you've got your breath and collected your wits, go in and face the music."

Tracy paused in the kitchen doorway. Across the kitchen and through the open door of his and Agatha's room she could see Duncan. He was wearing a dressing gown and sitting on their bed. Agatha was beside him with her head on his shoulder. His other arm was around Cam on the other side of him, and Susie was in his lap. Ken and Chris were at his knees and Eric stood over the family group like a guardian angel. She started across the kitchen to greet him but her feet, as though obeying a will of their own, took her instead through the door of her own room. She leaned back against it, eyes closed, hands clenched, thinking that the last moment in which there would be time to think was upon her. She must be sure that she was recognizing what might lie in wait ahead—for her and for Duncan and for everybody, even Caleb Lewis. While assuring herself that she was still thinking, she began to pack.

Louisa opened the door. She was weak with happiness and grasped at a chair back as she moved unsteadily toward the bed. "What a miracle! I'll never miss saying my prayers again. I thought I saw you come in. You haven't even seen him yet, have you? He's been asking for you." She was letting herself down on the bed when she saw the array of Tracy's things spread out upon it. She straightened to stare incredulously at them and then at Tracy. "What's the matter? Whatever are you doing? Packing! You're not. Have you lost your wits, child? Don't you realize? Duncan's back. We're saved. You most of all."

Panic seized her as she peered at Tracy's pale, set face. She groped behind her for the door and, turning, ran to break in upon the family reunion.

"Duncan," she cried, beckoning wildly to him from the doorway. "Tracy. Come. You must stop her."

"My God," murmured Agatha, raising her head.

"Tracy," said Duncan. "Where is she? I haven't even seen her yet. What's come over all of you? Why do you look so odd?"

"She's actually going," said Louisa. "You have to stop her."

Agatha pulled Susie from Duncan's lap into her own. Duncan looked with a mingling of bewilderment and impatience from his mother to Agatha and then to Eric. It was Cam who spoke up.

"Tracy married Caleb. She's going to live with him."

Duncan sprang up.

"She's what?"

"Caleb wouldn't give us anything to eat unless she married him. So she did."

"But this is incredible. What could the lot of you have been thinking of?"

"We had no choice," said Agatha. "We were starving."

"Uncle Garry married them," said Cam. "After the wedding Caleb went hunting and he just got back."

"And this very minute she's packing to go down to that cabin of his," said Louisa. "That's what you must stop."

"Garett?" said Duncan. "Even Garett lent himself to it? All of you. All of you taking advantage of that girl's loyalty to us."

His accusing stare came around to Agatha. Her lips tightened.

"We thought you were dead and we knew we soon would be. No one urged her to do it. It was her own idea."

Duncan gathered his dressing gown about him and strode out. He burst into Tracy's room with outstretched arms.

"Tracy! They just this moment told me what had happened. Thank God, I got back in time."

Tracy straightened slowly and turned to look at him. He stopped in mid-stride, his arms dropping to his sides. Her glance lingered on his disheveled hair and the dressing gown. A half smile twisted her lips.

"I remember when that gown was new," she said. "You wore it the night Chris was born. You could be home that night because you were on your way from the north with your regiment to join General Greene in Carolina. Seeing it on you when you came in made it seem for a moment almost as if we were back in Virginia and everything was still like it was then."

Duncan took another slower step toward her.

"Everything still is. And you are just as safe. That's what I came to tell you the moment they let me know. You don't have to go through with it. I will take every responsibility for that. You're not listening to me. I'm here. I'm right beside you. Can't you realize that?"

"Yes. I realize it. I'm trying to find words to say what I meant to say first—or try to say. Something, at least, about how happy I am that you are back, and safe and well. No one could ever be missed as they have missed you. No one could ever be as important as you are to them."

"Or they to me. And you, too. You are the same as one of us. You must never forget that. We never can. And you must also realize that I could have no more intention of letting that man have you than letting him have Agatha or Olivia."

"I am married to him. Didn't they tell you that?"

He dismissed the fact with a gesture of impatience.

"No contract is valid when threats are involved. If you are concerned about mere legality we can easily have it annulled. But the devil with all that. What counts is that I am here in time and that now you are safe. That man can go back to his wigwam."

"But he will not do that. He is as set on keeping that place of his as you are this one of yours. You are neighbors and you will go on being neighbors. As much as though he were the owner of an adjoining plantation in Virginia. You would not consider that so poor a match, would you?"

"Match? You can call it a match?"

"What else is it? You should be able to guess that it is not a matter of sentiment. It is a practical arrangement, serving his convenience, and mine."

"But it is very much a matter of sentiment with you, and a most misguided sentiment. The convenience of which you are thinking is our convenience. You conceive that you are doing us a great service. But you are not. You could be doing us no greater disservice. Your dishonor is our grosser dishonor. I tell you I shall never permit it."

"It is too late to ask for your approval. And we are not concerned with dishonor. You keep forgetting that I am married to him."

"You are merely talking wildly. It's no wonder. If we continue to discuss it I'll be talking wildly myself. But we've no need to continue. If you will compose yourself enough to listen I'll tell you why. Added to everything else that makes him impossible is a final abomination. He's worse than the ignorant offscouring of an Indian camp. He's an outright Tory. Clark has been able to learn why he wasn't known on this frontier during the war. He wasn't here. He was serving in the English navy."

He waited for her shocked revulsion. Instead she looked past him, her attention appearing momentarily to wander.

"But that only makes it even stranger," she said. "The way he speaks, I mean. His accent is a little more English than American but it is not at all the sort of English he might have learned below decks on a man-of-war. He picks each word with so much care, as though not only the meaning but the sound was important to him. Could he be so set on being his own man now that he's that anxious to let nothing remind him of having been an Indian or an English seaman or whatever else he may have been?"

"What the devil difference how he talks? How can you go on chattering about his confounded accent when I've just got through telling you he's a traitor? An enemy."

She remained calm.

"The war is over. It is no longer a crime to be an Englishman. For a man living this near the Shawnee it is even an advantage."

"Have you been bewitched? What can have come over you? You've always been so lucid, reasonable, intelligent. Are you trying to make me believe that you no longer have even any regard for your country? I can't make sense of anything that you have been saying. Surely you don't want to go to him?"

"No. But that is what I am going to do."

Olivia came running to Garett on his bench at the corner of the stockade.

"Garry. You've got to come. Duncan can't do anything with her. Maybe she'll listen to you. She always does."

"What can I say that the eloquent Duncan has not already said far better?"

"She's not listening to him. She's too full of the idea that it is for him that she's doing it. But somebody's got to make her listen. And, if anyone can, you can."

"Why are you in such a twitter? It wasn't so long ago that you were hounding her to the altar."

"I know. We had to then. But we don't have to any more. We have food and guns and everything. We just can't all sit back up here and let her go off to live in a hut with a man like that."

"A man like that." Garett pointed with his pipe. "Look at him down there now. He isn't waving his arms and running around in circles. He isn't bothering about why we are, or what may come of it. He's grabbing his chance to ship his hides and furs off to market by Bill Granger. He never misses a trick."

"Are you trying to tell me that Tracy's that calculating? That she's thinking about him as a girl back home might think of a suitor who had money?"

"Far from it. I'm merely suggesting that she's clear-sighted enough to put her finger on a few of the facts in the case. And that we might as well be, too. Tick some of them off for yourself. He has saved us and is waiting for his reward. He lives on our doorstep. He has the Slovers and the Indians in his pocket. He has the conscience of a savage. He is in a position to build us up or cut us down. Duncan's coming back hasn't altered a one of them. And it has added a new one of which Tracy could be the most sensible of all. Her secret is no longer a secret. We all know now that she is in love with Duncan. If she permitted his return to persuade her to stay, she would have Agatha after her with a sharper knife than yours has ever been. We would all be driven to taking sides. To Tracy, with her regard for the children as well as Duncan, the situation would be intolerable. So what else can she do? Think it over for yourself. If she can't stay here, where else can she go?"

Olivia sprang up from the bench, her face sharpening with fury.

"How could I have been so slow? It's just beginning to come over me. Of course, that's just what you want. She's been a brassbound virgin. You've never been able to get near her. But after she's a married woman, and restless and lonesome and unhappy down in that cabin, then everything might be different. That's what you're counting on, isn't it?"

"My darling," said Garett wearily, "if only this world were as simple as it appears to you, how much simpler all would be for the rest of us."

Tracy walked steadily across the bridge. Hebe followed a step behind, carrying her small cedar chest. At the edge of Caleb's clearing Tracy paused and took the chest.

"You can go back now," she said.

"Yes, ma'am," said Hebe.

She stammered, striving for some word of comfort or farewell, but then, her frightened stare going past Tracy to the cabin, she turned and ran. Tracy went on. The sun had set but the red glow of the sky shimmered through the forest's young green leaves. There was a curl of smoke from the chimney and the cabin door was open. She stopped at the threshold.

Caleb, stripped to the waist, was standing beside a basket of water before the fire, drying himself with a rabbitskin blanket. His back was to her, though she knew him too well to imagine that he was unaware of her approach. His damp skin, away from the line of tan on his neck and wrists, was a glistening white. His entire back, from his shoulders to his belt, was barred with a fearful pattern of welts and scars. At some time, whether in the course of Indian torment or shipboard discipline, he had been mercilessly flogged. Tracy shivered. This testimony that he himself had suffered violence and pain, perhaps degradation, made his lack of ordinary human feelings seem so much more an ingrained and essential part of him. He turned to glance at her in the doorway but waited to speak until he had drawn on a new buckskin shirt.

"You can put your chest on that shelf."

Tracy stepped into the cabin, placed the chest on the shelf, and turned again to face him. He still stood by the fire, surveying her.

"So he did not keep you from coming."

"He tried. They all did."

He continued to regard her thoughtfully.

"Still you came."

"I made a bargain. I am keeping it."

"Then there is the cooking place. There is the axe and the hoe. And there is the bed."

May

The weather, so long a bitter enemy, had become an indulgent friend. Each day, whether sunny or rainy, was pleasantly warm. The forest, once more a luxuriantly solid green, again seemed an encircling and protecting wall. Nature, released from the restraints of winter, was absorbed in the urgency of her annual increase. Redbud ornamented the river bank, azalea flamed on the ridge, strawberries and wild currants ripened, mulberries darkened, crabapple blossoms faded and dropped to make way for the fruit to come. Buffalo were calving, deer watching their still-hidden fawns. Birds, furiously concerned with their nesting, quarreled, mated, built, and sang with equal abandon. Waterfowl, littered marshy shores with eggs in such numbers that Polly, returning from her fishing, was able without straying from her path to gather an apronful.

In turning favorable the weather had lost significance. It was no longer the tyrant. The people of the station were able each day to awaken to the assurance that nothing beyond their control was to interfere with that day's labors. These were violent and demanding. The lengthening days remained still too short for half of what there was to do. May was first of all the planting month. The whole meadow, at last dry again, was dug up and checkerboarded with the traditional pattern of corn hills. The Slovers devoted themselves to the corn planting with unexpected diligence. Their lifelong acquaintance with hunger inclined them to take the same active interest in the brief, arduous labor of planting that they might take in the running down of a wounded buck. But they were not so inclined toward the next and more protracted task of enlarging the area of arable land. For them the process of cutting brush, grubbing roots, felling, piling, and burning trees was uninspired drudgery. Duncan, however, was insistent. There was better land for future crops to be had by attacking the forest margins of the meadow but he was determined first to clear the area between the station and the river.

"We have to get this patch of trees down," he explained, "so that movers coming down the river can see the station. Unless they can see it before they've drifted on past, not a one will ever stop to find out we've got good extra land. We've got to have more families. The Indians may not let us alone indefinitely and we can't hold this place without more people."

Olen was as always mildly anxious to please but not deeply impressed either with the reasoning or the need for new inhabitants.

"We got us no call to fret about Injuns," he said, "long's Caleb's here. And if'n he shoves off, we-uns can't hang on here nohow."

"But we can't fool along forever, depending on Caleb," said Duncan. "The place is ours, not his. We've got to get to the point where we can take care of ourselves."

Agatha brought their lunch to the woods where the men were working. It had been established that were the Slovers to go home for their midday meal it took most of the afternoon to get them back to work again. They accepted their portion with sheepish grins and mutterings and, made uneasy by Agatha's presence, withdrew out of earshot to eat. Clem and Ned followed them. Eric took his corn bread and ham and moved the other way to the bank of the stream. He worked as hard and long as any of the men, yet seized upon any moment's respite during the day to run back to the building of his bark canoe. Duncan sat down against a stump, rubbing his cramped hands over his knees. He had lost pounds, and the formerly faint frown line between his brows had become a permanent and deepening crease.

"You're working much too hard," complained Agatha.

"There's so much that has to be done. And to get anything at all out of Olen and his boys you have to work right along with them."

"If you make yourself sick, then everything will really go to pot. And Eric's as bad. Look at him. Instead of taking a few minutes' rest when he can, there he is sweating over that miserable canoe. Caleb can make a canoe, so he's bound to. Anything Caleb can do he has to prove he can, too."

"I'd gathered that most of the hero worship had soured. I don't think he's been near Caleb since Tracy moved over there."

"He hasn't. He's moped and snapped and been impossible to live with. Cam says he even grits his teeth when he's asleep. He'd put each of them on a pedestal—a different kind of pedestal, of course—and he can't forgive either of them for falling off. I'm not really sure which one he thinks has fallen the farthest. Don't smile. You're as bad as Eric. Tracy's going to live in that cabin has done something to you, too. You can't stand the idea that she did it because she thought we needed help. You're beside yourself with anxiety to prove you're a better man than Caleb Lewis."

Duncan's smile broadened. "But you don't think I am?"

"I know you are. A thousand times better. And in a thousand ways. But we're talking about getting along out here in this stupid wilderness. Take this matter of clearing. You've had six men working with you. And you haven't opened up as much land as he has working alone. He works hard, too, but he doesn't break his back doing everything the hardest way. He just girdled the trees before they budded, let them die, let the sun in, and planted his corn."

Duncan swung around to look across the stream. In the encircling wall of green forests there was one break. Opposite the station some hundreds of trees had become gaunt and lifeless skeletons. Through the bare trunks Caleb's cabin and the clearing immediately around it were now visible from the Jordan side.

"And what a wretched sight," said Duncan. "Like an abscess."

"True. It's a slovenly Indian trick. But he'll have a corn crop this year."

Duncan transferred his regard from the dead trees to her flushed face. "You seem to be inviting the case for the defense. The principal part of it is floating past." He rose to his knees and looked out over the river. "Not a boat in sight, as luck would have it. But during this one morning there have been seven. And they've been eight or ten every day this week. Four or five times as many this spring as ever before." He became suddenly earnest. "That's what counts. The number of people beginning to come to this country. That's what will go on counting and go on being the only thing that counts. Growth. This country's going to grow. And the people who will be most advantaged by it will be the people who are ready to grow with it. Compare us to the Slovers if you like. Five years from now they'll be just what they are now. Or to Caleb. No matter how he works on his place it'll still be just a one-man farm. They can't plan past tomorrow and he can't see beyond his girdled trees. Now consider our outlook. In five years we'll have twenty or thirty families. We'll have a mill and a store and a school and a church. We'll be a town.

That's the difference between our kind of people and the Slovers and Calebs. We're ready to grow with the country. Can't you grasp the significance of what I'm saying?"

"I do love to listen," said Agatha, "to anything you say."

The burst of activity to which spring had committed the people of the station knew one exception. The day after Tracy had left, Louisa had not risen until noon. The next day and every day thereafter she had remained in her bed. She declared she was not ill, but she had little appetite and grew more and more listless. Her one interest was in demanding of whoever came near her what they could tell her, however slight, about Tracy.

"Olivia and I saw her again today," said Agatha. "We took her a pan of Geneva's gingerbread. She was glad to get it. You know she was never much of a cook."

"How did she look?"

"Black as an Indian," said Olivia. "She works out in the sun all day. Caleb had brought seeds with him from the Shawnee and she's put in a big kitchen garden—pumpkins, squash, beans, melons—I don't know what all. Besides that she has to get wood and water and help him drag logs around and—well, everything that Daisy had to do."

"How does he treat her?"

"You mean besides working her like a slave? I don't think he beats her. Anyway, there're no marks on her."

"But how does he look at her?"

"He never does. At least not while we're there. He's too busy ever to look up or to say anything. She scarcely takes time to talk to us herself."

"Why hasn't she come to visit us?"

"She keeps saying that she will," said Agatha. "But she's got so much to do all day, and at night she's so worn out, that she keeps putting it off. That's her excuse."

"If you want to know what I think," said Olivia. "He won't let her come. He undoubtedly thinks if she started in running up here she'd get harder to handle."

Ken was the most frequent visitor at Caleb's cabin, but his reports were more enthusiastic than enlightening.

"Caleb's caught a pair of buffalo calves," he told Louisa. "They're not black like big buffalo. They're almost red. They play around just like our kind of calves, and butt and kick up their heels and suck your fingers. He's got them in a log pen so's the wolves can't get at them at night. And he's got another pen of baby turkey chicks. Fourteen of them, only so big. But they're growing fast. And he's got a pet coon that got tangled in one of his rabbit snares and didn't choke to death because he worked his fingers under the noose. It's already over being wild. It's just as tame. I call him Spec. He runs to meet me 'cause I always catch a frog for him on my way over there."

Cam's observations were more practiced and detailed, but even they failed either to relieve or confirm Louisa's fears.

"There's not much to see," she said. "They're just working all the time."

"How does she look, when she looks at him?"

"You mean, does she look as if she hates him? I don't know. She never looks at him, not while I'm there."

"And does he never look at her?"

"Oh, yes. Once in a while. But he doesn't take any notice. It's just like she was a stump, or maybe not there at all."

"Doesn't he ever speak to her?"

"Oh, yes. When he wants something. Like, 'Bring me the whetstone.' "

"Does she always obey?"

"Well, she doesn't jump as though she were afraid of him. But she does what he says."

"What does she say to him when she brings him the—what was it?—the whetstone?"

"She doesn't say anything. She just hands it to him."

"Haven't you ever heard her speak to him?"

"Only once. They didn't know that I was around. It was just getting dark."

"Really, Cam. I'm glad you visit them so often, but you shouldn't spy on them."

"I wasn't spying. I had a needle for her. She'd broken hers. But I didn't get a chance to give it to her. She was feeding corn mash to the buffalo calves. Caleb had just finished washing himself after he'd quit work. He walked over to the pen and said something to her but not very loud and I was too far away to hear it. That's when she spoke to him. I heard only the last word. That was 'animal.' He laughed. It's the only time I've ever heard him laugh. Then he went into the cabin and she followed him and they shut the door."

Louisa suppressed a moan and spoke hastily. "She was probably talking about one of the calves."

"That's what I decided. Because if she'd been calling him an animal, he wouldn't have thought it was so funny, would he?"

Duncan and Eric were of no use to Louisa. Duncan, whose judgment she valued above all others, was as tight-lipped on the subject as Eric. Garett had likewise remained aloof from the newlyweds but he was ready enough with his opinion of their situation.

"It's not too hard to guess why she doesn't visit you. She's ashamed. She's brooding over her social descent. She shrinks from facing us and our questions and our pity, particularly Duncan's."

"You don't think Caleb Lewis has forbidden her to visit us?"

"I'm sure he'd be glad to see her completely weaned from us. But I think what sticks most in his craw is plain resentment. No man is so callous he isn't griped by a woman's conviction she has debased herself by putting up with him. Marriage is no joke for the best of us and they're likely having a time with theirs. But I don't see what good could come of our trying to interfere. It's something they have to work out for themselves. Maybe she'll civilize him. Maybe she'll knife him in the night. Maybe she'll just decide she can't stand it and come back. She's made her big move, like Ken did when he strangled his dog, and there's nothing we can do now but wait and see what comes of it."

Louisa shivered and drew the covers around her. "All these years I've thought we Jordans were something a little bit special. But look what we have come to."

Duncan became increasingly concerned about his mother's decline.

"You must realize she's getting old," said Agatha, unpacking his lunch. "Tomorrow will be her sixtieth birthday."

Susie, who had come to the clearing with her, jumped up, instantly excited.

"It is?" she exclaimed. "Are we going to have a birthday party?"

Duncan and Agatha exchanged glances .

"Not a bad idea," said Duncan. "It might cheer her up. We'll take a day off. It'll do us all good."

"It'll only make her feel worse, if Tracy doesn't come."

"Tracy will feel bound to come. That's another advantage. It'll break the ice, get things on a more normal footing. Go ask her."

"I'm not at all sure that she'll feel bound to come, or that Caleb will permit it. But I'll try."

"Wait. We'll get three birds with our stone. Eric's the one to go. He needs some of the nonsense jolted out of him."

Eric came over from his canoe.

"The bark split again," he said. "That's the third time."

"Maybe you need Caleb to show you how to do it. You

can mention it to him now because we want you to go over there. Tomorrow's your grandmother's birthday. We're going to celebrate it. Run over and ask Caleb and Tracy to join us."

Eric paled and stiffened.

"No, Father. I—I can't do that."

"Why not? Caleb used to be your model."

"It's not Caleb. It's Tracy. She—she—I can't."

"She's not got leprosy, you know. All she's done is get married, which she was bound to do sooner or later."

"But not the way she did it. She didn't have to go through with it, not after you came back. I—I can't."

Eric backed off and ran to his canoe.

"Why, the sanctimonious young puppy," said Duncan.

"He's always looked up to her as a creature a cut above an angel and he can't get used to the idea she's mortal. But you should talk. You haven't been near them either."

"That's so. And not because I feel Tracy has fallen from grace. It's just that I can't stand the man. But, very well. I'll take my medicine. I'll go myself."

Duncan, crossing the bridge, saw Tracy on her knees in her garden among her sprouting vegetables. He veered off toward the sound of Caleb's axe in the edge of the woods. Caleb looked around from the log he was hewing. A dozen other squared timbers were piled nearby.

"A new cabin?" inquired Duncan.

"Barn for the stock," said Caleb.

"We're having a barbecue tomorrow. It's my mother's birthday. Will you and Tracy come?"

Caleb began whetting his axe blade with the stone.

"I have work."

"My mother is particularly fond of Tracy. She has been missing her."

"She has work, too."

"Does that mean that she has not visited us because you have forbidden it?"

"No."

"Then you mean she has not wanted to come?"

"I do not know. I have not asked her."

"Have you any objection to my asking her?"

Caleb tried the edge of the blade with his thumb and looked at Duncan.

"I agree with you. She is a fool. But she will be there tomorrow."

"Are you trying to tell me that she will not pay a visit to her own people unless you order her to?"

"Which way do you want it? Do you want her to come? Or not to come?"

"Of course I want her to come. My mother needs to see her."

"Then she will be there."

Duncan was still fuming when he rejoined Agatha.

"Things have got to such a pass that we can't observe my mother's birthday without getting that man's sanction."

"He must be pretty sure of himself to want her to start seeing us again."

"He's more sure of what he doesn't want. He doesn't want to admit that his wife has any reason to feel she's been degraded by marrying him. Now when she turns up tomorrow, I don't want you and Olivia to make it all worse by badgering her with questions. Just let her tell what she feels like telling."

"We'll do our best to remember our company manners," said Agatha tartly.

The next day Eric, bent on devoting the holiday's leisure to his canoe, was up as early as any working day. The family had not finished breakfast when he came running back from the point.

"There's a big boat turning into the stream," he announced.

Duncan and Garett ran out to the gate and around the corner of the stockade. Moored beside the lone sycamore was a huge, square, floating platform on which were three sheds, two wagons, a number of horses and cattle, and twenty-five or thirty people. Duncan grasped Garett's arm.

"Look," he exclaimed. "That must be one of the new kind of boats they were talking about in Pittsburgh last year. A flatboat. The first on the river. See what it can carry, so long as it has only to drift downriver with the current. A mover can bring along everything he owns."

Eric was already halfway back to the point. Duncan ran after him. Garett, following at his slower pace, was soon passed by the children. Olen, Jarot, and Jacob, stimulated by the prospect of the day's festivities, had also risen early to dig a barbecue pit. They dropped their shovels and joined the procession to the point. In the kitchen the women peered from loopholes. People were disembarking from the strange craft that looked so much like a floating barnyard and turning their stock out to graze on the new grass along the shore. Duncan and then Garett were shaking hands with the visitors. The Slovers had joined the assemblage. Everyone was talking and gesticulating. Cam was the first one of the welcoming delegation to return with a report. She burst in out of breath.

"A flatboat," she said. "A two-family flatboat. People by the name of Baxter. On their way to Kentucky. And who do you think's with them? Ida Lyman, Mark Lyman's wife. And her two children. One's four, the other only two. And Maggie Cobb. She's the girl they were always talking about who was waiting to marry Luke Lyman. That's why the Baxters stopped their boat here. To leave Ida and Maggie off with the Lymans. They though they were still here. Ida is crying, but Maggie looks as though she might be able to wait till they get to Kentucky. Anyway, Grandma, they'll all be here for your birthday party. Father invited them."

"Thirty extra people," exclaimed Agatha.

"Be enough meat," said Geneva placidly. "Thet buffalo Jat shot, she's gonna be roasted whole over thet pit they dug. They'll be a plenty to go round."

Garett returned with the next report.

"Baxter and his brother have fourteen offspring," he said. "Six of them boys old enough to work. Then there are three unattached white men and five Negroes—making a total of sixteen men and four women, counting the desolate Lyman ladies, and ten children, besides six horses and eight cows. A veritable colony. Duncan is talking Baxter's arm off, enlarging upon the many advantages of our situation here. He wants you all to do what you can to make them feel at home. Naturally, it would enormously improve our position if they could be persuaded to settle here."

The Baxter party, staring at all about them in eager, open-mouthed curiosity, were shepherded into the stockade. Hiram Baxter, a sturdy, graying fifty with a perpetual civil smile, had little to say but was giving encouragingly close attention to all of Duncan's observations. The Baxter women were ill at ease at first, especially when they were presented to Louisa, Agatha, and Olivia, but soon gained more aplomb and began to chatter about their experiences aboard the flatboat. Ida Lyman, small and dark and agitated, alternately sniffled dutifully over her great disappointment and scolded the two children clinging to her skirts. Maggie Cobb, big and fair and calm, surveyed the buildings, equipment, and people of the stockade with a regard almost as intent as had been Caleb's appraisal on the occasion of his first visit. She paused with heightened interest when she noticed Jarot and Jacob preparing the buffalo carcass for its suspension on a hickory pole over the fire pit. Jarot, exercising the prerogative of the hunter who had performed the actual killing, shoved Jacob aside so that he might be the sole object of her inspection.

"You the one that shot it?" she asked.

"Last evenin'," he said, swallowing hard but getting out the words. "Jest afore dark."

"Far off?"

"Up on the ridge."

Maggie surveyed the carcass again. "Most as heavy as a good two-year-old steer. How'd you get it in all in one piece?"

"Trimmed like she is—with the feet, head, and hide off and the guts out—she don't weigh more'n four hunnert pounds. Me and Jake we just tied her to a pole and lugged her in."

"Lavish o' buffalo in these parts?"

"Middlin' lavish. They come and go."

"Sounds most as good as havin' your own herd o' cattle."

"We-uns don't lack fer meat, not twixt spring and fall, leastwise."

Jarot, having completed the arrangement of the carcass on the spit that transfixed it, lifted one end of the pole to the notched upright in which it was to turn. Before he could get around the fire pit to lift the other end into position, Maggie had picked it up, given it a practiced jerk and a swing, and had fitted it into the notch of the opposite upright. Jarot permitted himself a direct look at her. She was tall enough to come to his shoulder and probably weighed a hundred and fifty or sixty pounds. But there was no fat on her. She was plump only where it was natural for a woman to be. The hand she raised to tuck back a lock of her straw-colored hair was calloused by years of hard work. Her blue eyes, looking right back at him, were as honest and matter-of-fact as a child's.

"Yer right strong, fer a gal."

"That one end wasn't no heavier'n a good-sized hog. Since Pa died I been doin' all the butcherin' back on our farm."

"Sell off yer farm?"

"Ma, she married agin. I'd heard some about this new country out here so I took a notion to come along out with Ida."

Jarot had finished binding a crossbar to the end of the pole. He grasped the bar, gave the carcass a quarter turn, and tied it with another leather thong in its new position. He glanced under his arm at Maggie's face as he spoke again.

"Luke Lyman, he ain't here no more."

"Ain't so many folks in Kentucky, Ida and me won't run across the Lymans somewheres down there." Maggie contemplated the gigantic roast on the spit. Its under side was beginning to sizzle. "I got me a Continental musket Pa brung back from the war. Reckon it would hit hard enough to knock down a buffalo that size?"

"It might, was yuh to stick it in his ear."

"What with did you shoot this one?"

"A Lancaster rifle. Want to see it?"

"Yes, I would."

They walked off together toward the Slover cabin.

"Take grateful notice," Garett said to Duncan. "You could be drawing most unexpected support from a most unexpected quarter."

The company was too numerous for the kitchen and in any event the roasting buffalo was becoming the center of attention. Louisa's chair was moved to the yard where she held impromptu court. The general excitement had restored some of her vitality. She seemed more her old self and betrayed her continuing inner anxiety only by the frequency with which her glance returned to the gate. But Tracy's appearance was delayed by another unusual event. After a month during which so many scores of craft had sailed unconcernedly past, on this one notable day a second boat had swung out of the river and poled into the stream.

"We've become a bustling port," said Garett.

Bill Granger, on his way from Louisville to Pittsburgh, tied his barge at the flat rock. He welcomed Duncan's suggestion that he and his four boatmen attend the barbecue and even volunteered to bring along a small keg of whisky. Duncan drew aside to read the letter from Clark which Granger had brought him.

"Good or bad?" asked Garett, watching his face.

"Both. Clark says the peace is already showing cracks. The Miami have started raiding outlying stations in Kentucky and the English have sent all the tribes new supplies of gunpowder from Detroit. He thinks the Wyandot and Delaware will stay quiet this summer but he's not so sure about the Shawnee. He's still after them to come in to talk treaty but they keep on putting it off."

"What's the good part?"

"Caleb. It's wonderful that we should be able to take comfort in being reassured our only neighbor is a Tory. Clark's found out a little more about him. When Caleb came back after the war, he went first to Detroit where he worked for a year in the English fur trade. Clark thinks it's safe to assume he's hand in glove with English Indian agents and traders like Alexander McKee and Matthew Elliot. At any rate, Clark promised to warn us if he considered the time had come for us to pull out and he doesn't think it has—yet. It's his judgment that if we can keep on good terms with Caleb we may feel reasonably safe here, at least through this summer."

"Which gives us some three months to recruit enough new settlers to hold the station with or without Caleb."

"Exactly."

The barbecue festivities, which had been given so much impetus by the arrival of so many unexpected guests from the outer world, were presently electrified by two more sensations. The first was Jarot emerging from the Slover cabin to saunter across the yard loudly strumming his mandiddle. He was drawing from it an inspiriting and provocative dance tune, but what brought the universal gasp of amazement from all who knew him was the circumstance that he had shaved off his beard. The band of dark tan across his nose and eyes, contrasting with the strange white of his lower face, gave him the rakish and somewhat piratical aspect of one wearing a mask. The second, immediately following sensation was Tracy's appearance in the gateway. She was smiling, her hair was carefully dressed in a high-piled, formal arrangement set off by an ivory ornament, and she was wearing her best blue silk gown. But what was far more astounding even than Jarot's beardlessness had been, was the final touch to her toilet. Her nostrils were transfixed, Indian fashion, by a single, small, vividly scarlet feather.

Louisa had taken advantage of the attention attracted by Jarot's music to have her chair moved to the corner of the shop where she would be nearer the gateway. Agatha and Olivia had scarcely got her settled when Tracy appeared in it. They sprang up, gasping and staring, but she bent swiftly past them to kiss Louisa. She straightened, laughed lightly, and touched a rueful fingertip to the quill piercing the delicate edge of the dividing membrane in her nose.

"I'm so sorry about this," she apologized. "But once I'd got it in I didn't dare take it out again."

"Why," asked Louisa faintly, "did he make you wear that ghastly thing?"

"He didn't. Far from it. It was my own last-minute inspiration. I was sure he'd object to my coming up here flaunting this squaw's gewgaw. But he fooled me, as usual. He took no more notice of it than he did of my dress or the way I'd done my hair."

"Is it as hard as that to find something about you to which he objects?" asked Olivia.

"Oh, no. He objects to practically everything about me. But he regards his opinion of me as of no more importance than my opinion of him."

Louisa looked helplessly from Agatha to Olivia.

"Is the man made of stone?" exclaimed Agatha.

"Granite," said Tracy. "A granite, white Indian. That's my lord and master."

"There must be some way to get back at him," said Olivia.

"So I would have thought. I still keep losing my temper and trying something new, however absurd, like this thing in my nose, in the hope of disturbing him. But it's no use. He simply takes no interest."

"You could stop working so hard," said Agatha. "That should catch his interest."

"It would trouble me more than it might him."

"When he comes up here today," said Louisa, breathing deeply, "I shall have a talk with him."

"He's not coming. He's too busy making more stock pens. Bill Granger brought some of the things from Louisville Caleb asked for in exchange for his hides and furs. They included a crate of young chickens, a pair of pigs, and a bull calf to grow up with his buffalo heifers."

Louisa reached out a suddenly trembling hand to grasp one of Tracy's.

"How, my dear, how, really, are you getting along?"

"I keep too busy to wonder. We both work, as you must have noticed, every hour of every day, from dawn to dark. That's a blessing in its own way. It helps to make it all seem more like the strictly business arrangement you, Agatha, said it might turn out to be."

"That only accounts for the days," murmured Olivia.

"At night," said Tracy, as calmly as she had explained the scarlet squill, "we sleep together, of course. I have no real basis for judgment but I should guess he is somewhat nearer an ordinary man in the dark than he is in the daylight."

"However can you stand it?" moaned Louisa.

"That I admit surprised me, too, at first. But I suppose it is something the average woman can stand more easily than she can any number of other trials. That must be so if you remember how many resigned wives you have known."

Duncan came striding, hands outstretched from the shop through which he had been showing Hiram Baxter.

"Tracy, I thought I heard your voice. I'm so glad you got here——"

He broke off to stare, dumfounded, at the scarlet quill.

"It wasn't Caleb's doing," said Agatha, coming quickly

to his rescue. "Tracy did it herself, trusting to aggravate him. But he took no notice of it. Like all husbands, he's blind at the oddest moments."

Duncan, recovering, took Tracy's hand, bent over it, and drew back to survey her.

"An Indian princess in a ball gown. Even that feather is bewitching. Bear with me for a second." He turned, lowering his voice, to Agatha and Olivia. "Talk to Ida Lyman and Maggie Cobb. If we could persuade them to stay it might help decide the Baxters to stay. Explain to them that they may have trouble locating the Lymans in Kentucky. Clark had them run out of Louisville when he heard how they had deserted us, and there's no guessing where they may have drifted by now. Tell the women, as if you were thinking only of their relief, that if they do stay here, we can send word to Kentucky and have the Lymans, when they can be found, come here to join them."

"You would really take the Lymans back," exclaimed Agatha, "after the way they have acted?"

"Why not? They're good workmen. We need them as much as we did before. We need anybody we can get."

Agatha and Olivia moved away slowly, reluctant to miss any further exchanges betwcen Duncan and Tracy. He turned back to her.

"Forgive the attention to business, even in this first moment of your first visit. But these are days we can't neglect a single item."

"I'm very aware of that. We keep busy on our side of the stream, too."

"It seems to agree with you. You look positively blooming."

"Thank you. Though it's not equally flattering that you should seem so surprised. After all I am not quite a fugitive from captivity. I have been working like a slave, that's true. But then, so have you." Tracy's color had heightened but she was addressing Duncan with the same artificial ease with which she had the others. "And there's one conpensation which you foresaw even before we left Virginia. That's a satisfaction in seeing things grow and other things take shape where there was nothing before. That's what we all came to this country for, isn't it? To make it over, to make something of what was nothing. It isn't easy. We didn't expect it to be. But in just the doing there is a reward of a sort."

"Courage," marveled Duncan. "The most remarkable courage."

"If you are intimating that I must be unhappy, of course I am. I am living with a man who's as much a stranger as when I first came to his door. But we've got thirty acres in corn and three pens of livestock and by this time next year all this will be doubled. That's why we came here, isn't it? To build, and keep on building. That's what you've always said, isn't it?"

"Yes," said Duncan quietly. "That's what I've always said."

The first tentative stampings and caperings of the dance were getting under way on the hard-packed earth of the yard as the persistent, shrill, thumping rhythm of Jarot's mandiddle became increasingly irresistible, even to the most diffident. Olen and Polly, whooping to signalize each change in the movement, broke the ice and were soon joined by Bill Granger with the younger Mrs. Baxter. Jarot sat on a bench, his great, sinewy fingers darting and thrusting among the strings with inventive abandon. He did not once look toward Maggie seated beside him on the bench, but the raptness of his gaze fixed on the air before him betrayed his consciousness of her nearness. Each moment his music vibrated with a wilder exuberance.

The oldest Baxter boy ran to drag Maggie from the bench and into the dance. She remained in demand, as the boatmen and the other Baxter youths sought their turns as her partner. Jarot continued to play with the same strident vivacity, but it was as though his hands were moving over the strings of their own quite independent volition. His whole attention was on Maggie, his burning eyes following her every movement, gesture, change of expression. Bill Granger, dancing with her, embarked upon an elaborate cakewalk which, on one of its strutting parades, carried them as far as the gate and beyond Jarot's range of vision. He continued to play, but as she went out of his sight he became rigid and his white face turned a brick red. They were back in a moment or two and prancing once more among the other dancers, but the cloud over Jarot did not lift. Duncan, having danced once with Ida Lyman, threaded his way among the weaving couples to do his duty as host by Maggie in her turn. She released herself from Granger's grasp but backed away from Duncan as well, and, evading the pursuit of other admirers, ran back, flushed and smiling, to sit once more on the bench beside Jarot.

His playing stopped in the middle of a bar and he turned to look at her, awed by the miracle of her return to him. His lips began to move, silently, and his fingers to pluck, soundlessly. Beads of sweat burst out on his forehead. He writhed and trembled. He was a man in torment. She stared at him, fascinated by his mysterious struggle.

Garett clutched Duncan's arm. "Look. Again the birth pangs of genius, by far the most painful seizure yet."

No longer marked by his beard, Jarot's face revealed nakedly the intensity of his emotion. It was an emotion too deep for expression but which yet struggled despairingly for the release of expression. The dancers, left stranded by the silence, turned to stare. Maggie leaned nearer to him, looking with helpless, puzzled sympathy into his haunted eyes.

Garett clung to Duncan. "Don't miss a second of this. I swear, I've the strongest premonition this time he's about to be delivered."

Jarot's fingers suddenly swept across the strings, bringing forth a single, harsh, triumphant chord. In the silence that followed the breathing of the crowd was audible. No one spoke or laughed. The silence continued. Jarot turned slowly from Maggie and bent over his instrument. Again his fingers began to move. At first there was no more than the faintest whisper of sound but it persisted and gradually gained form and body and rhythm and became a wailing, minor-key lament with a short staccato movement of eerie melancholy endlessly reiterated. His eyes brightened. His struggle was all but won. The last height was before him. He was finding words to go with the melody. As suddenly as when he had struck the initial chord he raised his voice in a husky, plaintive baritone:

"If'n I could sing
Ain't no words I'd find
'Cept them thet's about
When I seen yuh last."

He struck several minor chords and, brightening again, embarked upon a second stanza:

"If'n I could talk
Ain't nuthin I'd say
'Cept how long it's bin
Since I seen yuh last."

This time the succeeding chords were more confident. He was no longer so astonished by his achievement. He was able to recognize his aptitude and to welcome his own delight in it. With more and more assurance he kept on:

"If'n I could write
Ain't nuthin I'd spell

'Cept how good I felt
When I seen yuh last.

"If'n I could fly
Ain't no place I'd fly
'Cept straight to the place
Where I seen yuh last."

He paused momentarily, frowning, then, beginning again to beam, embraced the blessed release of one final burst of improvisation:

"If'n I could pray
. Ain't nuthin I'd ask
'Cept to find yuh agin
Where I seen yuh last."

His hearers, not realizing the phenomenon was consummated, waited appreciatively for more. Jarot, the excitement of his inspiration waning, was gripped by the significance of what he had done. He was afraid to look at Maggie even though her low, throaty chuckle indicated she might not have been displeased by his offering. Sudden panic seized him.

"Hey," he yelled, springing up, "thet buffler must be most done."

Tracy, sitting on a stool beside Louisa's chair, laughed and applauded along with the rest.

"That was really wonderful," she said. "Jarot's tried so long and so desperately and now he's finally brought something off. Maybe there's hope for all of us."

"There's none for you, child. Not while you're so bitter."

"It's good to be bitter." Tracy rose. "You need to be to keep on."

"You're not going? You haven't eaten. You scarcely got here."

"I've made you all sufficiently uncomfortable for one day. And I must get back to my chickens. They'll become another of my little chores. I'll send you the first egg."

"You mustn't blame Duncan. He has so many responsibilities."

"Of course I don't blame Duncan. Nor Caleb, either. I don't even blame myself. It's been one of those irrational accidents that you could see coming but couldn't escape, like a falling tree or an overturning canoe."

"That—that frightful object in your nose. That wasn't to annoy Caleb. You wore it to punish Duncan."

"No. No, that's not true. I'm sure it isn't." Tracy gave further consideration to the charge and again shook her head. "I'm very sure it's not. Duncan was always at a great distance. And now he's at an infinite distance. Caleb's the one who is near, the one I have to deal with." She bent to kiss Louisa. "You mustn't take it so hard. I'm tough and, as you say, I'm bitter. I'll manage."

Duncan found Garett in the gateway, watching Tracy crossing the bridge on her way back to her cabin.

"That defiant little feather," mused Garett. "And such a red one. No trace of white feather about that girl." He turned to look into Duncan's face. "So. The verdict, eh?"

"Baxter looked and listened with the most amiable attention but his mind had been made up before he landed. He likes everything about our location except the several disadvantages that it's on the north bank, it's too near the Indians, it's too isolated, and it's on land where Congress has forbidden settlement. He was on his way to Kentucky and he still is."

"And the two homeless young ladies?"

"They're no use to us without the Baxters. In any event, they're going along to keep on looking for the Lymans until they find them."

"Perhaps we should borrow Caleb's canoe and spend our days out in mid-river, hailing movers' boats. You know, like pitchmen at a carnival. We might steer an occasional unwary yokel into our tent."

"I've a better idea. Bill Granger's on his way to Pittsburgh. The corn's all in and the clearing can go on, at least after a fashion. So I'm going with him. By the time movers are this far downriver they have it long since settled in their minds that they're on their way to Kentucky. But if I can talk to a few of them before they've even got their boats loaded I might get them to thinking about heading for our place."

"Not bad," agreed Garett. "Not bad at all. It's about the last shot in our locker—so ram it home."

Duncan's announcement that he was again leaving the station drew from his mother none of the anxious protests he had expected.

"A wonderful idea," she said. "You can take Tracy with you."

"Stop and think. You have always had such good judgment."

"I still have. And it is for you to stop and think. This is a heaven-sent opportunity for her to get away. You can send her on to Virginia. Anywhere would do, anywhere that she was beyond the reach of that brute."

"It's out of the question."

"You've been working too hard, Duncan. You've got so wound up in your plans and anxieties. Haven't you seen how really wretched she is, what a truly dreadful time she's having? Have you so soon forgotten that she's doing it all for us? Perhaps we couldn't save her before. But we can now. And we must."

"So we do, as soon as ever we can. But that time is not now. Suppose she was wild to go and was here begging me to take her. . . . I would have to give her the same reply I am giving you. For a very simple reason. I cannot go at all if I must take her with me. I could not leave unless I were sure Caleb Lewis was here and still posing as the station's protector."

"But that day you came back from Kentucky—then you tried your hardest to keep her from going down there at all. You were not so afraid then of what Caleb Lewis might do."

"True. Because then I was staying here myself. Now we are talking about my leaving. And I can't if the station is falling apart. The Slovers, for instance, would clear out overnight if they weren't counting on Caleb."

"The station. Always the station. If only the Indians had taken it when they first came. And us, too. We'd have been more able to hold up our heads."

"That's ridiculous. Of what should we be so ashamed? You've been brooding too long. Tracy is not a child. She did what she did with her eyes open. We must help her as we can. But breaking up her marriage to Caleb does not come first. This land, this place, our home, and future—that comes first. Forgive me if I harp on what must be so self-evident."

"What you can't forgive is her going to him after you had tried to stop her. You're jealous."

Duncan laughed. "Thank God, you've not lost your sense of humor. Along with every year getting more and more set on your own way. Now chirk up. We're not so badly off. We'll get everything worked out and back in the place it belongs. Including Tracy. Just have a little patience."

The Baxters were trailing along the path to the point and their flatboat. At the end of the procession, Maggie and Jarot walked side by side, neither looking at the other, neither speaking. At the sycamore they came to a stop. Jarot thrust his rifle at her.

"Here," he said.

"You're givin' it to me?"

"Yes."

"What for?"

" 'Cause I want yuh to have it."

"Is that all you got to say to me?"

"Whut else kin I say to yuh?"

"You might ask what I might think o' stayin' on here."

"I might."

"Would you like to know?"

"I might."

"Then why don't you ask me?"

Jarot gulped, wet his lips, and shuffled his weight from one foot to the other.

"First you say, Maggie," she prompted.

"Maggie."

"Yes? Well . . . go on."

"Maggie . . . j'ever figger none on how yuh might make out was yuh to stay on here?"

"That ain't no way to say it."

"How'd yuh want me to say it?"

"Ask me straight out."

"Maggie, will yuh stay on here?"

"Yes, I will."

June

Summer had had the effect of seeming to tame and temper the wilderness. Every stir of air from the forest brought with it the pleasantly soothing aroma of pine needles, sun-soaked bark, moist leafage, resinous earth. Wild animals, apparently more attracted by the clearing's expanse of green corn than repelled by the nearness of people, returned again and again, sniffing and snorting with curiosity, to the edges of the woods. Deer, always the most stubbornly venturesome, began feeding in the corn at night. They had changed to their reddish summer coats, and the does were accompanied everywhere by their fawns. Everything living was responding to the increase in the warmth and length of the days. Serviceberries and purple raspberries had ripened, providing clusters of fruit which bears avidly stripped from the vines with simian dexterity. In lagoons along the river and pools at bends in the stream, wood duck cruised with their attendant fleets of ducklings. The first fireflies twinkled in the dusk. The corn had suddenly started to grow so fast that the taller stalks were six feet high. Tracy's garden had flourished and become an irresistible attraction to rabbits, woodchucks, and field mice.

She lay awake that morning in the first faint gray of dawn, listening to the birds' preliminary twitters and chirps which would soon burst into full-throated chorus as the light brightened. The night had in the last hour turned slightly cooler and she would have reached down to draw up the blanket had she not been aware that Caleb, beside her, had also awakened. She waited tensely for his first move which was usually, though not invariably, to spring silently from the bed to get at that day's work. There came a sudden snort of panic from one of the pigs. Caleb was in the middle of the floor, rifle in hand, in one leap so swift and lithe that the bed had scarcely quivered. For a second she could make out his pale, taut silhouette in the open doorway and then, his bare feet noiseless, he had slipped sidewise into the darkness along the outer wall. The morning before there had been the tracks of a panther at the edge of the clearing. The beast had evidently returned to make a closer inspection of the pigpen.

Caleb's shot came from the corner of the cabin. The panther's scream of pain and rage was repeated once from a greater distance, testimony that in the half-light even Caleb's marksmanship had managed only a hit, not a kill. He was in the room again, feeling for shot pouch and powder horn. Leaning the reloaded rifle against the wall, he returned to the doorway and stood there, half-turned, listening. The growing light accentuated the lean flat muscles of his shoulders and thighs and picked out the ladder of ridged scars on his back. He took a step over the threshold and again paused, strangely irresolute. She knew he was resisting his impulse to return to the bed. But she knew him too little to be sure whether he was resisting because he regarded the recurrence of his physical need for her as an admission of weakness or because he felt a preliminary delay added to his eventual enjoyment. He slipped from view and next she could hear him splashing in the stone-lined pool he had dug by the spring. His summer custom of taking night and morning baths in it was one of his least objectionable Indian habits. He was in the room again, reaching for his hunting shirt. Then he had dropped it and was coming back to her.

His second rising was only slightly more deliberate than had been his first. Her passing moment of victory in their constant duel was already ended. He dressed in silence, his selection of leather shirt instead of cotton indicating that this was one of the mornings he proposed to hunt. Even his silence was more aggressive than the most loudly proclaimed purposes of other men. He stuffed a handful of pounded corn and jerky into his pocket, picked up his rifle and strode out. The wounded panther would have left a trail of blood splotches. She knew he would not be back until he had completed his kill.

She dressed slowly and lingered over a breakfast of raspberries, followed by one of the trout Polly had brought the night before. Still unhurried, she set about feeding the stock, the coon playing about her feet and tugging at her skirt. She gave an extra portion of marsh hay to the calves, of acorns to the pigs, and of corn to the turkeys and chickens, and returned to sit on the doorstep. For once she felt less urge to fill every waking hour with the forgetfulness of constant activity. The rows of corn immediately before the cabin had grown so high that she could no longer see the station, shielding her from the perpetual reminder of the stark differences between her present and former existences. After the cool of the earlier morning it was pleasant in the sun. She leaned her head against the doorframe and all but dozed.

The green wall of drooping corn fronds rippled and parted. Eric stood before her. Taking care not to meet her eyes, he set down the heavy burden under which he had been staggering. It was a stone mortar, encrusted with earth and yellowed by age, of the sort Indians used for grinding corn. From his belt he took the stone pestle and carefully laid it in the mortar.

"Jat and I found it just now when we were grubbing out a stump," he said, still without looking at her. "It must have been buried by some flood. Maybe once there was an Indian town out there by the point. Olen thinks so because we keep coming on arrowheads and beads and broken pieces of clay pots." He kept on talking rapidly, as though he were crouched within the refuge of the continuing sound of his own voice. "You remember we've got an iron hand mill for grinding our corn. But I've noticed you have to pound yours in a wooden bowl. So I brought you this. You can make corn meal faster in it, and more at a time. Now I have to be getting back. I could see the Slovers sitting down even before I was out of sight."

Tracy tried helpfully to treat Eric's peace offering as an occasion of no special moment.

"Thank you, Eric. It will be a big help. But you've got so hot lugging the great thing. Let me get you a drink of water before you go."

She came out of the cabin with a buffalo horn of water. Eric drank it all, started again to go, and then seemed to have become deeply interested in the primitive design engraved on the horn.

"It appears to be an Indian attempt to represent a buffalo hunt," she volunteered. "Odd little figures, aren't they?"

"I only used the mortar as an excuse," said Eric, turning the horn over and over in his hands. "I was going to come over anyway. Since Father's been away I've been trying to think about—about things. I've had to. Uncle Garry can't do much and I've had to—sort of—feel responsible. About keeping up the place, I mean."

"Your mother says you've been working like a man."

"That part's easy. I'm talking about trying to think. I've been trying to look at things a little more like—well, maybe the way father would."

"That's not a bad rule."

"What I'm trying to say is I'm beginning to see what you've done couldn't have been so wrong."

"What makes you think that?"

"Because when you really stop to think you have to realize there couldn't be anything about whatever you did that could be anything but right."

Eric thrust the horn at her and bolted back into the corn. Tracy sat down on the doorstep and burst into tears. When she looked up, Caleb stood there, the carcass of the panther hanging over his shoulder. As always, to be suddenly made aware of his physical nearness, as when awakening beside him in the night or catching sight of him unexpectedly, stirred in her an instant throb of excitement as intense as a sudden realization of the presence of an enemy. This unwelcome and painful spasm of response was the more bewildering because she had schooled herself so resolutely no longer to fear or hate him. He, she had reasoned patiently, was in his way as innocent a victim of their predicament as was she. The sense of her own fairness made her the more determined to conceal from him this repeated inner tumult since it would be even more unfair to permit him to discover he was capable of arousing in her any sort of emotion. The instinctive defence at which she clutched whenever he approached her was to conjure up the image of Duncan to stand protectively between them. This figure of a man so different and about whom she felt so differently was a reassuring reminder that she herself could not have changed no matter how much her situation had changed. Caleb was for once giving her a second and more attentive look. He had never before seen her weep.

"You are maybe going to have a baby?" he inquired.

She sprang up. "I am what? My God, I trust not. I'm sure not. I don't see how a woman who felt as—as sterile as I do—could—could possibly."

He turned away and hung the panther by its heels to the rack on which he dressed his game.

"Bring me the basswood bowl," he directed.

She brought it to him. Cutting the panther's throat, he caught the blood in the bowl and, taking it with him, sprinkled the blood upon the earth around all the outer margins of the vegetable garden. He returned to the rack, ripped off the hide, and carved the flesh of the carcass into pieces the size of his fist, tossing the fragments into the hide spread out on the ground. Next he disjointed the bones and added them to the pile. Then, bundling up the hide with its contents, he walked to the back of the clearing and began dropping a fragment of flesh or bone at every step or two along the edge of the woods. He was soon out of sight behind the corn but when he came into view again from the other side it was obvious that he had continued the process around the whole outer circumference of the planted area. When he had used up the last of the pieces, he cut the hide into strips and tied them at intervals to the branches of trees. He washed at the pool and returned to the doorstep, shaking his hands to dry them in the sun.

"Were you performing some sort of Indian magic?"

"No. Just spreading panther smell."

"It certainly will smell. In this heat the place will soon stink to heaven."

"That is what will keep the deer away."

"Not for long. Animals, wood rats, ants, and bugs will eat up those scraps of meat in a day or two."

He was generally careful to enlighten specific instances of her ignorance.

"Still the smell of panther will hang on. Enough to keep deer out of the corn for maybe three or four weeks."

He went into the cabin, spooned powder from the keg into his powder horn, added a handful of bullets to his shot pouch, and filled his game sack with sugared corn. She realized that something had happened which he had not foreseen and that he was preparing to set out on a longer journey than one of his occasional early morning or late evening hunts. He came out again and glanced at the sky, the corn, and the stock pens.

"General Clark is here," he said. "At the bridge just now I talked to him."

He paused, still not looking at her. She sat down again on the doorstep and began deliberately taking the pins out of her hair.

"He wants me to go with him to the Shawnee," he continued. "I will be gone maybe four days. Maybe ten. I do not know how long he will want to talk to them or they will want to talk to him."

She rose, went into the cabin and returned to the doorway, a dab of soft soap on a chip in her hand, on her way to the pool to wash her hair. Several times since he had returned with the panther he had stepped around the mortar resting on the ground beside the doorstep without appearing to see it. Now he prodded it with one moccasined toe and looked at her inquiringly.

"Eric brought it," she said. "He'd noticed I needed one."

"Tell Eric I do not want him to come here when I am not here."

"So now you are afraid your wife might prefer a boy? Colonel Jordan is hundreds of miles away. So far he has been the one of whom you were the most afraid."

"And not only Eric," persisted Caleb calmly. "Garett, too. He never comes when I am here. Be sure he also stays away when I am not."

He turned to go but she set down the chip of soap and, her loosened hair shaking down as she sprang forward, overtook him before he had moved into the corn.

"Do you actually think that I hate you that much?"

"I think you do not care what you do."

"Otherwise I would not have come here in the first place—is that it?"

"No. You came to serve them. You still serve them. That, too, is what I think."

"What right have you to think anything, about people like us, about the rules they live by?"

"I can see what they are like." He glanced toward the station. He was tall enough to see over the corn. There came into his eyes that occasional glint of amusement that offended her more than anything else about him. "They talk much. But they must have other people do for them."

"You are so sure you are better than they are?"

"Even they can see that."

"Then why take my feeling for them as some sort of a reflection on you?"

"Because it shows I have picked a fool for a wife."

"You'd have done much better to stay with your Indians."

"I was born a white man."

"So I was born one of the Jordans' kind of people."

He looked at her. It was an impersonal appraisal that seemed to take no account of the pleasant disorder of her dark hair curling about her shoulders, the flush that had reddened her cheeks, or the flame of resentment in her gray eyes. His slow nod was grudging and fair.

"You have worked in my field. You have warmed my bed. You have tried to do some of your part."

"What is this other part you want of me?"

"I want you to remember that I am not a fool."

Clark, standing in the station gateway with Garett and Stephen Lockard, shook hands with them when he saw Caleb crossing the bridge. He joined Caleb at the foot of the slope and the two set off at a woodsman's trot up the trail along the stream toward the falls.

"George is a truly stubborn man," said Lockard, looking after them regretfully. "For me to pay a visit of several days to a comparatively unspoiled Indian town would have been the capstone of my western trip. But his first answer was no and so was his last. A recognized Indian trait is a high regard for the sanctity of ambassadors. I can't believe there'll be any serious danger." He took off his broadbrimmed hat, pulled a handkerchief from his pocket, and mopped his neatly trimmed, graying beard, his smoothly broad brow, and his closely cropped, silvering hair. He looked his age, which was approaching fifty, but there still was in his manner the eagerness of the young student just beginning to glimpse something of the extent of the horizons of learning. "I'm desolate to have missed finding Duncan here. Still, George and I will likely meet him on our way on upriver and, if not, I'll be able to look for him in Pittsburgh. But what about Thryza Carter? I haven't seen her since she was twelve, before the so untimely death of her father. Didn't I hear someone say something when we first got in this morning about her having recently got married? Where is she? And who is the fortunate young man?"

"She married Caleb Lewis."

"No. Not that stone-faced son of the forest George met down there when we first arrived? Not the mysterious friend of the Shawnee who has so engaged official curiosity that General Clark himself has come this far to confer with him?"

"You can see the roof of their cabin," said Garett dryly, "there over the top of the corn."

"I must see her."

"Want me to take you over?"

"Don't trouble. My sudden appearance will give her a pleasant surprise. And it happens that I have what may be a rather significant message for her."

Lockard crossed the bridge, pushed his way through the stand of corn, and came out into the narrow open space before the cabin. Tracy was seated on the doorstep, bent over so that her damp hair hung over her face, while she ruffled it with her fingers to speed its drying in the sun.

"It is not often that a naturalist has the extreme good fortune," said Lockard, "of coming upon a wood nymph engaged in her toilet."

Tracy, startled, tossed back her hair and looked up. She sprang to her feet.

"Stephen Lockard," she exclaimed incredulously.

"Have I aged so much that you have any doubt of it?"

"Of course not. But the last I heard, before we left Virginia, you were still in Paris with Dr. Franklin."

"So I was. For seven long years. But now I am again in

Amérique Septentrionale, making a long-anticipated inspection of this extraordinary western wilderness." He stepped back to survey her with the candid gallantry permitted an older man who had been a friend of the family when she was a child. "Not the least one of which I have just come upon. When last I saw you, you were a little girl in pigtails and starched muslin. Behold how you've grown up, and into how remarkably beautiful a woman."

"In a cotton shift and with her hair down," said Tracy. "Won't you come in? A backwoods cabin is one of the more special features of this wilderness you have come so far to inspect."

He followed her in. She stepped to her tiny mirror and began doing up her hair. He looked around at the plain, bare interior.

"Obviously the woman's touch," he remarked. "Neat as the captain's quarters on a well-run ship."

"Actually my husband's touch. I am an indifferent housekeeper. But he has the soul of a sailor, if he has a soul."

He did not miss her bitterness but he continued to smile.

"It could be that I have news for you about his onetime seafaring. Though that, of course, is none too likely, since he must have told you more than he has others."

"If you're talking about his past, he has told me nothing."

"Then I do have news for you, very welcome news. Presumably it has been resentment of the assumption that he was an English sympathizer that has led him to refuse any explanation. But his connection with the Shawnee makes his case so important that General Clark has gone to some trouble to look up his history. His serving the English during the war was not by his own choice. It appears that the first year of the Revolution he shipped from New Orleans aboard an American marchantman. The ship was captured and he was impressed into the English navy. Instead of accepting his lot he served the English so badly that he was repeatedly punished with all the severity for which that harshly disciplined service is noted. In the West Indies—during the engagement between Rodney and de Grasse, to be exact—he finally managed to escape. These personal difficulties with the English have led Clark to suspect that Mr. Lewis might after all be more inclined to lean toward our side than that of our late enemy. At any rate, he has sought him out on the chance that he will help persuade the Shawnee to listen to our government's peace proposals."

"I'm glad you've told me this," said Tracy. "It helps explain a number of things. But I somehow doubt Caleb's wartime experiences have inclined him to any side other than his own."

Lockard's exceptionally intelligent eyes, perpetually alive with curiosity, crossed her face as she spoke and roved on to the drinking horn lying on the table.

"I gather that in your case marriage, as in so many others, has not resulted in an immediate, miraculous relaxation of every tension." He leaned forward to pick up the buffalo horn. "This, by the way, is not of Shawnee manufacture. It is a product of the culture of the so little known Indians of the far western plains. I saw one very much like it in a collection in Paris sent by a French trader from the banks of the Missouri. Notice the design, crude and misshapen, yet vigorous. Since you are a married woman it is permissible to point out the extravagant glorification of the buffalo bull's maleness. In every quarter of the world of which I have heard any report, savage magic is more preoccupied with the encouragement of procreation than with any other aspiration."

His head turned instantly as a low bird note drifted in from without through the open doorway. He tiptoed to the threshold and waited until a repetition of the call enabled him to locate the bird perched in the top of one of the taller cornstalks. "Clearly a representative of the grosbeak family but with a color configuration never before described." He whipped his notebook from his pocket. "You will pardon my taking a couple of notes? This will make the thirty-seventh new species I have identified since I left Pittsburgh. I visited the great Linnaeus while I was in Europe, by the way. You will be interested to know that he showed me a letter he had received from your father the year before he died. It contained a list of Virginia toadstools." The bird flew away as he edged nearer. He put the notebook back in his pocket and turned to Tracy. "May I be so bold as to ask, what is that peculiar odor?"

She explained the use Caleb had made of the panther's remains. Lockard laughed.

"A fascinatingly practical evolution of an almost universal primitive rite. Most savage peoples are convinced that blood will promote the growth of their crops. In some instances, unhappily, they require maidens' blood. In others it is considered sufficient if young women spend a night reclining in the newly sown fields. I trust I'm not boring you with my display of erudition?"

"Indeed no. We've been looking at the wilderness as just trees through which to chase game or to be cut down to make room for corn. It's a wonderful relief to be reminded people can actually have wider interests. Are you on your way to Kentucky?"

"Alas, no. I've already been there and my too brief tour is almost over. So soon as General Clark returns from his embassy we will continue on upriver and at Pittsburgh I shall set out for Philadelphia."

"Then you must have already seen a great deal of this western country. Really seen it, I mean, with eyes able to see more than trees and soil and game. What did you see that interested you most?"

"Aside from the present moment," said Lockard, bowing, "I was most captivated by a deposit of enormous bones I came upon around a salt spring in Kentucky. Evidently at some earlier period numbers of much larger animals than any now living roamed this immense valley, including one much on the order of an elephant, though considerably exceeding in size any we now know in India or Africa."

"Surely you're joking?"

"Very much to the contrary. I have the proof in General Clark's canoe. I am taking back with me to present to my old friend Tom Jefferson a thighbone somewhat taller than a man and a tusk more than ten feet long."

"Oh, I'd like to see them."

"Then most certainly, my dear, you shall. This very minute."

They pushed through the corn to the stream bank. On the bridge Lockard paused and indicated the station cornfield.

"The Jordan meadow has been returned to its original role. Once it was an Indian cornfield. Most such small, apparently natural open areas in this wooded country are to be accounted for in that manner. You realize, of course, the origin of this knoll in which the stockade was built. It, too, was made by man. There are scores of such mounds up and down the Ohio, many of them much larger than this one. Who built them? We do not know. Surely not the Ten Lost Tribes or the legendary Welsh, as some claim." They walked on along the path downstream. "But their numbers must have exceeded by many hundredfold the present number of Indians. They flourished and then they disappeared, leaving no trace but these mounds, not even a legend."

Clark's two canoemen, leathery veterans of his Revolutionary army, had established their camp under the sycamore on the point and gone to sleep in the shade. Aroused by the approaching murmur of Lockard's voice, they grunted wearily when they had awakened enough to identify the source and rolled over to go back to sleep. Then one of them caught a glimpse of Tracy and they sat up to watch her. Lockard went to the canoe drawn up on the beach and lifted from it two long, heavy objects wrapped in deerskin. He untied the lashing and revealed the monstrous bones.

"This is a tusk," he said, "and that one is as clearly a legbone. Most of those smaller ones are teeth. You can imagine the proportions of the catlike animal which would have canines the size of those. The ground about the salt spring is a bog. Animals of our time still come to lick the salt. But these great earlier animals were so ponderous they sank in the mud and were trapped. The salt in the mud no doubt helped to preserve their skeletons. There are acres of such bones. We can see them, we can feel of them, we can know such animals once existed. But that is all we can know. The range for speculation is unlimited. Could the mound-builders have lived at the same time as these giant animals? Could they, too, perhaps, have been giants? Can you not begin to imagine the questions for which we as yet have no anwers? You must forgive me for rushing on like this. I have been talking steadily—it could have been for hours. I get carried away when I reflect on such matters. I assure you it is occasionally possible for me to stop talking, and I can prove it by doing so."

"Only don't prove it now," begged Tracy. "You can't guess what a comfort you are to me. Please keep on, and on, and on. Don't stop talking to me as long as you are here."

Stephen Lockard's visit was also an event in the Jordan household. Each evening they sat late with him, plying him with questions about mutual friends in Virginia, listening to accounts of his long journey which, beginning in Paris, had taken him to London, Boston, New York, Philadelphia, Richmond, and Louisville, before bringing him here, and relishing particularly the light thrown on what had been going on in the outer world by his anecdotes of recent contacts with figures such as Franklin, Washington, and Jefferson. But presently they became even more interested in the preoccupation to which he devoted his days. Each morning he rose early and, armed with his notebooks and collector's kit, set out upon an enthusiastic investigation of the flora and fauna of the region. Upon each of these scientific excursions, which lasted as long as there was light to see, he was accompanied by Tracy in the role of guide, assistant, and disciple.

"A real change for Tracy," said Agatha. "She may have been going days at a time without hearing a word spoken but she's making up for that now. If she remembers a tenth of what Stephen says she'll have enough talk to think about to do her for the next ten years."

"Stephen must be fifty," mused Olivia, "but he's always so bubbling over with ideas. Would you guess all of their talk is strictly scientific?"

"He was a great friend of her father's," said Louisa reprovingly. "They went to King's College together. And then they both taught at Mr. McDonald's school. That was before Stephen went to Philadelphia to write for Dr. Franklin's paper."

"Olen's gone out with them twice," said Eric, bringing up another defense. "And I went yesterday. Mr. Lockard doesn't shoot too well. When there's a bird he wants to add to his collection we shoot it for him with that little fowling piece of his. Once in a while there's a larger animal which we bring down with a rifle so that he can examine the markings. I shot a long-tailed fox yesterday which he was sure had never been listed before. I skinned it for him so that he could take the hide with him."

"Sounds scientific as all get out," said Garett.

"Oh, I don't doubt he's adding this and that to his collection," said Olivia. "But I keep thinking about that particular idol of his, Dr. Franklin. He must be all of eighty, but I seem to have heard he still has quite a taking way with him."

"What Olivia's getting at," said Garett, "in the light of her inimitable confidence in humanity, is that were Caleb to turn up suddenly, all might not appear so Arcadian. Maybe we'd better consult the oracle. Cam, come here."

"I was with them all yesterday afternoon," said Cam, "after they had come back with Eric's fox. They had specimens spread out all over the cabin floor—butterflies, and flowers, and bugs, and dead birds, and even two snails. I was helping them sort them. He was teaching Tracy the Latin names for everything. It was just like school. Only they laughed so much."

The report Cam brought back the next evening produced a ripple of deeper concern in the family council. It had been an excessively hot day and her face was red from the heat as well as from excitement over what she had to tell.

"I saw them up by the falls just a little while ago," she began, developing her narrative with careful regard both for exact accuracy and maximum suspense. "Oh, it was all right for me to go that far. Polly was going up there to fish and I went along with her. Only it was so hot that Polly sat down before we got there and went to sleep under a bush. I was just going to come back when I heard Tracy laugh. I left Polly and went on. Then when I saw what they were doing I squatted down quick so that they didn't see me. So you've all got to promise me you'll never tell Tracy I told you."

"I promise," said Garett, "on condition this proves a revelation proper to unveil in the presence of your grandmother."

"Oh, they weren't doing anything bad. Only sort of funny. You know that pool just below the falls? They were taking a bath in it."

"What's funny about that? Nothing could have been more sensible on a day as hot as this. I took a swim myself this afternoon, right down here in the pond."

"Only you wore your pants. And they didn't have any clothes on."

The three women looked at one another. Garett continued to smile.

"The Arcadian idyll," he murmured, "would seem to have taken on idyllic proportions."

Cam sighed, content with the effect she had created.

"Of course, they couldn't see each other. You know that big rock that sticks out in the pool. They were on each side of that. And when they got out to dress, the rock was still between them. Then, when they got out, I didn't stay any longer. I ran back here."

"You're so hot, dear" said Agatha. "Why don't you go wash your face and put on a fresh dress?"

Her voice was gentle and yet Cam withdrew hastily.

"My inimitable confidence in humanity," Olivia taunted Garett.

"What they were doing was foolish," said Agatha, "but for all we know just as innocent as it was foolish."

"Stephen Lockard is a gentleman and our guest," said Louisa, coming firmly and directly to the point. "I trust Tracy as I would myself. There's no occasion for us to take any position. For us to let them guess that we feel the slightest anxiety would be insulting to them as well as excessively bad taste on our part."

"I agree we could easily make things worse," said Garett. "It's their affair, not ours. I even confess to a crass hope that they're enjoying it. But when Caleb gets back it can become very much our affair."

"We should insist on Tracy staying up here while he's away," said Louisa. "It's not right for her to be alone down there in that cabin in the woods, especially at night."

"I asked her to come up here," said Agatha. "I told you then I'd asked her. The day he left. But she said she had too much to do, too many things to look after. I got the distinct impression that no matter how bad a time she's been having she feels more comfortable down there than to be seeing too much of us."

"That's absurd," said Louisa. "I still can't believe she stays away from us for any other reason than that he insists upon it."

"Besides, she's not been too lonely," said Olivia.

"For Olivia all roads lead to the same Rome," said Garett. "Anyway, Mother, nothing's to be gained by bringing her up here, even if she would come. Caleb's a man who knows his own mind. If he'd wanted her up here he'd have sent her up before he left. And you must remember our foremost problem is to smooth his feathers, not to ruffle them. I assured Duncan that while he was away I'd keep the peace with the man. It would seem to follow, Eric, that some reliance on your woodsman's craft is indicated. You probably could use a relief from your clearing labors. Why don't you start in tomorrow morning keeping an eye on the old Indian trail above the falls? Caleb's due back most any day now. We don't want him walking in on some chance tableau involving his wife with a stranger which any husband might misinterpret. A few minutes' warning of his approach might be a salvation—ours as well as Tracy's and Stephen's."

Eric returned late in the afternoon of his first day's trail-watching with an immediate report on results.

"I ran into John Turtle. He was coming this way." Eric grinned sheepishly. "For the best part of an hour we stayed behind trees, each of us making signs for the other to come out first. But finally we met and shook hands. I'm glad I didn't try to shoot him. He had a letter from General Clark. Then we sat down and had quite a long talk."

"Talk?" said Agatha. "Has he learned so much English? The last we saw of him the only words he knew were 'friend' and 'broder' and 'swap.' "

"They're still the only words he knows. But Indians are wonderful at making signs. If you pay attention and watch closely and make them do it over and over again, you can catch on after a while to almost anything they want to tell you."

"Why was he so anxious to talk to you?" asked Garett.

"He kept making a great show of being our best friend, just as he did when he took all our food. He was pretending to be just passing the time of day, but what he was really trying to do was give us a scare by proving how much the Shawnee knew about us. He knew that Father had gone. He knew about Jat's new wife. He knew about Mr. Lockard being here. He knew how much clearing we've done."

"Caleb could have told him all that," said Garett.

"That wasn't the way he told it. He kept grinning all the time. And he knew things Caleb couldn't have told him, like Mr. Lockard's and Tracy's collecting. But what hit me hardest was that he referred to Caleb by the same slighting, sarcastic sign for 'big white man' that he made for General Clark. And when he referred to Mr. Lockard and Tracy in the pool he laughed as though that were a good joke on Caleb. I don't think the Shawnee feel as close to Caleb as they did before he sent Daisy home and took Tracy in her place. And I don't think there's a possible shadow of doubt that they've been watching everything we were doing every day since the snow went off."

"Eric," exclaimed Louisa, "you can't mean that all this time they've been hanging right around the edge of the woods, that they have been able to see us while we couldn't see them? Really, Garett, the longer I'm here the less certain I am that this is quite the most suitable place we could have chosen for a home."

"I wish Duncan would get back," said Agatha.

"I can even wish Caleb would," said Olivia.

"Where's the letter?" asked Garett.

"It was for Mr. Lockard. I gave it to him when I ran into him and Tracy down along the stream. They were turning over rocks looking for salamanders. He'll be along in a minute."

Lockard came in. His bows of greeting were hurried and unaccompanied by his usual flurry of urbane remarks. He sat down gravely and ran his eye again over the opened letter in his hand.

"George is not coming back here," he said. "He wants to talk to two other Shawnee chiefs who are off in a hunting camp somewhere in the forest to the east. He instructs me to take his canoe on upriver and wait for him at the mouth of the Muskingum. He says the Shawnee listened to him politely for five days but have given him no answer. He also says Caleb Lewis will be back here some time tomorrow." He refolded the letter and put it in his pocket. "Eric, would you be good enough to tell General Clark's canoemen that we will be embarking this evening? Explain to them that the General advises our traveling at night until he is able to rejoin us." He watched Eric go out and then, his gravity deepening, turned to survey the three Jordan women and Garett. "I am not one, as you may have noticed, who is ordinarily at a loss for words. But I find myself very much in that condition now.

As a preface to what I am about to say, may I remind you that Edmund Carter was my dearest friend. He was an unworldly man but equipped with a singularly fine mind. These qualities his daughter has inherited. I was fond of her when she was a child and I find my regard for her reinforced now. It is a pity her father did not live to enjoy the fulness of her development into womanhood. The bright, warm-hearted child he and I once knew has become one of the most intelligent, sensitive, truly fastidious women it has ever been my good fortune to encounter."

"You don't have to praise Tracy to us," said Louisa. "We know her."

"Then how could you have permitted her subjection to this totally odious marriage? Or, if that originally was in the nature of an abduction, which I can only assume it must have been, why do you not save her from it now?"

"Please, Garett—wait," said Louisa. "Mr. Lockard, do you consider yourself her faithful friend?"

"I do. And I think she accepts me as such. With one reservation. She positively refuses to consider her personal situation any concern of mine."

"Then make it yours. Before you leave, go down there. Plead with her. Make her come back to us."

"I'm surprised at you, Mother," said Garett. "It's not usually your way to sidle off from the truth. You know your challenge is foolish. You know she won't come. No, Stephen, the truth is as plain as it is simple. You have eyes and the brain to use them. You can see it, too. The truth is that this hole in the woods which we inhabit is too narrow for civilized niceties. The truth is that he is stronger than we are. He knows it. We know it. And she knows it. There you have it. If you can see a way out, I'd be happy to hear of it."

"I do not," said Lockard. "But there must be. There has to be."

Lockard stood at the edge of the corn in the deepening twilight, watching the swift graceful movements of Tracy's shadowy figure as she fed the stock. Not until she had returned to the cabin doorway did he step out to confront her with a gesture that was as abrupt as a decision suddenly reached. Her face was only a pale blur in the darkness except when the brief flash of a firefly lighted for an instant her wide eyes.

"I've been thinking over that letter from General Clark," he said, "and I've decided I'd better leave tonight."

Silently she slipped past him into the cabin. From the

doorway he saw the first faint gleam as she lighted the candle from a coal on the hearth. The glow lighted her face as had the firefly. But this time the revelation endured. The golden brown of her skin in the sun seemed now an ivory pallor. She rose and placed the candle on the table. He entered. They faced each other across the table.

"I knew all along how short the time would be," she said. "And now it is over."

"It does not need to be over. He is returning tomorrow. But I am leaving tonight. Come with me."

Her face paled, her eyes closed, she took a long shuddering breath. When she did not reply he plunged on with more and more urgency.

"By this time tomorrow you will be beyond his reach. He cannot blame the Jordans. He can only blame me, a stranger, and I, too, will be beyond his reach. You cannot fear his pursuit, for we shall, by the day after tomorrow, have joined General Clark under whose wing you will be completely safe. At Pittsburgh we can consult with Duncan. You must know how heartily he will approve of what you have done. Then I will take you on to Virginia. But we do not need to plan so far now. All we need to consider now is what you do tonight. And to face what will happen to you if you do not seize this opportunity, the like of which may never come again."

She opened her eyes. Whatever the inner turmoil with which she may have coped during his plea, she was calmer now.

"Please sit down," she said.

"Why?" he demanded. "Why do you hesitate?"

She took the other stool across from him and leaned toward him, spreading her hands beseechingly out on the table top.

"I want to tell you. I want to, desperately. I have had nobody to talk to. When I am alone, no matter how hard I try to think, I become confused."

She paused. He tried to help her.

"You conceive you must stay to guard the Jordans."

"That is true. But it is not so true as it was at first. He wants to stay here, and he cannot if he ruins them."

"Then from what do you shrink?"

"I will try to tell you, if you will only listen. I will try to confess to you as honestly as though you were a priest."

"Shall we say, rather, your physician?" He smiled. "I would not want to be set apart from other men except by the warmth of my regard for you."

"What most sets you apart for me is that you are able to

think. That is more good to me at the moment than your sympathy. If I stay here instead of going with you it will be because I have begun to feel, just these past few days while he has been away, that I might after all be of some use here. I'm trying to get at something that's still so unclear to me that I don't seem to hit upon words that say what I think I mean."

"Keep trying. When you do find words they will tell you as much as you are trying to tell me."

"Perhaps what it comes down to is that I committed myself to this marriage as cold-bloodedly as he did. I have been punished for that. And the damage that has been done to me has already been done. Nothing worse can happen to me. But there is possibly a slight hope for him. He is struggling, however awkwardly, however blindly, to better himself. There may be something in him worth saving if it can be saved. No other possible good can ever come out of any of this. Should I throw that away, too?"

"So what it really comes down to is the perpetual feminine illusion that any man, even this one, can be domesticated."

"Don't goad me. I don't want to improve his manners. I don't want to make a husband of him. What I think I do feel is a kind of sense of justice. Perhaps if I stay I can manage to help him, if only a little. If there *is* a chance for him, even though I have none, shouldn't he have it?"

"What chance, as you call it, is there for him?"

"Maybe there is none. Those scars on his back are more than skin deep. The one spark of warmth in his life was his regard for Corbit Revel and that ended in a terrible disappointment. Everything that has ever happened to him has inclined him the more to put his trust in nothing but his own strength and cunning. Yet this is the only spot where he had ever even caught a glimpse of something that appealed to him, and all these years afterward he has come back to it."

"You argue his case with great spirit. Are you absolutely certain that this sense of justice is tempered by no trace of any more personal impulse? Do not answer unless you choose."

She laughed harshly. Her reply came with a rush, as though it were one she had been eager to proclaim.

"Why shouldn't I choose? Of course, I am certain."

Lockard stroked his beard. "I can see that while you have had a difficult time, his has not been an easy one. But I can also see that there is hope for neither of you. Get away, my dear. Get away while you can. Get away now, tonight." He rose, came around the table and placed a hand on her shoulder. "You are endowed with so much that can still make your life a full one. You have so much to look forward to. So very much. Come with me and begin."

She laid her hand over his. "You've been a Godsend, Stephen, at a time I needed it most."

Lockard, looking up past her, snatched his hand from her clasp. She turned. Caleb stood in the doorway.

He set his rifle against the wall beside the door, unslung his game sack and dropped it to the floor, hooked his thumbs into his belt and regarded them thoughtfully. The lacings of his leggings were filled with shreds of leaves and bits of bark, his moccasins were frayed, there were wrinkles of weariness about his mouth and eyes, and his face was smudged with a two-day beard. He must have made the long journey from the Shawnee town in one headlong plunge through the forest. His unnatural calm clothed his presence with a kind of total menace. Nothing about him forecast the possible range of his intentions. Tracy could hear Lockard's breathing behind her. She started up from her stool into a position between Caleb and her guest. But Caleb did not move from his place in the doorway.

"This is Mr. Stephen Lockard," she said. "He was an old friend of my father's, and of mine, when I was little. He came here with General Clark, as you probably know."

"How do you do, Mr. Lewis," said Lockard. "I am delighted by the opportunity to meet you before leaving." The conventional words echoed meaninglessly across the cabin's silence. "General Clark wrote me to meet him at the Muskingum and I came over to say good-by to Mrs. Lewis."

"Mr. Lockard is a naturalist," said Tracy. "That was also one of my father's interests. I have been able to help him with his collecting while he was here."

"As I've already remarked, Mr. Lewis," said Lockard, "it's been a great privilege to meet you." He edged forward and picked up his hat from the table. "But I shall have to be going now." He was speaking carefully as though to one slow of understanding. "General Clark suggested we travel at night and I shall have to be off."

He took a tentative step around the table. Caleb did not move from the doorway. Lockard glanced helplessly at Tracy. There were beads of perspiration on his broad brow. Caleb continued to regard them silently and thoughtfully, his stare transferring from his wife to her caller and then back to her.

"How do you like my place, Mr. Lockard?" he asked.

"Your place? Ah . . . very much. What you have done with it in one season is remarkable."

"And my wife. You find her remarkable, too?"

"Why—why, yes—of course. But she has always been that. You see I have known her since she was a little girl."

"Look at her." Lockard's gaze remained fixed on Caleb's expressionless face. "Do not look at me. That is not what a cabin at night is for. Look at her." Lockard looked desperately at Tracy. "She is not so little any more." Lockard wet his lips. "Is she?"

"Don't answer him, Stephen," said Tracy. "You don't have to, any more than I do."

Lockard maintained his outward urbanity. "A husband has certain inquisitorial rights, recognized in even the simplest societies." He looked back at Caleb with a smile. "No, Mr. Lewis. No, of course not. She has quite grown up since last I saw her."

"But to you she is still like a child."

"Caleb," said Tracy. "Must you try so hard to be disgusting? Because there is no need to try, not for you."

Caleb stepped forward to the table.

"I swear, Mr. Lewis," said Lockard, "since you seem to feel so strongly the need to be reassured, you have been in no way wronged. There has been nothing between us. Not so much as a gesture; not even a thought."

"Stop it, Stephen, stop it," cried Tracy. "Can't you see what he's doing? He's making you grovel just to prove something to me. All he's really proving is his resentment of anything he can't understand."

Her blazing eyes came around to Caleb. He was grinning.

"I'll tell you why Stephen is here," she said. "He came tonight because I asked him. I have been begging him to take me back to Virginia with him. You are able to understand so little. But maybe you can understand that."

"You will be in his canoe and in his camp many nights on your way to Virginia. But when he thinks of that he thinks only of telling you about frogs or reading to you out of a book. Is that what you want me to understand?"

"All I want you to understand is that I'll be glad to be in his camp, or anywhere but in this cabin."

Caleb seized her arm and jerked her around until her back was to Lockard. Deliberately he raised his open hand and slapped her. It was not a hard blow but he repeated it with the back of his hand from the other side. She screamed with rage. Lockard sprang forward in protest. Caleb released her and looked at him. Lockard's shoulders sagged. He picked up his hat and walked on around the table. In the doorway he turned.

"You may have proved that I am weak. But have you proved that you are strong enough to hold her?" He looked bleakly at Tracy. "It is just possible that you have."

He went out.

"Your father's friend," said Caleb. He stood aside, opening her way to the door if she were disposed to take it. "If you do not hurry he will be in Virginia before you."

She darted to the fireplace, snatched up a stick of wood, and struck at him with all her might. He caught the descending blow with one hand and, continuing to laugh, twisted the stick from her grasp. She lifted the brass kettle and swung it at him. He inclined his head no single fraction of an inch more than was necessary to evade its swing. The kettle flew from her fingers, hit the wall behind him, and rebounded to his feet. He stuck his toe against it before it came to rest and accelerated its roll back toward her. She looked about wildly for another weapon. His mocking glance went to the hatchet leaning beside the fireplace. She came at him with it. He held her against him, her arms pinioned to her sides, until she dropped the hatchet. He was still laughing. His physical superiority fired her fury to a final pitch of infantile frenzy. She writhed in his grasp and bent, striving to sink her teeth into one of his restraining hands. He was still laughing, more amused than ever. He shoved her away and stood watching her, his thumbs again hooked in his belt. She overturned the table, extinguishing the candle, and ran out the door.

She paused in the corn, panting, listening for his pursuit. But the empty doorway behind her remained empty. He righted the table, relighted the candle, and sat down on the edge of the bed. He was still chuckling.

She worked her way through the corn with infinite care to make no rustle. Once across the bridge she began to run along the path down the stream. The canoe camp on the point was deserted. Not too far out on the dark river there was the faint glint of what might have been the splash of a paddle.

"Stephen," she called. "Stephen."

There was no reply. She sank to her knees and waited for Caleb to find her. But he did not come. At length she stumbled slowly back along the path. When she reached the rock she kept on up the slope. Reaching the shadow of the palisade she kept close to it and edged around the corner toward the gateway. She had no way of knowing whose turn it might be to be standing guard on the fire step above.

"This is Tracy," she called softly.

"Tracy. Good God, what's the matter?"

She gasped with relief upon recognizing Garett's voice.

"Not so loud, Garett. Don't wake up everybody. I just want to talk to you."

The gate swung open. Garett drew her in and dropped the oaken bar back into place.

"I thought you people ought to know straight off," she whispered. "I've no idea what Caleb may try to do. Because I've left him."

Garett gave a low whistle. "And high time, too. But why whisper it? Shout it from the housetops. Come along. Let's roll out the family and drink to such news."

"No, Garett. No. I can't stay here. This will be the first place he will look for me."

"He can't look till he gets back."

"He's already back."

"Oh. So that was the last straw."

"Stephen was going to take me to Virginia. But Caleb frightened him so that he left without me."

"That Caleb has a genius for detecting clay feet." Garett let go of her arm and stroked his chin reflectively. In the darkness she could not see his face but she could imagine his quizzical grin. "Have you then some idea of where you will go, where he will not as promptly know where to look for you?"

"No. I haven't thought. Anywhere. Anywhere but here." The need to find some more sensible reply to his question forced her to begin to think more connectedly. "Yes, I mean. I do have a very clear idea. Give me a paddle, a sack of something to eat, and a rifle. I'll take Eric's canoe. Going downstream with the current I can easily get to Kentucky in a few days. And if I travel only at night he can never catch me before I get there."

"So you're really through with him?"

"Yes," said Tracy fiercely.

"What a good thing."

Garett leaned past her and struck the barrel of his rifle sharply against the iron triangle suspended by a rope beside the gate. The clang of the warning gong echoed across the silent yard. He seized Tracy's wrist and began towing her by main force toward the kitchen door.

"No, Garett," protested Tracy. "No."

"Yes, Tracy," Garett mimicked her. "Yes."

"Garett," called Olivia from the doorway. "What is it?"

"She never goes to bed before I do," murmured Garett.

"Even when I'm doing my turn on night watch. Astounding woman, really." He called ahead to her. "Light a candle."

He dragged Tracy after him into the kitchen. A glow spread from Olivia's candle. She turned, holding it up.

"Tracy," she exclaimed. "What's wrong?"

"Nothing," said Garett. "Quite the contrary." He thrust Tracy into a chair and stood over her. "Sit there. And be quiet. All I want from you for the next ten minutes is that you spend them keeping in mind that I'm commander here."

Eric slid down the ladder from the loft, the children scrambling down after him. Agatha and Louisa, struggling into dressing gowns, came out of their rooms. All stared, astounded, at Garett and Tracy. Louisa ran to Tracy's chair, but Garett held her away.

"Sit down—all of you," he directed. "And be quiet."

Polly, her bare feet sticking out below the blanket wrapped around her, came to a stop in the doorway, her blinking eyes searching the gathering anxiously for a first inkling of the cause for the alarm. When she saw Tracy she grunted with relief and turned to call out into the darkness toward the fire step of the stockade.

"Olen. Jat. Jake. You-uns kin come down. 'Tain't Injuns."

"Call them in," said Garett.

The Negroes from their cabin and the rest of the Slovers thronged in and ranged along the wall. They stared at Tracy and Garett, sudden acute curiosity replacing their earlier alarm.

"Light more candles." said Garett. "I want to be able to see everybody's face. Besides, it's an occasion for illumination. We're about to be able to look one another in the eye for a change."

While more candles were being lighted, he went to the mantel, took a pistol from its case, charged it, and thrust it in his belt.

"Something has come up that's better settled now," he said, "than to let it wait until morning. Eric, go over to Caleb's cabin and tell him that Tracy is here."

Louisa sprang past Garett and sank to her knees beside Tracy, wrapping her arms around her. Eric darted out the door.

"Now," said Garett, "we're about to hold what Duncan liked to call a town meeting." He surveyed the company. "Everybody will have to make up his mind which way he wants to jump." He swung around to Tracy. "When Caleb comes up to get you, will you want to go back to him?"

"No," said Tracy. "And I will not. But I don't want to stay

here, either. I never intended that. You dragged me in. The last thing I want is to make trouble for all of you."

"That's for us to decide. We're very good at deciding how much trouble we can tolerate." He surveyed the company again. "Well?"

"What else can we do?" said Olivia. "Of course she can stay here."

"Did you expect we'd say turn her out in the woods?" said Agatha. "Or over to him?"

Louisa tightened her clasp about Tracy. "We'll never let her go again. Never."

Garett, still impassive, looked across at the Slovers. The men were exchanging uneasy glances. Maggie nudged Jarot, seemed about to speak up herself, and then waited, watching Polly. Polly selected a chair and worked her blanketed bulk comfortably into it.

"When a man and the woman he's wedded with takes to fightin' twixt theyselves, thet ain't no time fer other folks to take sides. 'Specially when both man and wife is young. Fore long they'll go to noticin' how cold the bed's turned. Let 'em alone fer a spell and they'll figger out some way to git it warm agin."

The Slover men nodded and grinned, pleased by the ease of Polly's solution.

"But we still have to decide," said Garett, "what we'll do if he comes up here and tries to take her back whether she wants to go or not."

Polly chuckled. " 'Tain't never easy to take no woman thet way. Not when she fer sure don't want to be tuk. And me I wouldn't never hold with nuthin like thet. But it ain't nuthin fer none o' you menfolks to fret about. Ain't no call fer nobody to take to wavin' guns nor axes. One broomstick will do. Yer women and Maggie and me—all we got to do is stand in the doorway and he kin never come near her till she says she wants him to."

"The judgment of Solomon," said Garett.

Eric stood in the doorway, breathing hard from running.

"Did you tell him?" demanded Louisa.

Eric nodded. He squirmed unhappily, as though he were the bearer of peculiarly difficult tidings.

"I had to wake him up. He was asleep—or acting like he was."

"But did you tell him that Tracy was here? And that she was going to stay here?"

"Yes, I told him that. He just turned over and went back to sleep."

July

The procreant heat of summer settled upon the little valley. Occasional evening thunderstorms kept the earth moist. The corn shot upward, the faint whispering rustle of its growing now and then audible on a still night. In the meadow it stood nine and ten feet high and on the virgin soil of Caleb's bank it was twelve. The green jungle of towering stalks was so dense and luxuriant as to seem an added defense, a kind of moat interposed between the station and the shadowed edges of the forest. On the open side toward the river, where the clearing was under way, smoke from the burning piles of logs and brush wreathed and drifted lazily. The great river, now widely visible, was no longer lonely. More than a thousand boats had passed so far this one season. Beyond the smoke and the corn and the river, the wilderness was intent upon its own increase. All manner of fruits and nuts and roots and seeds were ripening. Bear and buffalo were mating. Their roars and bellows rumbled through the hot afternoons and in the warm darkness of the nights.

The dismal wail of a wolf, complaining of a poor night's hunting, roused Garett just before dawn. As he listened he heard the nearer scratch of Ned's bare feet on the doorstep and then the faint creak of the opening kitchen door. Ned, having stood watch the second half of the night, was coming to announce the night was ending. His palms patted on the bedroom door. Olivia, still half asleep, clung instinctively to Garett to keep him beside her. He caught her hands, kissed them, the curve of her shoulder, the tip of one ear, and got up.

"Worst thing about summer," murmured Olivia drowsily.

"Is what?"

"The nights are so short."

"Don't tell me you've so soon forgotten how long ago we went to bed?"

"No." She stretched and smiled, her eyes still closed. "Of course I haven't. How could I?"

He completed his hasty dressing, kissed her again, picked up his rifle, and went out. The sky in the east was beginning to pale. He drew a deep breath. In the summer's warmth more of his strength had returned to him than he had enjoyed since Yorktown. He beat on the door of the Slover cabin. The steady drone of snoring within broke into a confused chorus of grunts and wheezes. Since Eric's encounter with John Turtle, Garett had insisted on an inspection of all the nearer edges of the woods every day at the first streak of daylight. The Slovers had not protested so violently as he had expected; the early morning search for Indian sign served to postpone by a couple of hours other tasks to which they objected more, such as hoeing corn or clearing land. He knocked next on the door of the shop. The summons, as usual, brought a low laugh from Maggie and an immediate howl of anguish from Jarot. Jarot was a slow awakener and it was one of Maggie's delights to expedite the process by tickling him while he was still somnolently defenseless. His spasm of resistance and her vigorous persistence all but shook the cabin. Much of their marital love-making verged on physical contests that amounted to feats of strength.

Ned had roused the sleepers in the Negroes' cabin. Geneva waddled out, yawning, and went into the kitchen to kindle the breakfast fire. Hebe gathered an armful of wood and followed her. Clem went to the grindstone and began sharpening his axe. Olen, Jacob, and Jarot let themselves out the gate and separated to make their respective circles through the nearby forest. Garett climbed to the fire step over the gate to listen and watch in the growing light. Polly, rifle in hand, climbed to the fire step on the opposite side of the stockade. There was nothing out of the ordinary to be heard or seen except the flicker of a campfire on a small island half a mile up the river.

"Jest movers," called Polly. "Yuh kin see the nose o' their boat a-stickin' out behind thet willer."

Garett's survey of the encompassing walls of green came around to the tremendous stand of corn on Caleb's side of the stream. A wisp of smoke rising into the still air behind the tasseled crestline of the corn was the one sign of the existence of his cabin or his presence in it. He was their only neighbor and the center of their perpetual interest, but his every activity down to his simplest daily tasks took place behind that masking green barrier. For all that could be seen of him from the station, he might as well have lived a hundred miles off.

Eric came out, chewing on a great hunk of cold roast venison, and climbed up beside Garett. He, too, looked across the stream.

"Smoke," said Garett. "He's still there."

"Oh's he's going to stay," said Eric. "When he came he came to stay; and that's what he's going to do. He's still working just as hard as last month or last fall. He's clearing another strip back of his cabin and he's filling his barn with hay from the marsh. I went hunting with him last evening."

"What did he have to say about Tracy, or about us?"

"He didn't have anything to say about anything. When you hunt with Caleb you hunt. You don't talk. He only spoke once. A mile or so downriver on a burnt-over slope there's a patch of the biggest and sweetest blackberries you ever saw. He shot a bear that was feeding on them. Then he ate four or five handfuls of the berries. That's when he finally said something. He said 'Good.' "

"He said a little more than that two weeks ago when you went down to his cabin to get Tracy's things. I never got quite the straight of it."

"He had her stuff all packed in her chest and didn't say anything at first. Then when I started to walk off with it he called me back and handed me his second rifle, a light one he'd taught her to use. He said to tell her not to wander outside the stockade without keeping it always with her. I told him she had said she didn't want anything of his. He said this was hers. When I told her that, she didn't say anything but she took the rifle."

"Better not tell her about the blackberries. She'll be right out after them."

"She'd spotted them a week ago. She's going after them today."

"She's been working harder than she ever did for Caleb. From daylight to dark she's off dragging in something to eat or grabbing something you or Olen have shot so that she can pickle it or smoke it or salt it away. She's been after me to have a cellar dug under the storeroom, so there'll be a place to lay away more. I suppose you can't blame her. After what our getting hungry last winter cost her, she wants to make sure we never get hungry again."

Eric had grown in more than stature. There was a new air of maturity about him and his most common expression was the wrinkled brow of concentrated thoughtfulness.

"I wonder. She's always looking for berries or wild celery or something on his side of the stream. It's almost as though she wanted to keep going where he might catch sight of her every now and then."

"You could be right. But, if so, hers would seem a fairly dim hope. The man's about as impressionable as this gun barrel. I thought you'd given him up for good and all. Are you taking up with him again?"

Eric squirmed uncomfortably. "He's a lot different from us. But the ways that make him different aren't all bad. I like to hunt with him. Every time I'm with him in the woods I learn something new. Look—Jat's come out into the clearing. Clem and I can get going."

Eric jumped to the ground, slung his rifle over his shoulder, gathered up axe and saw, and set out for the clearing with Clem. Olivia came from the kitchen with a plate on which were a square of hot corn bread spread with goose liver, a mound of stewed serviceberries stiffened with pine-nut meal, and the half of a cold roast duck. Garett took a last look around, saw that Polly was still at her post, and dropped to the ground beside Olivia.

"Maggie's door is open," she whispered.

"It is? Then by all means let's stroll out where she can see us."

Garett seized the duck, began eating it and, with Olivia beside him carrying the plate, sauntered around the corner of the shop. Through the open door they could see Maggie making the bed. Toward the back of the former Lyman quarters still stood the forge, anvil, workbench, and rack of tools. The forward half of the cabin had become Jarot's and Maggie's home where were ranged their bed, table, and cooking place. Garett and Olivia, looking at each other, walked slowly past.

"Surely is a nice day," remarked Garett.

"Couldn't be nicer," agreed Olivia, slightly louder.

Maggie looked up from her bedmaking.

"Come right in," she said, cheerfully.

"We were just out enjoying the beautiful morning," said Olivia.

"We don't want to trouble you so early," said Garett.

"No trouble at all," said Maggie. "Come on in and get at your rat-catchin'. Never no tellin' when Jat'll get back and whenever he does his grub is waitin' for him. I already got your fire started."

Garett and Olivia, murmuring apologetically, hurried past her to the back of the shop. He started to put the half-eaten duck down on the plate, but Olivia pushed it back at him.

"Finish your breakfast first," she insisted. "Once you get started you'll forget all about it."

Garett took two or three more hasty bites of the duck,

crammed some of the corn bread into his mouth, and turned to poke at the charcoal in the forge. Olivia set down the plate, picked up the hand bellows, and began blowing on the fire. He thrust a wedge-shaped piece of iron into the coals.

"When you get time," said Maggie, regarding them from the doorway, "Jat and me we need a new skillet the worst way. Our old one that Polly give us has got a hole burned through the bottom of it."

"The very next thing we do," said Garett, "will be to make you one. Soon's we've finished this pair of hinges for Geneva's cupboard."

Maggie went out and presently Tracy took her place in the doorway. Her rifle was slung to her shoulder and she carried a basket in either hand. Garett and Olivia were by now completely absorbed in what they were doing. He was taking up the glowing iron with tongs and transferring it from the forge to the anvil. She dropped the bellows and handed him a hammer, with which he began to give the iron carefully measured strokes. Without looking around he handed the first hammer back to her and she instantly handed him a second lighter hammer with which he continued his shaping of the metal. They were bent intently and together over their work.

"Vulcan himself," said Tracy.

"Not to speak of Aphrodite," said Garett, grinning at Olivia. He glanced up at Tracy's baskets. "You better hold up your berrying for the moment. Our spies aren't back yet. But it ought not to be long before Jat shows up. Jake must always take a nap while he's out and Olen see a turkey or something to stalk. But Jat likes to get back to his Maggie."

Tracy stepped aside so that they could see past her into the yard. Maggie was crouched over her array of bark boxes ranged along the palisade opposite the buildings. She had brought with her from the east a packet of assorted fruit-tree seeds—apple, pear, peach, cherry. These she had planted in boxes and already the seedlings had sprouted. But this morning she was moving the boxes and arranging them on the ground in a rectangle that suggested the outlines of a cabin. She stood back, studied the effect, and moved three so as slightly to enlarge the smaller of the two rooms.

"It won't do Jat much good to hurry back to his Maggie," said Tracy, "if he puts off much longer building her a cabin of their own. You can hardly blame her for getting tired of living in a factory."

Garett laughed sheepishly and poked the wedge of iron back into the charcoal. Olivia began at once operating the bellows.

"I can't imagine getting to my age," he said, "before discovering it was so much fun to make things with your hands. And what a blessing Olivia takes to it, too."

"What a blessing that Olivia is so easy to manage," said Olivia.

"What makes that so simple is that no more is required than to encourage her to get her finger, her nose, or her elbow into everything."

"Not everything," amended Olivia placidly. "Only into everything that's yours."

"Polly's getting down," said Tracy, "so evidently all's judged still well. Cam wants to go with me. Is that all right?"

"It is if she stays with you."

Garett and Olivia became again engrossed in their project. Tracy and Cam let themselves out the gate. Hebe, with her two buckets suspended from a shoulder yoke, accompanied them as far as the bridge on the first of her many trips to the stream each day to keep the station suppied with water. In the kitchen Agatha had spread out on the table a softly tanned deerskin from which the hair had been scraped, and with a bit of charcoal was marking it with the outlines of a garment. Polly, summoned by Chris, came in to advise her.

"All the children's clothes seem to have fallen to pieces at once," said Agatha. "I can't see anything for it but to start dressing them in buckskin."

"Ain't nuthin' in this world so oncomfortable as buckskin," said Polly. "A buckskin shirt is hot when it's hot, and cold when it's cold, and wet when it's wet. And buckskin pants is worse. But one thing is sure. Buckskin wears a sight better'n cotton."

Cam came running in.

"Polly," she exclaimed, "Tracy and I just saw a really big catfish. He's lying on the bottom right alongside the bank. Tracy thought you might want to come down and spear it."

"Whereat?"

"Just a little below the bridge on Caleb's side of the creek." Cam began to speak with more care as she came to the more significant part of her report. "We had to take the path on that side in order to get around to the blackberry patch down on the river that Eric was talking about. When you go down that path a little ways you get to a place where you can see past the edge of Caleb's corn into his barnyard. Caleb was working with his calves, trying to break them to wearing a yoke. The bull calf from Kentucky was behaving but the two buffalo heifers were kicking and jumping and trying to fight off the harness. Ken was over there watching. When we got to where we could see, Tracy pretended her shoe was untied and stopped so she could watch, too. That's when I saw the catfish and then she told me she'd wait there and for me to run get Polly."

Polly, accompanied by Cam carrying the fish spear and followed by Lina at a more leisurely pace, joined Tracy on the stream bank.

"He's still right there," said Tracy. "He hasn't moved."

Polly gripped the spear. Her bulk seemed to drop away from her. For the next few seconds she moved with the quick lightness of her long-lost youth. Leaping through the fringe of reeds lining the stream bank, she struck downward mightily with the spear. The immediately ensuing upheaval cast a shower of water over the onlookers. Polly, drenched and whooping in triumph, took a turn of the line about her ample hips and leaned her weight into the pull. Tracy seized hold of the line to help. The threshing monster was dragged up on the bank. Polly drew her knife and, watching for her chance among its convulsive contortions, drove the blade to the hilt between the eyes. The great fish lay still. Polly regarded it complacently.

"Must weigh more'n a hunert pounds." She knelt, withdrew the knife, and began to disembowel the fish. "Weather like this it's best to clean 'em straight off."

Cam, her interest in the episode satisfied, strolled off around the end of Caleb's cornfield to indulge her greater interest in a closer inspection of his calf-breaking. Lina wandered on lazily along the path, looking for an inviting place to sit down. She had grown very large about the waist these past few weeks but she carried herself with the serene grace of a ship gliding over a calm sea.

"When is she due?" asked Tracy.

"Some time next month. She's gittin' along real good. She won't have her no trouble." Polly glanced across the estuary at Eric and Clem still working alone at their clearing. "Olen and Jat and Jake—they kin surely figger ways to spend time with their pokin' around through the bresh these mornings. But they don't feel so foolish doin' it as they done at first. Not since they found out Caleb he was out lookin' around every mornin', too."

"He is? Does he think then there's any real danger?"

"Not yet, he don't. But he don't like the idee o' even one Injun snoopin' around. Not without his knowin' about it."

Lina had found a spot that suited her and had settled down against the moss-covered trunk of a fallen tree. She appeared to be dozing in the sun. On the path across the stream Betsey came into view from the direction of the marsh. She was carrying a string of half a dozen ducks.

"She nets 'em in the marsh over around thet island we snuk to thet night," said Polly. "Nuthin Betsey craves so much as smoked duck. They's about the only thing she ever gits hungry fer. She's kept arter 'em 'till she's got most four dozen strung to the rafters."

"She looks so much better lately and seems to be in so much better spirits."

"Thet's a fact. I figgered out why quite a spell back but she only tol' me herself jest last night. She's on her way to havin' her another young-un."

"What! Who?"

"Nobody here. But yuh mind thet day o' Louisa's birthday shindig when Bill Granger's boat stopped off and he brung up thet keg o' whisky?"

"Surely not Bill Granger?"

"Betsey ain't sure whether 'twas him or which one o' them no-count boatmen o' hisn. Anyhow, arter they all got theyselves good and drunk and arter it got dark she was down there on thet boat with 'em most o' the night."

"But—but I thought she wasn't well. Even if she had drunk too much too, how could she stand it?"

"She never tuk a drop. She knowed whut she was doin'. I reckon she figgered it was a case fer kill or cure. Anyhow, she come through it. She tuk to her bed fer mebbe a week but when she got up she stayed up and tuk to eatin' more and stopped actin' so mean. Soon's we can't keep it from 'em no longer, Louisa and Agatha and Olivia they'll most likely go to lookin' down their noses agin, but me I ain't yellin'. Betsey she can't abide it not havin' a brat of her and when a body wants somethin' thet bad it's no more'n right fer 'em to have it." Polly wiped the blade of her knife on a clump of grass, struggled upright, and poked at the fish with one bare foot. "It's too heavy fer me to lug up the hill. When Olen turns up I'll send him down to fetch it." She looked off toward the continuing commotion in Caleb's barnyard. "I misdoubt me some Caleb he's ever goin' to git them buffler to pull even in the traces. But Caleb he ain't no hand ever to give up easy. Thet's one thing yuh might's well git straight in yer head. He ain't bin actin' much like it but he wants yuh same's he done from the start. It was you, then, and nobody else. He fooled me some then, but he ain't foolin' me no more."

"You have to admit he has a marvelous way of showing whatever it is he feels, if he feels anything."

"A man like him's got a right to expect his woman to be the first to give in."

Wagging her head, Polly trudged away toward the bridge. There came a splintering sound from the direction of the barnyard but Tracy took care not to look again. Hastily picking up her baskets, she hurried on along the path past the drowsing Lina toward the river bank. When she had pushed through the willows to the beach to turn downriver toward the berry patch, she saw a barge anchored a hundred yards out and a man rowing a skiff from it into the mouth of the creek. He twisted at his oars to see where he was going and, catching sight of Tracy on the bank, swung the prow of his skiff toward her. Twisting again, he called out:

"This Revel Creek?"

"Yes, it is," said Tracy.

He pulled again on his oars, drove the bow of his skiff into the bank, and began fumbling in his shirt.

"I got a letter for Garett Jordan," he said. He stretched from the seat to hand it to her. "I told his brother in Pittsburgh I'd drop it off here."

The moment Tracy had hold of the letter he picked up his oars and, obviously relieved his mission had cost him so little time, began vigorously to row back to his barge. Tracy ran all the way to the station. The gate was open now that the scouts had at last returned from their morning patrol, but they had not yet left to join Eric in the clearing. Olen, Jarot, and Jacob, all brandishing shovels, were circling about the center of the yard, studying the ground and striking at it with shovel points to illustrate their varying views on some debate that absorbed them. Polly and Maggie, equally interested, were taking an earnest part in the discussion. Garett and Olivia were watching from the doorway of the shop. Tracy ran to Garett.

"A letter from Duncan," she announced.

Garett tore it open. In it were two folded sheets of paper, one of them sealed. Olivia, pressing against him the better to see, snatched the sealed one.

"It's for Agatha," she said. "I'll take it to her. She won't want to wait an extra second for it."

Olivia ran to the kitchen with Agatha's letter. Garett smoothed his and began at once to read it aloud to Tracy.

"Dear Garett:

From all I have been able to learn since reaching Pittsburgh the general situation in this western country has changed materially since we came through here last fall and, I am sorry to say, the chance has been very much for the worse. I have been able to talk to men as well-informed as John Neville, John Heckewelder, and George Morgan. All agree that conditions in the west, particularly north of the Ohio, are drifting toward a possible crisis. The man who has agreed to deliver this letter on his way to Limestone is in a hurry to be off and so I will try to say what I have to say in a few plain words. The principal event which has so much changed every prospect has been England's persistence in maintaining her garrisons at Detroit and Niagara, which forts formerly under the peace treaty, they had agreed to turn over to our country. This enables English traders to continue to move freely among the Ohio Indians to furnish them with guns, gunpowder, and whatever else they desire. This in turn has encouraged the Indians to renew their objections to American settlements north of the Ohio. They are said to be even now holding councils in which they are shaping their demands that the Ohio be recognized as the permanent boundary between our country and their tribal lands. Congress has become so aware of the threat that it in turn has renewed its prohibition of any settlement whatever across the Ohio. General Harmar arrived here last winter with his detachment of federal troops but his soldiers are too few to offer more protection to the frontier than the garrisoning of one or two log forts. So far Harmar's best thought on the most likely way to prevent a new Indian war is to discourage white settlement on the Indian side of the Ohio. In a number of recent instances he has even ordered his soldiers to burn cabins found on that side in order to require the settlers to withdraw. In spite of all the talk about the Indians renewing the war, which from their point of view was not actually ended by the peace treaty between the United States and England with regard to which they were not consulted, it does not appear that important hostilities are likely this summer. They are still occupied with their many conferences in which they are endeavoring to work each other up to united action while Joseph Brant, the Mohawk king, is said to be planning to go presently to London in the hope of enlisting further English aid. Before making any general move they will undoubtedly wait to know the result of his embassy. What we do have to be prepared for, however, is the possibility of nuisance raids this year and the probability of more general attacks next summer. In the meantime be constantly on your guard. I shall return within the month and have every hope of bringing with me a sufficient number of new families to make our position more secure. Until then be sure to keep on the best of terms you can with Caleb. I have written this so hastily that I have scarcely had time to read what I have written. Do not let it give you the impression that I am discouraged, for I am not, as I know you are not. We have seen our country come through many severe trials before and it will continue to do so. As will we.

Yr' aff't bro,

Duncan

"Well, well," said Garett. "Looks like Duncan's finally beginning to get his eyes open."

"He's not been so blind," protested Tracy. "Last year when he made all his plans for us to settle here he had no reason to expect anything like this. Nobody foresaw then the English would hang on to their lake posts. That's what's made all the difference."

"Admitting Duncan can do no wrong, suppose we turn to a safer subject. During your singular sojourn with Caleb, did you get no inkling from him of this apparent change in the Indians' temper?"

"None. Though that doesn't signify. He might not have told me if he knew."

"At any rate he seemed to feel no growing need to be watchful himself. He didn't hesitate, for example, to leave you alone when he went off hunting."

"I'm sure he is still quite certain that neither he nor his property is in the slightest danger."

"And it didn't bother him that the Shawnee were creeping up to spy on the station?"

"He might not have known that. There were no Indians ever hanging around on his side of the stream, you may be sure, and you must remember he never hunts on this side. He could have learned for the first time about a number of things like that when he went to the Shawnee town with General Clark. Naturally, I know nothing about him since he got back. I do know that he made the two-day journey in one, whether or not his hurry to get back meant anything. And Polly tells me that now he looks around the woods every morning just as you make the Slovers do."

"It's obvious that something has come over him. For one example, can you guess what the Slovers are doing out there now?"

Garett nodded toward the activities in the yard. Jarot and Jacob had begun to dig a hole over which Olen and Maggie were erecting a scaffolding.

"Surely not another barbecue pit?"

"No. A well. That crossbar will be to support the rope and pulley to hoist buckets of earth. When Olen met Caleb in the woods this morning Caleb asked him why we didn't have a well in the stockade. The slightest suggestion from Caleb is to the Slovers the equal of a royal command. It's a fact that if we ever were besieged it'd be a big help not to have to depend on carrying water up from the stream."

Tracy's eyes became increasingly thoughtful as she contemplated the diggers. "On this mound they'll have to dig a ways to strike water. You or Duncan could never have got them to work that hard. It had to take a hint from Caleb. It's the first real sign of his taking our side."

"Don't go too fast. It may not be a free choice for him. In Clark's letter to Stephen he remarked on the existence among the Shawnee of a peace party and a war party. He said Caleb seemed to have as many old friends in the one lot as the other but some of the more ardent leaders of the war party were beginning to cool off on him. What I'm getting at is that if he's bound to keep his place here he may sooner or later be obliged to take our side."

Tracy appeared not to be listening. "In planting the idea of the well on Olen he could only have meant to help us. Now that he's made this overture, isn't it up to us to make some gesture in return?"

"Such as your going back to him?" The smile on his lips was mocking but his eyes were troubled and thoughtful.

"No," declared Tracy with instant violence.

"Then you haven't, as Polly put it so much more neatly, as yet begun to miss him?"

"Don't be absurd. All the same, there's still this one thing about him we have to face. He is sacrificing something on account of us. If we weren't here he could have that place of his to the end of his days and the Shawnee would have no slightest objection. It may cost him a great deal to befriend us and we do have to try to meet him at least part way. I haven't spoken to him since that night I left. But I'm beginning to wonder if I shouldn't try to have a talk with him. An intelligent talk, I mean, just for once."

"No harm in trying. I've one suggestion. While you're at it try also to remember that intelligence has a way of coming down as the temper goes up."

"I'll do my best. But none of you up here can have any idea how really infuriating he can be."

"I have some idea. And I think Duncan assembled a very good one."

"No wonder. Two men could not be more different."

"I know. Duncan's everything that's wise and reasonable and noble."

"No. Those aren't the ways they're the most different. Caleb isn't stupid, or irrational, or ignoble, at least in the kind of world he knows."

"That's the right frame of mind. Give him the benefit of every doubt. Just hang to that thought and go down there and see if you can't find out just where we stand with him."

Tracy met Cam and Ken on the bridge.

"He put the calves back in their pen," said Cam. "They broke the yoke and he's gone to the woods to find a piece of ash to make a new one. Are you still going berrying? Where'd you leave your baskets? Don't you want Ken and me to go with you?"

"Your mother just got a letter from your father," said Tracy. "You'll want to hear what he said, won't you?"

"Oh, yes," said Cam.

She and Ken went flying up the hill. Tracy kept on, wedging her way among the tremendous stalks of corn, until she came out into the narrow dooryard before the cabin. The coon came scuttling from under the doorstep to clutch at her skirt and make murmuring little squeaks of greeting. The door stood open and she saw that the interior of the cabin was as neat as ever. Caleb was nowhere in sight. She walked on toward the barn and stockpens. Her garden was doing well and had been kept carefully weeded. The calves were crusted with dried sweat and still rolling nervously bloodshot eyes, but appeared otherwise well-kept and flourishing. Two of the hens that had been setting when she left were stalking importantly about their pen followed by trails of cheeping chicks. The sow had not yet farrowed but, sprawled contentedly in the sun, was of a size to promise an imminent and significant increase in the pig census. The young turkeys were two-thirds grown and Caleb had been obliged to contrive a latticed roof of saplings to keep them from flying out of their pen. She walked back to the cabin door and sat on the step.

Caleb's return was so noiseless that she was aware first of his shadow before looking up to see him. He stood before her, axe in hand, his rifle slung to one shoulder, and a roughly squared section of ash log balanced on the other. He eased the log to the ground, set the axe against the wall, and leaned on his rifle, looking down at her. The Indian impassivity of his gaze kindled in her the familiar flare of resentment. She drew in her feet with the immediate impulse to rise and walk away from him.

"You have come back?"

He must have intended his words to convey as much unconcern as did his manner. But he hurried them ever so slightly. She settled back on the doorstep.

"No. I have come to talk."

"What is there to say?"

"Some of the things we should have said before I came back that first time."

"I am listening."

"You have been helping us."

"When you say us, do you mean us? Or them?"

"I mean everybody at the station. I think we, at least I, owe you something in return. So I want to help you."

"How will you do that?"

"I will come down every morning and every evening—all day, if necessary—and do all the work I did when I was living here."

"What good is that?"

"You have much more to do here than one man can do."

"I do not need help." He nodded in the direction of the station. "That is what they need."

"Everybody needs help."

"I do not think I do but I know I do not want it."

"What is it that you do want?"

"The same as in the beginning. I want a wife."

"Do you still want me?"

"Yes."

"Why? You have never been satisfied with anything about me." He did not answer. "Have you?"

"You might learn."

"So might you. Though we do not seem so ready to learn, either of us." She rose to face him. "It will do no good for me to come back and I will not. But there is something else we can try. I have come down here to talk to you. Why, tomorrow or the next day, do you not come up to the station to talk to me? Any white man would do that if he wanted to persuade his wife to come back to him. You are not obliged forever to act like an Indian. Come as often as you like. You will be welcome. I'm not promising anything. I'm only saying that there is no slightest hope whatever for what you say you want so long as we go on feeling as we do about the other's kind of people."

He had listened attentively and appeared to give her appeal some consideration. But after a moment he shook his head.

"No. If here you feel always the feather in the nose, then here is not the place for you."

"That is how you have made me feel."

"Then it is better you do not come back." She turned to go. "But you are here already." The words burst from him. "Why do you not stay here?"

"Feather and all?" she taunted him.

He did not reply. She started away and he made no move to stop her.

Lina squirmed into a more comfortable position against the log and opened sleepy eyes. Across the stream, nearly a hundred yards wide here where its estuary broadened before curving against the sandy point to empty into the river, Eric was swinging his axe against the base of the last tree standing between the station and the Ohio. She watched him contentedly for a while and then dozed again. A rustle in the undergrowth caught her attention. She opened her eyes. A great six-foot rattlesnake was slowly worming his torpid length from the stretch of sun-baked open along the path into the comparative shade and seclusion of a tangle of juniper brush. She watched idly. Then, struck by a sudden thought, she sprang up and broke a long dead branch from the fallen tree. With its forked end she began teasing the snake, preventing its escape into the shrubbery and forcing it to retreat toward the more open bank of the stream. She worked with the huge reptile coolly and smilingly. When she had maneuvered it to the location she had selected, she struck it several harder taps. It coiled to strike, its fangs gleaming, its rattle buzzing fiercely.

"Eric!" she screamed. "Eric! Help!"

Eric dropped his axe, snatched up his rifle, and ran to the stream bank. He paused there, half-crouched, the rifle ready, his glaring eyes frantically searching the woods behind her for evidence of the danger threatening her.

"A snake," she cried. "A big rattler. He's after me."

Eric instantly threw down his rifle, stripped off his powder horn, and plunged into the stream. His flailing arms whipped the water of the estuary into a froth in the desperate urgency of his swim across. He scrambled, dripping and gasping, up on the bank beside her. She had already found a weapon for him. It was a long heavy pole of water-soaked driftwood. He grasped it.

"He's right there," she said, pointing.

The rattlesnake had been neglected while Lina had become belatedly concerned over how well Eric could swim. While she watched his crossing the creature had started to move off. But upon Eric's leap toward him he coiled once more, lifted his great triangular head, and resumed his lethal buzz.

"Watch out," said Lina. "He's so big he kin strike a good ways."

Eric shook off her clutch and sprang on to the attack. He swung the heavy pole and continued to hammer wildly until he had beaten the reptile into a pulp. He dropped the pole and straightened, breathing deeply and swaying with a momentary faintness mingled with his relief.

"He surely was a big one," he whispered. "Never saw a bigger one."

"You come very quick," she murmured. "I only had to yell oncet and there yuh was a-churnin' crost the crik."

"Of course," he said.

He looked around at her. In the brillance of the sunlight his vision of her was breathtakingly near and clear. He looked at the flaxen brightness of her hair curling about her shoulders, at the startling glow of her dark eyes against the whiteness of her skin, at the moist red curve of her lips, at the satiny sheen of her throat, at the pleasant lift of her bosom. But then his glance reached the swelling bulge at her waist and he looked abruptly and painfully away.

"I ain't never bin skeered o' snakes," she was saying. "I can't figger whut got me in sech a fret all on a sudden over this one. Must o' bin 'cause o' the time thet's on me."

He looked helplessly at her again. Usually she seemed so calm and peaceful, almost sleepy. But now she seemed vibrantly alive. Her eyes were shining, her lips parted, her breast rising and falling. She seemed on tiptoe to accept and to welcome something extraordinary, something mysterious. She lifted her hands and pressed them against that portion of her that seemed thrust out toward him, that he was struggling so desperately not to notice. Hastily, he looked away again.

"He's gittin' thet spry, and strong, too," she went on. "Sometimes he gits to jerkin' around like a frog in a teacup. Look—he's right here. Most as close to yuh as I be. Yuh don't have to be a-feared to look." She took one of his hands and held it against her. "Here, yuh kin feel, too. Whut's in there is jest as much yers as mine."

He jerked his hand away.

"I don't want to feel. I don't want to look. I don't even want to think about it."

He plunged into the stream and swam back to the security of the other side as furiously as when he had rushed to the rescue. Lina looked after him, smiling sorrowfully and forgivingly.

Through all the next week the station was in a continual tumult of activity. The well-digging progressed earnestly and succeeded beyond every expectation. Long before the shaft had been sunk to the level of the stream, water gushed into it and rose slowly in the well, cool and black and glistening, to within ten feet of the surface. Olen was astonished to the point of alarm by this apparent violation of natural law and was only partially reassured by Garett's suggestion that there must be some subterranean channel leading from the heights of the adjacent ridge which their digging had chanced to intersect. With the well achieved so much more easily than had been anticipated, the Slover men were encouraged to undertake the construction of a cabin for Jarot and Maggie. Eric, Ned, and Clem, the major clearing completed for the moment, began the excavation of Tracy's proposed cellar under the storeroom.

There was but one untoward incident to disturb this productive week. In the course of one morning's patrol Olen sighted a bull elk with a broken arrow protruding from his shoulder. He whistled for Jarot and Jacob to join him and the three set out to back-track the elk in order to determine how near the station the Indian had shot him. They advanced with extreme caution at first but then went on more boldly as they observed that the elk's gait had been normal during the hour before Olen had sighted him and that there were no splatters of blood marking his course. Crossing the old Indian trail above the falls they came upon clinching evidence. Here they found where the elk had bedded down for the night and where upon getting up he had lingered to browse. It was clear that the Indian hunter's range had been at a considerable distance and that his unsuccessful arrow had been launched days before. But in setting out to return to the station they came upon another kind of Indian sign that gave them new pause. Near the stream crossing, a tree beside the trail had recently had a strip of bark peeled from it. On the gleaming fresh surface of the scar had been painted a number of the odd, sticklike designs of Indian picture writing.

"Injuns—mostly Shawnee, I reckon—bin using thet trail off'n on," said Olen in reporting the discovery to Garett. "But ain't bin no Injuns foolin' around in the woods this side the trail. Not since we-uns bin goin' out every mornin'. Thet I kin swear to."

"But the picture writing must mean something," said Garett. "Could it have been meant for Caleb?"

"Nope. We-uns tol' him about it 'fore we come back up here. When we tol' him whut it was like he knowed whut it meant without goin' to look at it fer hisself. 'Twasn't war sign. 'Twas woman sign." Olen chuckled. "Some Injun'd lost track o' his woman and he painted the tree there so's any other Injun comin' along who happened to run crost his woman would tell her he was a-lookin' fer her."

"Admirable device," agreed Garett. "Good's a notice in one of our newspapers."

During the week the moon waxed until there came the

night it became a perfect great ball of copper rising above the wooded hills across the Ohio into an evening sky still faintly blue. In the kitchen the first candle had not yet been lighted. Tracy came upon Agatha leaning her head against the wall beside a loophole, gazing out at the moon over the river. In its pale reflected light her face looked even paler, her eyes large with yearning, her lips trembling like a child's. When she was thus off guard, she looked as lost as any child could ever look. She was but half a woman when Duncan was away from her. For all the devotion she lavished upon her children, she lived only for the moment of his return. Tracy shuddered, brooding over her own loneliness which was so much greater because for it there could never be hope of relief, and went out into the dusk of the yard.

The shadow of the palisade darkened the area of the half-finished new cabin, the well, and the woodpile, but the other half of the enclosure was bathed in the glow from the rising moon. Garett stood guard over the gate with Olivia leaning beside him on the fire step. She said something and he drew her closer to him. Jarot and Maggie sat on the shop doorstep. He was softly strumming his mandiddle and her low laughter was even softer. The Slovers had retired except for Lina who sat on a bench before their door. She was idly combing her hair, humming as she inclined her head first one way and then the other. Eric was crouched in the shadow behind the woodpile, watching her. His figure, barely distinguishable in the darkness, was as rigid as though chained to the ground. From some distant, undoubtedly likewise moonlit recesses of the forest drifted the faintly echoing rumble of a bull buffalo's longing. That tremor in the warm air seemed to Tracy to merge with Jarot's strumming, with Maggie's soft laughter, with Olivia's whisper and Garett's murmured response, with Lina's humming, with Eric's anguished tension, and to share with the moon's radiance in the universal invitation of the midsummer night. She turned abruptly back into the dark house.

Louisa, her arms clasped about her knees, was sitting up in bed, staring at the loophole in the wall before her. The shaft of moonlight that came through it fell upon her calm face, etching more deeply and yet making more beautiful the lines of age upon it. Tracy came in.

"Shame on you," she chided. "You should be asleep."

"I can remember when I couldn't sleep on a night like this," said Louisa. "And when I get to remembering, I still can't."

Tracy sank down on the edge of the bed, keeping her face turned away from the shaft of moonlight. Louisa reached out, touched her, and then withdrew her hand.

"Caleb says I'm a fool," said Tracy, suddenly giving way. "He could not be more right. There could never have been a more utter fool."

Louisa touched her again and waited.

"It is worse this time than when last he went away. Even then when I thought he might be dead. *So* much worse. That day his letters came. While Garett was reading his to me, all I could think about was what he must have said to Agatha in the one to her. When he is here I can stand it. I know I have to. But when he is away I sometimes don't see how I can."

Louisa cleared her throat before replying with unsympathetic calm.

"So you've made up your mind that living for a while with another man, even Caleb, has made you want Duncan more than ever."

"It's dreadful to admit it. But it must be so. Only you can hardly call it making up my mind. I scarcely seem to have a mind."

"Mind or no, you've surely been in a state ever since you came back. You've been tearing around as though you didn't dare ever stop for a minute."

"So I have. And for the same reason. When I was down there I worked as hard as I could from morning till dark because I couldn't endure thinking. I still can't endure it."

"For fear you may decide which man you most want not to think about?"

Tracy started up with a cry of protest and sank slowly down again. "How can you say such a terrible thing?"

"I didn't say anything. I only asked a question. And if I were a girl as mixed up as you are I wouldn't rest till I'd found the answer. You'll only feel worse the longer you put it off."

Tracy's shoulders sagged, her head bowed, her hands were twisting a corner of the bedspring into a knot.

"I'm worse than mixed up. I really must be losing my mind. Even my dreams are crazy. I've often dreamed of Duncan. Last night I did again, after I'd finally got to sleep, and then I woke up grabbing at you to make sure I really was here with you. For right in the middle of the dream it came over me that it wasn't Duncan any longer I was dreaming about. It was Caleb. Yet in the dream I'd gone on feeling just as if—as if—oh, I don't believe it. I can't believe it. I can't." She clutched at Louisa. "It's all very well for you to sit there mumbling as though the answer were easy."

"It's never easy for one who's been raised as you have," said Louisa, her pitiless calm unshaken. "Least of all for one who's so sure she has to think before she can tell what she feels. But the answer's as simple as bringing an iron near to a magnet. You've been away from the both of them for a while. Being near either of them again now will tell you fast enough whether it's he or the other. You can't go to Duncan to find out. He's hundreds of miles away. But Caleb's right down there in his cabin."

"You can't be suggesting I go back to him!"

"You left him once. You can leave him again."

"You're more mixed up than I am. No one's been so set against him as you've always been."

"As I still am." There was no emotion in Louisa's voice, only an immense weariness. "But I am also an old woman. One of the few advantages of age is that you begin to see how little use there is in trying to make anything go away just by going on saying it isn't so. You've already been hurt all you could be. You can't be hurt any more. And this time you'll finally know. Or is knowing what you are the most afraid of?"

Tracy stood up.

"No. I'm not afraid of knowing. I—I want to know. I have to."

She moved from the doorstep along the shadow of the wall to the ladder in the corner of the palisade behind the kitchen. The yard was deserted except for Garett and Olivia over the gate and all of their attention was alternately on the forest beyond and on each other. She climbed to the fire step, swung over the parapet, and dropped to the ground outside. On the bridge she began to run, but at the edge of the corn she paused. To force her way through it would set up an unavoidable rustling. She shrank from giving Caleb so premature an advertisement of her approach. Circling carefully around the cornfield she crept past his pool. At the corner of the cabin she came to a sudden halt, frozen. From within came the murmur of Caleb's voice and Daisy's giggling reply.

She crept away as silently as she had approached. The storms of rage which had so often protected her from him before failed her now. The one sensation that overwhelmed and possessed her was of her own terrifying inadequacy. She seemed to be falling and continuing endlessly to fall in sickening helplessness into bottomless depths of shame from which there could be no faintest hope she might ever escape.

August

It had not rained in more than two weeks. Day after day the sun blazed from a cloudless sky and each day the heat became more oppressive. The ground inside the station baked hard, pitch oozed from the logs of the palisades, springs dried up, the stream shallowed, the broad leaves of the corn yellowed, the forest turned tinder dry. Only the new well resisted the dryness and the heat. Every morning Olen peered down it, grunting with satisfaction upon being again assured that the water level had not fallen by so much as an inch. By now he had taken all credit for having personally selected the precise spot beneath which had so long lain hidden so manifest a miracle.

The third week the inevitable forest fire cast its towering black and yellow shroud across the sky. Later in the year there were often such fires, set by Indians in the course of their immemorial fall game drives. But in weather as dry as this one was bound, sooner or later, to be set going by chance —by burning grains of powder from a careless hunter's primer pan, by a mover's abandoned river-bank campfire, by a bolt of lightning from one of the distant thunderstorms murmuring along the horizon. Once started, such a fire spread endlessly across the limitless expanse of woodland, devouring in a day years and centuries of patient growth, in a pitiless devastation that would rage on unchecked until finally subdued by the next heavy rain. This fire was an immense conflagration, though happily on the other side of the Ohio. It burned over the southern hills for days, at times seeming to smolder, at others casting huge billows of flame from treetop to treetop. A strange traffic coursed to and fro upon the river. At each flare-up the water was dotted with the heads of swimming wild animals—bear, wolves, panthers, rabbits, herds of deer and elk and buffalo. The majority were seeking desperately to flee the flames, but almost as many, deranged by their terror, were struggling as desperately toward them. The night sky was as fiery as the open door of some monstrous furnace. By day, if the wind veered to the south, choking clouds of smoke rolled across the river to curl about the station.

Yet this season of heat and drought and fire offered certain redeeming compensations. The corn had matured until every morning there were new young roasting ears turned tender enough to eat, and the blueberries in the marsh had suddenly ripened in incredible profusion. The people of the station, long since wearied of their principal diet of fresh meat, drank deeply from their enchanted well and gorged blissfully on green corn and blueberries. At last there came a night when a prolonged thunderstorm quenched the great fire and left damp cool air after its passing.

"Them blueberries," said Polly next morning, "they's right at their best. But they'll go bad fast arter the soakin' they got last night."

A berrying bee was organized to gather a major supply to be dried and stored away for the winter. Maggie, Betsey, Cam, Ken, Geneva, and Hebe assembled to accompany Polly. Tracy, who had seemed so much more affected than anyone else by the heat that during the whole three weeks she had seldom ventured from her room, bestirred herself and joined the group. Garett called Eric.

"So many people will keep up a chatter loud enough to carry for miles. Take Jat and cut over the ridge to East Creek. Look particularly to see if there've been any Indians back around that Shawnee hunting camp Jat spotted over there last week. Then work your way to the river and down to the marsh."

Eric nodded.

"I saw Caleb again last evening just before the rain," he said. "My trigger spring was broken and I asked him to show me how to put in a new one. That seemed as good an excuse as any. I like to drop in on him now and then."

"And a good idea, too. What did you decide?"

"You can't tell. He acts just the same. And he's working just as hard. With Daisy to help he's been able to get more done, in spite of the heat. He's cleared another couple of acres back of his stockpens. His corn's not as yellowed as ours. It'll be a week or two later than ours getting ready to harvest. And he'll have more. He's been able to keep the deer out of it better than we have."

"He didn't have any sage remarks to make about Indians?"

"No. But while she was away Daisy learned a little English from some trader she worked for in the Shawnee town and she likes to show it off. With the help of a few signs she was telling me that John Turtle paid Caleb a visit night before last. He talked with Caleb a while out in the yard and then went off again without even waiting to have anything to eat. When I asked her if they'd had some sort of an argument she wouldn't talk about it any more."

"On the other hand, it could as well mean some sort of a reconciliation with the Shawnee—signalized by Daisy's return."

"It could. But I hardly think so."

"You think she just came running of her own accord when she heard about that picture writing up on the trail."

"I think Caleb put that there himself, all right, to save him the time and trouble of going after her. But I don't think the sign meant any more than that he'd simply decided he needed her again. There's no use John Turtle or anybody else trying to argue with him. He doesn't listen; he just keeps on going his own way, whatever that is."

Eric and Jarot set out. The rain had obliterated the earlier sign of Indian hunters in the valley of East Creek. After they had made sure there had been no new tracks since, they zigzagged down the valley and climbed the lower slopes of the nose of the ridge thrust out into the main river bottom. They could see the berry-pickers scattered through the marsh below but were immediately gripped by a much greater interest in what they could see in the estuary of their own creek beyond. There was a sizable flotilla of boats drawn up on the shore of the point from which upwards of half a hundred men were disembarking. The figures were too far away to identify but the craft were trading bateaus, not Indian canoes. The berry-pickers were unaware of this fleet's arrival, since in the marsh any view of the open river was cut off by the offshore island and of the estuary by the fringe of brush along the nearer side of the point. Eric and Jarot, keeping to the more open higher ground, ran around the marsh and on to the point. In another quarter of an hour they were running back to the marsh, Jarot making for Maggie and Eric for Tracy. The berry-pickers straightened in surprise to greet the messengers. One after another, as they heard the news, they snatched up their half-filled baskets and began to run toward the point. Tracy was the farthest away and the last to hear.

"Father's back," Eric announced. "And General Clark's with him along with a dozen boatloads of soldiers."

The vanguard of berry-pickers, too excited to go around by the path, burst through the shrubbery out to the point and there paused to stare. The newcomers did not look much like soldiers, for instead of wearing uniforms they were dressed in odds and ends of buckskin and linsey-woolsey, and most of them were as ragged and shoeless as the poorest mover. But there was a small brass cannon in one of the beached bateaus; a flag on a staff thrust upright in the sand; beside the staff two neat, pyramidal stacks of muskets, to one of which a drum was hanging; one of the ragged men was pacing solemnly back and forth along the path with a bayoneted musket on his shoulder, and most of the others were engaged in spreading their rain-soaked blankets to dry in meticulously straight lines on the ground under the direction of a fiercely mustached, older, and stouter man who had the frayed stub of a plume in his battered, three-cornered hat. At Polly's puffing approach the sentinel ceased his measured tramp and confronted her with musket at port.

"Be yuh sure enough soljers?" she inquired.

"Company C, First American," said the sentry stiffly.

Captain Valentine Telford, stripped to the waist, was shaving at a little mirror hung on the trunk of the sycamore. He was young for his rank but bore himself with a cultivated and unmistakable air of command. Without looking around and without raising his voice, he spoke distinctly and coldly.

"Sergeant, a sentinel on post does not carry on a conversation with bystanders."

"Yes, *sir,*" said the mustached man. "Jenkins—look alive."

The sentry hastily resumed his pacing back and forth. Captain Telford slowly turned, razor in hand, to survey the group of gaping onlookers which by now included Jarot, Maggie, Betsey, Cam, Ken, Geneva, and Hebe.

"Sergeant, could you postpone the entertainment of visitors till you've got camp established?"

"Yes, sir. Most certainly, sir."

Sergeant Redfern advanced scowling on the berry-pickers. They backed away, continuing, however, to stare with unsatisfied curiosity at the cannon, the flag, the stacked muskets, the Sergeant's hat, and the eagle tattooed on the Captain's back. Cam and Ken were torn between their interest in the novelty of this military spectacle and their desire to waste no more time before seeing their father. After a brief struggle they scampered off toward the station. The others lingered.

Captain Telford resumed shaving. Tracy, running along the path from the marsh, rounded the spreading hazel bush where the path took its turn, and all but plunged into him. It was his turn to gape, open-mouthed, at this flushed and startlingly vivid face that had sprung so suddenly and at such close quarters upon his view. He had paid scant heed to the other intruders but this new invasion struck him instantly as a different case. With one hand he had been stretching his lower lip in order to get at it with the razor and she was so near that for a second he could feel her hastened breath on that raised bare forearm. He peered over it at her. It began to come over him how very much different, in truth, was this one from the others. His military aplomb toppled. His blush was not so apparent on his tanned and still half-lathered face but it spread like a crimson tide across the whiteness of his naked torso.

"Oh, I beg your pardon," said Tracy. "I had no idea the path ran right into your camp."

She stepped around him and ran on, the grinning Eric at her heels. The Captain, for the moment forgetting his soldierly dignity, craned to look after her. His expression did not escape Betsey's sharp eyes. Taking advantage of Sergeant Redfern's pause to tug on at his mustaches while taking a second and less passing look at Maggie, she circled him and sauntered toward the sycamore. The Captain peremptorily gestured her nearer. As she advanced her scrutiny was open and direct, but he had regained his usual color and seemed undisturbed by her contemplation. He inclined his head in the direction of Tracy's receding form.

"Who was she?"

"Tracy Lewis."

Betsey waited. He concentrated on the next two strokes of his razor before making another equally casual remark.

"Bit awkward for a soldier to be taken quite so completely by surprise."

"Eh?"

"Never mind. But when you see her next time will you convey my apologies? Tell her I do hope she wasn't too upset?"

" 'Tain't likely." Betsey ran another appraising glance over his muscular arms and chest. "She's bin married long enough to git her eyes open."

"Oh?"

" 'Course she's a widder now—sort of. She lives up at the station."

"Oh."

The young Captain appeared capable of making quick decisions.

"Sergeant Redfern, will you please be good enough, and without further delay, please, to clear the camp of visitors? Also to have my locker brought ashore and my tent set up?"

He waited with increasing impatience for these instructions to be carried out, ducked into his tent, threw open his locker, and set about arraying himself in his new dress uniform.

Cam came running from the kitchen door to meet Tracy and Eric in the yard.

"General Clark's on his way back to Louisville to build a fort. We're going with him. We're going to give up the station and move to Kentucky."

Eric bolted past her and on into the house. He came to as sudden a stop, astounded. The whole atmosphere was one of excitement and jubilation, his mother tearful with happiness, Garett's quizzical grin more overt than usual, Louisa and Olivia laughing, the children whooping, the Negroes chattering.

"Cam says—Cam says—" Eric could not get the words out.

"It's all true," said Agatha. "Isn't it wonderful!" She saw his expression and slipped an arm comfortingly about his shoulders. "Your father'll tell you all about it in a minute. But first he wants to talk to Tracy."

She glanced past him at Tracy and nodded toward the office. Tracy went in and closed the door. Duncan had his little brass strongbox open on his desk and was sorting papers in and out of it. He whirled to face her. He looked as buoyant as the day of their arrival when they had stood together on the top of the mound.

"You can't begin to guess what a relief it was," he exclaimed. "To learn you'd left him, I mean. You represented the one complication that made me hesitate for a second about this move to Kentucky. But now there can be no question of your going along with us. Can there?"

"None. So you really are giving up this place."

"I'm giving up nothing. This land's still ours. It will always be. And in time we'll be back on it and have everything here we ever counted on. Can't you grasp what it really means? This isn't a retreat. It's a seven-league-boots advance. The opportunity opened up suddenly through some men from the East I met in Pittsburgh. I've got hold of pre-emption rights on a fifteen-thousand-acre tract on Green River. Actually by way of an option on shares in a land company. You can hardly call that a disaster. I'm attached to this place, too. But by the time we get the Green River tract developed the Indian situation will have improved enough so that we can come back here and build this one up next."

"Then all you've lost is just the year we've spent here?"

"I wonder you're not even more bitter. I'm not forgetting what this year has cost you. We can never forget what you did for us. Never. And we'll never stop trying to make it up to you. If there's anything on this earth anybody can ever be sure of, you can be sure of that."

"I'm sure you—all of you—will want to. But if I seem bitter it's not because of that. What I keep thinking about is that the year was a sort of test of his kind of people and our kind. It was almost a personal duel between you and him as well as between me and him. And look how it's coming out."

"That's nonsense, and you know it. The way it's coming out is that we'll have holdings so broad there'll be proper places, besides mine, for Garett and Eric, and Cam when she marries, and the others, and you, too, you may be sure. While he'll have just a cabin in a clearing, if the Indians let him keep that. My view hasn't narrowed. It has widened, vastly. Can't you see that?"

"Dimly. I can see what you see."

"Good. I've so much more to tell you the moment I can. But so much to do that has to be done this instant." He paused on his way to the door to give her one more earnestly beseeching look. "I can't tell you how happy I am that you're back with us. You belong with us. You're one of us."

He went out. Eric was waiting for him. After one glance at his son's face he smiled understandingly and placed a hand on his shoulder.

"I don't wonder you're taken aback. I was myself, at first. I couldn't stop thinking of all our work and all our hopes. Any more than I can stop thinking now of the way you've taken hold while I was away. Later I'll go more fully with you into my reasons for the move. But what it amounts to is that we have little choice. With the turn the Indian attitude has taken it had become clear we couldn't get settlers to join us here. Even if we were able to hang on here alone—for years to come that's all we'd be doing, just hanging on. While down there where we're going we'll have a thirty-family town established before snow flies."

"But do we have to depend on what other people do? Why isn't it what we do that counts?"

Duncan removed his hand from Eric's shoulder. "You'll just have to trust my judgment. We haven't time now to debate how I arrived at it. Naturally, if we're going to move, the sooner the better. And if it's to be soon, it must be at once, in order to take advantage of Captain Telford's military escort. River travel is becoming as dangerous again as it was during the war. Two flatboats were taken not thirty miles from here just this week."

Eric's face was getting whiter. "That only makes it seem even more like—like running away."

Duncan stiffened. "You have become a man in size. I must ask you to act like one. You will take Clem and Ned and begin at once moving our stores down to the rock. That's an order."

"Yes, Father."

Duncan turned to address the others in the room.

"Will each of you start picking out what he wants most to take. Space is limited, so we can't take everything. There will be room, however, for everything we really value."

He went out into the yard. The Slovers were gathered, silent and staring, about the well. He walked over to them.

"We have to leave today," he explained, "so that we can travel with the soldiers. So better start right in getting together what you want to take."

" 'Twon't take us no time to pick up whutever we own, Kunnel," said Olen.

Polly jerked her head toward the open gateway and the cornfield beyond. " 'Twon't be more'n two-three weeks till thet corn she'll be eared out good."

"We can't wait for it," said Duncan shortly. "And we won't starve without it, you may be sure."

Clark and Captain Telford came through the gate. The General's faded buckskins were made to seem the more dingy by contrast to the Captain's resplendence in his blue broadcloth uniform, pipe-clayed white crossbelts, dangling dress sword, and high, plumed shako. The young Captain veered off to take up a strategic position where, while waiting politely for the General, he could see, without seeming to peer, through the open door into the kitchen where the women of the household were dashing about. Clark came over to Duncan.

"I'm shoving off now," he said. "I have to get on to Louisville at the earliest. But I've advised Captain Telford to wait for you."

"He won't have to wait long," said Duncan. "We'll be loaded before dark. I know you're anxious to get your fort started."

"Good. I just had a talk with Caleb Lewis. He didn't tell me too much, but what he did say fits everything else I've been able to pick up. The Shawnee haven't threatened him directly. But what friends he's still got among 'em keep on nudging him to get out soon's he harvests his corn. They say if he stays here he's bound to get mixed up in the trouble that's coming at any white holding on this Indian side of the river."

"When is he getting out?"

"He says he's not. I made him a proposition to throw in with me when he pulled out here this fall. I've got a property across from Louisville that I never find enough time to work on myself."

"You trust him that much?"

"Well, the Indians are near enough through with him so's he's stuck with staying a white man, and I'd trust him to look out for anything he figgered was his."

"Still, he turned you down. You'd have thought he'd have jumped at the chance."

"He said he liked it here."

"Maybe then I could ask him to keep an eye on my place for the next three or four weeks. We're going to have to leave some things behind I'd like to be able to send back for, and there's that corn crop which would be worth something at Louisville prices."

"No harm in asking him."

"And not much use, either, I'd say, on second thought. Chances are the main reason he's staying on here is he'll be able to consider the whole place his from now on."

"He'll earn it if he does. Beyond about next spring whoever tries to hold this station will have to hold to it hard. Well, I'm off. The turn things are taking, I think you're making a very sensible move, as I told you when you first mentioned it back in Pitt. This country north of the Ohio—I doubt it's going to be quite the place to raise a family for the next five-ten years."

Clark waved to Captain Telford, who came to attention with a smart salute, and strode out the gate. The Captain made instantly for Duncan.

Tracy was helping Geneva sort and pack her kitchen utensils. There was a smudge of soot on her nose, and she was wrapped in one of Geneva's voluminous aprons with the strings tied around her under her arms. She looked up to see Duncan with the now so brilliantly caparisoned Captain bowing at his elbow.

"Tracy, may I present Captain Telford," said Duncan, his eyes twinkling. "For the past week my very good friend and for the week to come our providential protector. Val—Mrs. Lewis. Before we get to Louisville let us hope you are privileged, like us, to address her by the much more agreeable name of Tracy."

The Captain bent low over her hand, which was at the moment slightly grimy.

"We can pray for the future," he said, "but for the moment, Mrs. Lewis, my most earnest wish is to strive to correct the sad impression made by our first encounter."

"Which leaves us the new problem," said Tracy, making a civil effort to match their masculine humor, "of how next to correct the impression I must now be making." She glanced from her soot-streaked apron to the Captain's immaculate attire. "Best take flight while you may, Captain Telford. We are all so busy that if you linger here you may become inveigled into some most unsuitable task."

"I shudder but I do not flee. I am completely at your mercy, whether that mean scouring pots or—name what you will."

"You are too kind, Captain Telford, and we shall be sure to take the most ruthless advantage of you." She smiled brightly at him and, continuing to smile as brightly, turned to Duncan. "Your every move today is so breath-takingly swift. Even to starting so soon making everything up to me."

Duncan laughed and took her hand. "That's because I'm so happy you're back with us." He glanced at the Captain who, continuing to grin, was listening politely to their banter. "This may not be too poor a start, but it is only a start. I hope to do better." His glance came back to Tracy. "But why do you look at me so strangely? Just as when last I returned, you keep studying me as though you were having difficulty convincing yourself that I was really here."

"I'm sorry, Duncan. So much has been happening that I must be in a kind of daze. I assure you that I could not be more convinced that you are here." She stood on tiptoe and lightly kissed his cheek. "And I couldn't be more happy that you are. So many things are getting straightened out today."

She drew back and looked up at him, her smile broadening at his bewilderment. Suddenly the hand in his clasp went limp. She was no longer looking at him but past him. He wheeled. Caleb stood in the doorway.

Duncan immediately started toward him. The two confronted one another at a corner of the table. Caleb hitched the strap of his rifle over his shoulder, reached under his leather shirt, and pulled out a belt in which there were a number of pouches. He dropped the belt on the table. It fell with a solid clunk. The two men were the same height and their eyes on a level. Their glances were equally direct and challenging.

"You are leaving," said Caleb.

"Yes."

"I am staying."

"So I understand."

"I have come to buy your place."

Duncan continued coldly to study his adversary. Everyone in the room had ceased what they were doing to watch and listen. Tracy had backed against the fireplace. Her eyes were burning.

"I can understand," said Duncan, "with some difficulty, that is, your wish to buy. But there would seem to be a greater difficulty. You cannot afford it. I admit the buildings and the corn are not worth much, thanks to your Indian friends. But the land will still be here for years to come."

"I came to buy everything. Take with you what you can. Whatever you leave will be mine. For it—along with buildings, corn, and land—I will pay you now fifty guineas and I will give you a note promising to pay you in three years from today whatever more either General Clark or George Morgan say the land then is worth."

"Guineas, did you say? Do you know what guineas are?"

Caleb undid one of the pouches in the belt and shook five gold pieces from it. Duncan contemplated him with new antagonism and yet with a kind of grudging wonder.

"That was quite a risk you ran, working in the English fur trade the very year you deserted from the English navy; but it would appear to have been a profitable one."

"I have come to buy," said Caleb. "Do you want to sell?"

"I do. You have made, under the circumstances, a very reasonable offer. I may say that I should prefer to see the property come into the possession of almost anyone else. But these are not times we can pick and choose." Caleb was opening more of the pouches and shaking the heavy yellow coins out on the table. "I further feel, Mr. Lewis, that I should caution you. In this country now, gold pieces are so scarce as to be literally unheard of. They are worth many times more than their face value. I assume you are aware of that."

"I have already said that I have come to buy."

"And I have said that I will sell. I will make you out a bill of sale."

"I do not want that. I want Corbit Revel's title."

"So you would. A final righting of the injustice over which you have brooded so long. Very well, come with me to my office and I will sign his original grant over to you."

"And I will sign the note saying what more I will pay."

He followed Duncan into the office. Garett picked up one of

the gold coins, tossed it in his hand, and dropped it, ringing, back on the table top. He crossed to Tracy.

"That Duncan," he marveled. "He's lighted on his feet again. He'd sunk our last penny in this place. Then, before he'd hardly started to face up to the fact it was a dead loss, a land company angles to get him as western manager and throws in as bait a larger tract in a safer region. On top of that comes this offer out of the blue of enough to give his new development a running start. Just to be privileged to finger one of these solid gold guineas, people in Kentucky will rush to build him three such stations as this."

Tracy did not reply. His roving glance, passing over the meat block upon which had been piled the contents of Geneva's cupboard in preparation for packing, settled on the protruding neck of a brandy bottle. He snatched at it.

"Glasses, Geneva. Glasses for everybody. A libation is in order."

Bottle in hand, he followed Geneva about the room, forcing glasses on everyone and spilling a dash of brandy into each. Duncan and Caleb came out of the office.

"A toast," cried Garett, lifting his glass. "A salute to the new lord, and lady, of the manor. May their tribe increase."

Caleb's glance passed over Tracy as calmly as it did the others. He kept on out the door and through the gate. At the bridge she overtook him.

"There's one thing I want to know," she said. "That I have to know."

"There could be more than one," he said. "But who could tell you?"

"Last winter," she accused him, "when the Shawnee took all our food—it really was you who put them up to it—you who sent them—you who told them exactly what to do and how to do it. Wasn't it?"

He regarded her thoughtfully. "What do you do when you want something so much you are sure you must have it? Do you wait? Do you pray? Do you hope for someone to give it to you? Do you just sit and shiver? Or do you reach for it?"

"Reach for it? Is that what you call what you did? You plotted and schemed. You took advantages any savage would scorn to take. You sat over here like a great spider. From the moment you came you began to plan to get our place away from us. And the awful part is that you have. You have wound up getting exactly what you wanted."

"No." He glanced up toward the station and then up the stream along the border of the cornfield toward the falls. "I was ready to be a neighbor. It was not Colonel Jordan's land that I wanted. That was Corbit's to give and he did not give it to me. It is mine now but it is mine because I have paid for it."

She stared at him wildly. "Then why did you do it? Could you have been so out of your mind that you could put us through all that just to get you a white wife?"

"No. I was for a little while so out of my mind that I was sure there was just one white wife I had to have."

Her laugh was harsh with venom. "Then there is still one slight consolation. That was one game you lost. You no longer have her. After all your reaching you've come out with just what you had when you started. Daisy."

"That is so. It is also so that I am no longer out of my mind." He glanced up toward the station where Captain Telford had appeared at the corner of the stockade. "The young soldier is waiting for you. Do not keep him waiting. He could be your Daisy. He is another of your kind of people."

Caleb walked on across the bridge and into his cornfield. Tracy's clenching of her hands made her aware that she still was swathed in Geneva's apron. She tore it off and wadded it under one arm. Slowly she began to climb the slope. Captain Telford watched her, frowning, one hand on the hilt of his sword. But when she joined him he was surprised to see that she seemed quite casually calm.

"Was he annoying you?" he demanded, still frowning.

"I was just saying good-by," she told him cheerfully. "After all, we were married, for a while."

"I watched him while he was talking to Colonel Jordan. I have never seen a man to whom I took a more instant dislike. It is perhaps as well that I will not be here long enough to be obliged to meet him. Colonel Jordan's brother just now gave me a brief account of the circumstances of your marriage. If you will forgive my saying so, I have never heard of a more heroic sacrifice."

"You are very kind. But do not make it worse than it was. He did not mistreat me. It was just one of those instances of a leap in haste followed by repentance as hasty."

"You must believe me," said the young Captain, "when I say that I deeply sympathize. And that any service I can render you—here, en route, after we reach Louisville—will gratify me as deeply."

"You can be of service to me this minute, as a matter of fact." Tracy's hand fluttered to the tightly buttoned neck of her gray homespun gown. "I lost a locket in the marsh this morning. I'm sure I know just where it must have fallen. But everybody's so busy packing and we women and children are not supposed to wander off from the station alone. Would you mind walking over there with me?"

"Would I mind!" The Captain offered his arm with a flourish. "I warn you, madam. Do not mock me. I am a very forthright fellow. Do not be misled by my outwardly sunny nature."

She tossed the apron against the foot of the palisade and laid her fingers on his arm. They descended the slope and set out along the path toward the point. She glanced up at him.

"You do look the part."

"Of being a very forthright fellow?"

"No. Of being a soldier. A born soldier."

"Does that so astonish you?"

"Yes. Since the war all anybody's been thinking about is how to make money. Especially out here where everybody's rushing around so wildly looking for land. Even Colonel Jordan. Why are you so different?"

He replied with sudden sincerity. "Very simple. I love my country. It's young and helpless and needs defenders more than ever. I am honored to be one of the few it has. Nothing else would do me."

"I'm glad I asked," said Tracy, the tips of her fingers pressing his arm ever so slightly.

They had reached the edge of the camp on the point. The sentry presented arms. The lounging men sprang to attention.

"At ease," said Captain Telford. "Sergeant Redfern, send Corporal Rhodes with twenty men to report to Colonel Jordan at the station. They are to assist in any way they can in moving his cargo from the stockade down to the bank. Send Corporal Heston with the boats to that flat rock you can see from here to begin loading. Heston is boatman enough to see that the loads are divided equally. Remind him to make sure no boat is overloaded."

"Yes, sir," said the Sergeant.

Tracy and the Captain walked on. At the turn in the path by the hazel bush she looked back toward the station, her eyes darkening. He was watching her, noting her every change of expression.

"A great pity, really," he said, "to have to give up the place after you'd all worked so hard, and Colonel Jordan had made such a promising start with it."

"I know. But I know, too, it's all for the best. He'll have so much better chance where we're going. We'll all be much better off."

They walked on. The path was narrower now. To avoid the

shrubbery on either side she leaned closer to him. A projecting root tripped her and she clutched at him to regain her balance.

"Mrs. Lewis, you weren't hurt?" He covered the hand on his arm with one of his own and gazed down into her face beseechingly. "Do I have to call you Mrs. Lewis?"

"I don't like the name much myself. But, after all, I'm no longer Miss Carter."

"It's a dilemma easily avoided. I don't deserve it yet. But may I call you Tracy?"

She dropped her eyes. "Yes, Captain Telford."

"Thank you, Tracy."

She gently withdrew the hand under his. "The path is so narrow. Perhaps I'd better walk ahead."

She went on. He followed, giving himself over to the luxury of contemplating uninterruptedly this one aspect of her at least. After several excursions among the folds and contours of the gray gown his attention centered on the gleam of bare skin visible between its collar and the curls at the nape of her neck. Since she could not see it, there was no need to conceal his smile. It was a smile that suggested he was passing rapidly from the stage of dawning hope to that of eager anticipation. She paused in the shadow of a low spreading dogwood to look ahead into the open marsh.

"I'm trying to remember just where it was," she explained. "There was a little pool. I was in such a hurry I jumped across instead of going around. That's where it must have fallen."

He bent to look into her averted face.

"The locket must have meant a great deal to you. You seem so disturbed."

"I'm just being foolish," she said quickly. "I don't know why, but all of a sudden I was thinking again of our leaving. And then of all the other people this year who've had to give up places on the north bank. I've heard that many of them were so bound to hang on that the Army actually had to burn their cabins to make them move."

The Captain's smile vanished. He drew himself up as though throwing the mantle of authority about his broad shoulders.

"That was across the river along the stretch between Pittsburgh and Wheeling." He nodded judicially. "I burned out a dozen or so of them myself. But don't waste your sympathy. Most of them were scum. Bush rats, runaways, troublemakers. But no matter what they were, they'd been repeatedly warned, repeatedly ordered to leave. Congress had prohibited settlement on that side. Laws are meant to be obeyed and it's the Army's duty to see that they are."

"Then our settlement here couldn't have been legal, either?"

"Strictly speaking, it wasn't. But it represents a rather different case. Up there the squatters were just across the river from our older settlements. They stirred up the Indians and constituted a threat to the law-abiding people on the Pennsylvania and Virginia side. Here there are no settlements on the other side and the station's been in the hands of superior and reputable people. When General Harmar heard about it he agreed with General Clark that it was actually an advantage to have a station on this stretch of the river."

"Then the Army just chose to make an exception in our case?"

"It amounted to that. Though not an official one, of course. We've merely looked the other way, as it were."

"Well, I suppose you need to worry even less about it now. It certainly should make no trouble with the Indians now that Caleb owns it. He's almost a Shawnee himself. He grew up among them."

"He did?"

"They still accept him as one of them. So there's not much chance they'll object to his keeping the place. He has friends among the English, too. People like Alexander McKee and Matthew Elliot. And he was in the English navy during the war."

"But didn't I hear Colonel Jordan say something about his having deserted?"

"Oh yes. But that was after the war. He was too anxious to get back to Detroit to wait for a discharge. As you just saw, he knew he could make money in the fur trade."

All preoccupation with gallantry had been swept from the Captain's candid young countenance. His thoughtful frown was stiffly official.

"His having the station begins to sound like making the Indians a present of a fortified post right smack on the Ohio. Does General Clark know him?"

"He doesn't know about his buying the place. But he's met him several times. He thinks he knows him quite well. He thinks he's changed. He trusts him."

"You should have reason to know him better. What do you think? Do you trust him?"

"What does it matter what I think? It's General Clark's judgment that counts."

"Not with me, it doesn't. George Rogers Clark is a great patriot and an extraordinary man. He's also one of our Indian commissioners and I've been instructed to build a fort to cover his negotiations with them. But he's no more a general than you are. He has never been a line officer. He served only with the Virginia militia during the war and he's been just a civilian since it ended. He can't speak for the Army of the United States, while I must. I have my orders and the duty of carrying them out is my personal responsibility."

"Then I should think you'd feel like talking to Caleb yourself and then making up your own mind about your duty. Oh, look."

She ran swiftly away from him along the path and knelt among some low bushes with her back to him. By the time he had recovered from his astonishment and had overtaken her she was rising and wheeling triumphantly to face him. From her fingers dangled the locket at one end of its chain.

"Isn't that wonderful," she exclaimed. "I just happened to catch sight of something glittering in the sun. And there it was. Right there beside the path." She bent to examine the locket. "Look, you can see where this link was soldered to the locket. That was where it broke. That must have been how I lost it."

The Captain nodded absently. His face was stern.

"Remarkably fortunate, your finding your lost locket so promptly. But that it gave you an opportunity to tell me what you just have is far more fortunate."

He stood aside. She walked on before him. At the camp he spoke to Sergeant Redfern with crisp decision.

"Detail another twenty men to help move Colonel Jordan's goods down to the landing place. And I want ten more, in your personal charge, to come with me. Have them fall in with muskets and bayonets fixed."

The slope between the station and the flat rock was crawling like an ant heap as men scrambled back and forth, laden with sacks, bales, bundles, boxes, and articles of furniture. Captain Telford, preceded by Tracy, and trailed by his column of reinforcements, encountered Duncan at the landing place.

"I'm giving you another twenty men, Colonel Jordan," he said, "in the hope that the loading may be further expedited. Sergeant Redfern, will you post your guard at the bridge? Instruct them that no one is to cross, either way, except by my personal permission. Then come with me."

The ten with bayoneted muskets took up their station. Captain Telford, followed by the Sergeant, strode across the bridge and on into the corn. Duncan watched in growing astonishment. He turned to Tracy.

"What's come over the man?"

"A certain act of Congress prohibiting settlement on this side of the river. I gather he's remembered that he's a federal officer and that it's his duty to enforce it."

Duncan stared at her incredulously.

"This is your doing. Why? Can you tell me why?"

"Very easily. I just couldn't stand the idea of Caleb's taking over this place. We've put too much of ourselves into it for him to have it."

"You mean what you can't stand is Daisy's moving in."

"No. Daisy counts for nothing. It's Caleb's having it. After the way he's treated us. That's what I couldn't stand."

Captain Telford stepped out of the corn and looked about him at the cabin, the barn, and the stockpens. There was no one in sight. He glanced into the cabin, made sure that it was empty, and went on around the corner. There he came to another pause. Daisy was on her knees in the garden, digging onions. She looked up, grinned shyly, and got to her feet. The day was warm. Her plump body glistened with sweat. Her working costume consisted of a bark apron about her hips. She stared with mounting admiration at the Captain's military finery, then, recalling her manners, bent to pick from the ground a sleeveless, vestlike garment of ragged doeskin. This she slipped on, giggling, and looked up to give the Captain another less shy and more sociable grin.

"Who are you?" he asked.

Daisy struggled with her recently acquired stock of English phrases and came out with:

"Caleb's woman."

Captain Telford looked around to share his disgust with Sergeant Redfern and became aware that Caleb stood leaning on his rifle three paces behind the Sergeant.

"I see," said the Captain. "There seems to be a new Mrs. Lewis."

Caleb's glance took in Daisy and came back to his visitor. "Have you come because you want this one, too?"

Captain Telford took a long breath and counted ten. "No. I have come to announce what I had conceived to be a somewhat disagreeable duty. I find, instead, that it is one in which I can take considerable satisfaction. I must remind you that settlement on this side of the river is contrary to law. I am an officer sworn to uphold the law. I am here, therefore, to inform you that I shall be obliged to burn your station."

Sergeant Redfern's hand crept to the butt of his pistol. But Caleb neither replied, nor moved, nor changed expression.

"If you wish to come with me to my camp I can show you a copy of the order which directs me to take such action in every such case, without exception."

"I do not need to see it. I am sure that you can read."

Captain Telford took another long breath. "It is the stockade that chiefly concerns me. I do not propose to permit a man of your stripe to maintain what amounts to a fortified post right on the Ohio. If you accept the situation quietly I will leave you the corn and this cabin. But I must warn you that if you attempt to create any sort of disturbance I will leave you nothing."

Again Caleb made no reply. The Captain strode off toward the corn. Sergeant Redfern fell in step at his heels, giving the impression of a man laboring to look back over his shoulder while continuing to stare straight ahead. Caleb started to walk after them. Captain Telford swung around.

"You will not be permitted to cross the bridge."

"I do not want to cross the bridge. But you have said you will burn my place. Do you also forbid me to watch you do it?"

The Captain went on. Duncan was waiting for him beyond the guard posted along the bank at the other end of the bridge.

"Are you actually going to burn him out?" he demanded.

"Yes. Will you let me know, please, when you have removed as many of your effects as we have space to transport?"

"But, Captain Telford, I really must lodge a most vigorous protest against this action."

"One does not protest the law, Colonel Jordan. One merely obeys."

"But we've always had tacit permission for this location. And I've sold the station to him in good faith. You're placing me in an impossible position."

"As I understood the transaction, he purchased from you whatever you were unable to carry away. However, that's a matter for you to settle with him."

Duncan glanced across the stream. Caleb sat on the other bank, his forearms on his knees, his rifle lying on the ground beside him. He appeared to be taking a merely sardonic interest in the activity on the station side. Behind him, Daisy crouched, peering impassively from the first row of corn.

"May I cross to talk to him?"

"Certainly, if you wish."

As Duncan approached, Caleb got up and waited for him

to speak with the same composure with which he had been watching the loading of the boats.

"I wanted you to understand, Mr. Lewis, that I had nothing to do with this. I protested as strongly as I could. But Captain Telford considers his duty clear."

Caleb nodded. "Under that foolish uniform the young man is a soldier."

"One thing I can do. Since I am unable to hand over all that you paid for, I am ready to make an adjustment on the price you paid."

"Nobody else will blame you. Why should I? It is not your stockade that he will burn. It is mine."

"I must insist that you say what you consider the buildings worth so that I can return that portion of your purchase price."

"I would not have paid a shilling for them. This land. This stream. This valley. This place that Corbit picked. That is what I bought. I can build another stockade."

"Why try so hard to pretend? You've no need to grope for excuses. For what could one man, even one as headstrong as you, do against soldiers and bayonets and cannon? Actually nothing would have pleased you more than to have been able to sit in that house and remember that we built it for you."

"It is always easier to forget than to remember. When you first came you were able to see a little of what Corbit saw here. Like a tanager flying into a bush. For a moment you saw a streak of light. Then it was gone. Now you have forgotten even that."

"You are a childish fool."

"The young man is calling you. Your people are ready to go. They are leaving from the same rock on which you landed."

The line of loaded bateaus rocked in the shallows at the point, their prows grounded on the sandy beach. Most of the soldiers and passengers had already taken their assigned places in them. Duncan stood on the shore waiting for the arrival of Captain Telford and his guard detachment. From the station on its mound flames leaped into the air.

In one of the boats Eric lay prone, his face buried in his mother's lap. Her hands crept caressingly through his hair, over his neck and shoulders. She tugged gently to make him look up but he stiffened against her touch.

"It wasn't your father's fault," she murmured. "He did all

he could to stop it. He tried to give Caleb some of his money back. What more could he do?"

In another boat Tracy sat between Garett and Olivia. She stared not at the smoke rising in the sky but out over the river into the distance. Olivia had an arm around her. Garett was holding one of her hands.

"There's one consolation, my dear," he said. "It was a close, hard game, with neither of you ever giving an inch. But you would certainly seem to have taken the last trick."

"I can still see him sitting there by the fire those first nights," said Olivia. "That awful unblinking stare of his. There he sat, sizing us up. It was our being Corbit Revel's people that meant the most to him. He was beginning to think he wanted to be like us, to have one of our women, to live in our house, to belong to us."

"No, that wasn't what he was beginning to think," said Tracy, spacing the words as though each were being forced from her. "What he wanted, even from the first, was that we should belong to him. We weren't punishing him when we pushed him away, and took back our woman, and took even the house away from him. Because long before he'd made up his mind that we weren't up to being counted Corbit Revel's people."

Captain Telford came along the path at the head of his final file of soldiers. Duncan went to meet him.

"Where are the Slovers? When they didn't show up here I assumed they were helping you."

"And I thought they were with you." The Captain scowled. His temper had been deteriorating steadily this last hour. "Everybody was instructed to assemble here."

Duncan strode on and came to a stop upon seeing Olen shambling along the path toward him. He was alone.

"Go get your family," directed Duncan impatiently. His temper too, had frayed. "And be quick about it. If you're not here in five minutes we'll go without you."

Olen shifted his weight uneasily. It always pained him to deliver unwelcome news. He gulped, clawed at his beard, and stared past Duncan at the sycamore.

"We-uns ain't a-goin', Kunnel," he said. "We-uns reckon we'll jest stay on here and string along with Caleb."

September

The setting sun appeared to be sinking into the farther end of the long westward reach of the river. The twin channels on either side of the island were transfigured into mirrored paths of crimson and gold. A flukey breeze, riffling the water, brought from the unbroken walls of forest on either hand puffs of air which smelled alternately of the heat of the day and the first cool of the evening. On wide mud flats along the shrunken edges of the Ohio, cranes and herons stalked stiffly or stood on one leg, blinking into the sunset. Fleets of ducks drifted with the current, quacking conversationally, from time to time a tail rearing abruptly upright as its owner dove expertly for some morsel on the bottom. Thrushes and catbirds and mocking birds raised their defiantly cheerful evening chorus in one last spasm of thanksgiving before yielding to the silence imposed by the night.

A herd of buffalo trailed single file from the north bank woods, drank noisily, and then, following the old cow who was their leader, waded on out through the river's late summer shallows. The half-grown calves, now as black as their elders, shouldered, splashed, and butted one another. As the herd neared the island the old cow's head came up. She sniffed suspiciously. After one warning grunt, she veered away from the island. The herd, bunching together in her wake, trotted behind her through the midstream shoal, swam briefly through the slightly deeper southern channel, and galloped into the woods.

The twilit loneliness of the river was suddenly relieved by the appearance of a solitary boat, wallowing around the bend above the island. The flat-bottomed scow, of a draft so shallow as to enable it to negotiate the seasonal low water which for weeks had denied the river to heavier craft, was poled by a man whose mien suggested he bitterly regretted having clung this late in the year to his determination to get on to

Kentucky. With his ragged family of a wife and a half dozen small children clustered about him, he was driving his pole wearily against the muddy bottom while peering ahead nervously for a safe haven in which to camp for the night. Perceiving the island, he poled his scow toward it and ran aground on the shoal that stretched upstream from its point. Cuffing first his whimpering children and then his scolding wife, he got out in the water, shoved his ungainly craft free, climbed aboard again, and drifted disgustedly on past in the deeper channel, unaware of the coldly narrowed eyes watching him from the shadowed island.

Stretched on the ground in the shrubbery at the water's edge were a dozen Indians, observing expressionlessly the mover's progress. Their oiled dark bodies remained so entirely without any twitch of movement that they had the appearance more of animals than of men. Beside them were two bark canoes as carefully hidden as they from anyone passing in the open river. One of the Indians looked at the sky and grunted. All sat up, reached into their game pouches, and began to eat a handful of pounded corn and jerky.

Fifty yards away, in the center of the little island, Tracy sat against a tree, watching the slowly darkening sky. The days since she had been taken had fallen into a routine so unvarying that she knew each hour of the twenty-four what next to expect. Her every daylight hour had been spent in the heart of such a thicket as this. It was always on an island in mid-river. Always at dark her captors reassembled and got back into their two canoes. Always she was prodded into the prow of the first. The other trailed a quarter of a mile back. The Indians paddled hard all night on upriver. They hid on another island at dawn and waited through the daylight for the return of darkness. There had been eight such days and nights since the night she had been snatched from her bed in a house on the very outskirts of Louisville. The memory of that outrageous moment was so vivid that she was still moved more by chagrin than dismay each time she reflected upon the savage cunning with which they had managed to carry her off while there were a hundred people within call.

There was a faint rustle in the shrubbery in the direction of the Indian bivouac. She looked across at the gnarled and wrinkled squaw, squatting five feet away, watching her, who had been her constant companion since her abductors had returned to their waiting canoes hiddden in the Louisville marshes. The old crone's eyes were steadily upon her, day and night, for she seemed never to sleep. It was only at this moment that her attention ever wavered for a second. She, too, had heard the rustle and her glance always flickered toward it. It was the moment before another departure when one of the braves brought a strip of jerky or a dab of pemmican for the women to share. Tracy waited, with a kind of perverse satisfaction in the predictabilty of the gesture, for her keeper to snatch at the food. But the old woman instead gave a slight start. Tracy, too, looked around and was herself immediately overwhelmed by astonishment. The figure outlined against the pale sky was not one of the Indians. She scrambled up to her knees.

"Eric," she gasped.

He knelt beside her, grasping her arm reassuringly.

"I hope you haven't been having too bad a time," he said.

"I didn't hear anything. Where'd the Indians go? How'd you find me?"

It was getting too dark to see his face clearly but she could sense the forced cheerfulness of his grin.

"You're not saved, worse luck. I'm their prisoner, too. Have been since the night they took you. Only they've kept me in the second canoe and would never let me come near you."

"Then why are they letting you talk to me now?"

"I suppose they've got so far away they're beginning to feel safe."

"But how'd they take you?"

"My own fault. They may not give us much time to talk, so let's compare what we know as fast as we can. You remember that had been the day of the election. I marched that night in the torchlight procession. I was pretty set up that Father'd only been in Louisville two weeks before they'd picked him to be a delegate to the state convention. But when everybody got out to Major Belden's and they'd started that dance—well, I didn't feel like dancing. I took a walk, off where it was quieter. I don't know just where I went, through some woods and down along the Beargrass. Anyway, when I got back it must have been nearly midnight but the dance was still going on. At the edge of the woods there were maybe a dozen Indians lying on their bellies back of a rail fence, looking toward Major Belden's house and the barn where the dance was. I'd gone off by myself to try to think. Anyway, I wasn't paying any attention. I stepped right on one of them before I knew they were there. They grabbed me. It was that easy. They made me lie down with my face against the ground. Then after about an hour they made me run with them through the woods down to the river. I hadn't heard any noise around the Belden place or sounds of alarm or any shooting, so I decided they'd given up trying to do anything there. How'd they get you?"

"I didn't feel like dancing either. I told Mrs. Belden I had a headache. She took me to a back bedroom. I lay down on a bed. I must have dozed. There was an open window just beside the bed. The next I knew the quilt on which I was lying was jerked over my head and I was bundled in it so tightly I couldn't make a sound. Then I realized I was being carried out the window but there wasn't a thing I could do to help myself. This same quilt." She plucked resentfully at the quilt on which she was kneeling. "It's all so fantastically irrational. We'd spent a year wandering about the woods on the Indian bank and now the both of us are taken right in sight of Louisville."

"When small Indian parties get among the settlements they don't pick and choose. They just hide and watch and wait for a chance to steal a horse or burn a cabin or axe somebody or do anything else miserable they think they can do and still get away. It just happened that night to be our bad luck."

"I can understand the bad luck part. I'd heard everybody talking about the danger from Miamis, and how they'd been getting bolder every week this whole summer. So being captured wasn't so outlandish. But what I can't understand is why they're taking us this far upriver."

"They're just on their way home. That's the big reason Indians like to take prisoners. So they can show them off to their home folks."

"But the Miami towns are up in the Wabash country. That's off the other way altogether."

"These Indians aren't Miamis. They're Wyandots. Their towns are up by Lake Erie. So they are on their way home. They're probably planning to head north up the Scioto or the Muskingum."

"But what were Wyandots doing as far away as Louisville?"

"That bothered me, too, at first. But Indians travel a lot more than most people think. They're always visiting each other, like Cherokee wandering around up here or Northern Indians seeing the sights clear down to Florida. These Wyandot could have been visiting the Chickasaw, or the Osage, or the Missouri. Then on their way home it probably just struck them as a good idea to take along a Kentucky captive or two."

"What do you think they intend to do with us?"

"I don't think we're in too much real danger. The Wyandot aren't supposed to be at war with us, not yet anyway. We'll be able to get in touch with some English trader and get talk about ransom started."

It was too dark now to see his face at all but in his tone there was the continuing earnest effort to reassure her.

"The wonderful part about being taken by Indians," she said, "is that there's some comfort to be had in any prospect short of burning."

"They haven't burned anybody," said Eric hastily, "not in more than two years."

There came the brief harsh squawk of a disturbed wood duck that was the usual signal for a new start. The old woman instantly grasped Tracy's arm and turned her toward the beach. Eric slipped off into the shadows. Tracy took her accustomed place in the prow and the first canoe shoved off. The six Indians of its crew settled to the tireless, night-long rhythm of their paddling. Tracy squirmed until she had arranged the folds of the quilt under her knees. For the first time she was permitting herself to realize the extent of her weariness. During the whole interminable stretch of eight days and nights, she had remained so determined to keep always on the alert for the faintest opportunity to escape that she had dozed only in snatches. But there had been an immense relief in discovering Eric was near, even if only as a companion in misfortune. She was no longer alone. If there was anything to be done he would know when and what. For this once she might rest. She pushed the old woman away to make more room, curled up on the quilt in the bottom of the canoe, and let herself drift into the deepest of sleeps.

Hours later she realized dimly that they must be camping again. The canoe was being dragged up on another beach and she was being lifted from it. She was more weary than ever and bitterly resentful of being disturbed. It was so much more inviting to drop back in the refuge of sleep.

When finally she began at last to awaken of her own accord, ever so slowly and still reluctantly, it was to the smell of broiling trout. Not once during all that driving dash up the Ohio had the Indians built a fire. It crossed her mind vaguely that they must have turned off the main river into the Scioto. The persisting smell of the grilling trout began to make her aware that she was hungry and she began tentatively to stir. Her limbs were sore and cramped from those nights in the canoe, but the long sleep had left her rested. Though she had not opened her eyes she could tell that it was daylight. A deeper mystery began to pluck at her attention. She was not on the hard ground but on a surface comfortably soft, and there was a clean blanket over her in the place of the quilt which had come to smell so strongly of Indian grease and pitch from the canoe and river mud. Slowly, only idly curious as yet, she opened her eyes. Instantly she was in the grip of a fantasy far wilder than the desperate sensation of being carried off by Indians. She had awakened in Caleb's cabin in the very bed which once she had shared with him.

Driven by an immediate spasmodic impulse to protest, she cast aside the blanket and swung from the bed. Daisy, squatted on the hearth, glanced over her shoulder and grinned amiably. Tracy sank back on the edge of the bed. Daisy swiftly transferred two of the smoking trout from the skillet to a bark tray, added a square of hot corn bread, and advanced, her offering extended. Her grin was broader than ever. Her attitude was unmistakably, and therefore the more grotesquely, hospitable, even welcoming. Tracy sprang past her to the doorway.

Caleb was working in his cornfield, engaged with furious energy in the harvest of his corn. He moved steadily along the row, bending down the tremendous stalks, his knife flashing, ears of corn flying over his shoulder into little heaps on the ground behind him. He had thrown aside his shirt and the muscles of his arms and shoulders and the scars on his back stood out in the sun. The summer had tanned him nearly as dark as an Indian. She clung to the door frame, suddenly and irrelevantly aware of her hair hanging in a tangle about her shoulders and of the torn and bedraggled blue silk dress which had suffered so rudely since she had been taken in it. She sank down on the doorstep and covered her face with her hands. When she looked up again he was standing before her, buttoning one of the white linen shirts that she once had so rebelliously made for him.

"It's no use your trying to make me believe you somehow saved me from those Indians," she said.

His eyes were grave and intent with something of that look of concentrating all his faculties that was in them when he lifted his rifle to take aim. Then his lips parted slightly in what for him was almost the equivalent of a smile.

"I have counted on my fingers all the different things you might think," he said. "But that you might think I would try to fool you never came into my mind."

"Then you admit that you had this done to me because of what I had done to you when I burned your stockade."

"Yes. So soon as the Slovers told me that it was you who burned it I knew what I had to do. When you left me the night your father's friend was here, I waited. When you did not come back I decided you knew what you wanted. You had been here long enough to know and there is no use having a wife unless she does know. Then the burning was like finding a trail that I had lost. It came over me that I had not after all made a mistake in the beginning. A woman who can get that mad at me is the one I must have."

She stared at him.

"And now that you've had your Indians dump me back in your cabin, how long will it take you to discover you are still making mistakes?"

"Not long. In a month if you want still to go back to Louisville I will take you back."

"You will not have a month. I have friends. Colonel Jordan; Captain Telford; General Clark. They will come for me."

"It is true that they will be looking for you. But they will not know where to look. They will think first of the Miami. Before anybody comes here we will already know what we will do."

"If you wanted me to believe any of this, why didn't you come to Louisville to talk to me?"

"You would not have listened to me in Louisville. It was only here that there could be another chance for us."

"Along with all the other chances of what might happen to me while I was being bundled through woods and in and out of canoes by a pack of wild Indians?"

"You were never out of my sight from that first minute I wrapped you in the quilt."

"So you were right there in the second canoe. I half guessed it. But you never came near me. Why? I was as helpless there as I am here."

"There was no use to talk to you until you were ready to listen."

"And a week of believing I was a captive of the Wyandot might make me more ready to listen?"

"Yes. That is a part of what I counted on."

"Well, I am listening. You're so quick with all your answers. Have you thought up an excuse for carrying off Eric, too?"

"I did not plan that. Once we had hold of him I could not let him go to tell your people too soon where you were."

"During this month you expect me to try again to get used to you, am I supposed also to get used to Daisy?"

"You make too much of Daisy. You have not once had reason to think about her since that day I first saw you. But if the sight of her bothers you I will send her back to the

Shawnee." The hint of a smile was again around the corners of his mouth. "That will make Jake very sad. He had been sidling around her. To have a wife as willing to work as she is would be for him a very good catch."

She dropped that topic and clutched at another.

"Did you give Eric to your Wyandot?"

"No. He is here. Up there with the others."

"He is?"

She started up, desperate to escape his steady gaze, to delay, until she could breathe again, his detection of her surrender.

She ran through the corn but came to a stop on the bridge. All of the meadow corn had been cut. But this monument to the Slovers' month-long surge of industry was as nothing to the tribute presented by the spectacle of the rebuilt stockade. A wall of palisade poles once more ringed the crown of the mound. The vision burst upon her like the sudden unfurling of a banner in the sun. That which she had herself destroyed seemed miraculously to have been restored to her. Elation possessed her. She ran on up to the open gateway and again paused, hungrily, to stare.

An immense crib of leather-bound saplings, already half filled with corn from the meadow and with storage space waiting for Caleb's, stretched along the back wall of the stockade. In the center of the yard were great piles of logs, some of which had already been notched and squared, though actual construction of new housing had not yet commenced. The inhabitants still occupied brush shelters set up against the wall beyond the site of the one-time Slover cabin. Olen and Jacob were at work with axes, squaring more of the timbers. Jarot and Maggie were carrying logs already shaped to other piles nearer the spots where they would be used. Polly and Betsey were raking and sifting the ashes of the former buildings to recover nails, locks, hinges, and other items of ironwork. Eric was on his knees, bent over a strip of birch bark kept flat on the ground by stones at its corners, drawing lines upon it with a charred stick. When he saw her in the gateway he sprang up, leaned down again to pick up the strip of bark, and ran to her, brandishing it exultantly.

"Look. I can remember all the dimensions of father's plan for the first buildings so that we can put them up again just like they were before. We won't have to guess where doors and windows come or stop to saw holes after the walls are up. We can cut every timber the right length to fit and get everything up in half the time."

"Eric," said Tracy.

Her voice broke. For a second he misinterpreted her emotion.

"You're wondering why I didn't tell you, last night when we were talking, that it was Caleb himself who had taken us?" He laughed. "That's easy. He told me not to. And I had to do whatever he wanted. Because I had to make sure he'd let me stay here."

"Stay here? Eric! Is that what you really want to do?"

"It is. It certainly is." He saw that she wanted to believe and sought eagerly to convince her. "That night I was walking around in the woods, I'd kept on thinking about everything until I'd decided to run away and come back here. So it was the greatest luck in the world when I was taken. That'll make everything so much easier for Father and Mother to understand. There just couldn't have been better luck. I still can hardly believe it."

He seized her hand and ran, pulling her after him, to the nearest brush hut. Lina sat on a stool nursing twin babies. When she saw them coming she bent unhurriedly to slide the two small bundles into a cradle and rose to face them. She gave Tracy a quick welcoming smile but her entire interest was in Eric. She stared at him in hungering happiness, still unable fully to grasp the good fortune of his return to her, her fingers meanwhile fumbling slowly to draw the front of her cotton dress over her plump white breasts with the moist glowing nipples.

"See," said Eric, pulling Tracy down over the bright new cradle which smelled of fresh basswood and Indian sweet grass. "Two of 'em. Two boys. Two more rifles."

"Maw said I was a size to have me four," said Lina, "but they was only the two. Look—yuh kin see how much they take arter Eric."

"They're beautiful babies," murmured Tracy.

The young parents had already turned away from the cradle. They had eyes only for each other. Lina's fingers at the buttons of her dress were trembling. Eric, leaning closer to help her, was trembling, too. Tracy walked back toward the gate.

The Slovers had straighted from their labors to watch and now surged forward to greet her. But Polly, so smeared with ashes as to look even more disreputable than usual, peremptorily waved them back and came on alone. She took Tracy by the arm, led her aside in the gateway, and looked sharply into her face.

"Of course I'm going to stay," said Tracy. "You do want me to, don't you?"

"It ain't fer we-uns to pull on thet string one way nor t'other. Long's Caleb wants yuh, then sure's Christ's good we-uns do, too. We ain't total foolish. But if'n thet's whut yer aimin' to do they's something I figgered I'd best tell yuh straight off. Me and Olen we-uns had us a mess o'brats 'fore them yuh see here. Nine o' them's still livin', five boys and three gals, all married. Week 'fore last we got us a chance to send word back to 'em by a mover who'd changed his mind about Kaintuck and was headin' east. Come spring they'll all be out here."

"How wonderful for you," said Tracy, "to have all your family together again. And if there is another Indian war, with nine more men there'll be so much better chance to hold the stockade."

"Caleb figgers on holdin' the stockade. Make no mistake about thet. But there's something more yuh got to figger on yerself. Them young Slover sprouts and the men the gals married up with, they had theyselves thirty-some young-uns when we left and they's likely had half a dozen more by now. Thet's a slather o' folks to find room in one stockade no bigger'n this. Come real Injun trouble yuh and Caleb won't be able to stay quiet-like down in that cozy little cabin o' his'n. Yuh'll have to shove right in amongst us. Thet's whut I figgered yuh better know about so's it wouldn't come at yuh one day like something jumpin' out'n the bushes."

"Thank you, Polly. I'm sure we'll manage. But there's an equally friendly warning I might give you, about another kind of family problem that may prove harder to handle. As soon as Colonel Jordan finds out Eric is here, he's going to try to take him away. Eric's his oldest son and he's made many hopeful plans for him."

"Soon's a boy's growed enough to make him boys of his own," said Polly, "he ain't a boy no more. He's a man. And it's a man's place to make up his mind fer his ownself about whereat he belongs." The calm with which she had begun her reply gave way as she continued to consider the question. Suddenly she became as livid with rage as when she had defended Lina's choice before the Jordan tribunal. "Whut kind o' talk is thet? Whut kin the likes o' them Jordans say thet makes any sense about whut's good fer Eric? Eric's a good boy and he's on his way to bein' a good man. But he ain't never goin' to be up to whut's come to him. Thet gal is thet ready to give, and she's got thet much to give, and she's bound to give all of it only to him and never to nobody else. Most men never gits theyselves even a sniff o' luck like thet." She paused for breath and began as suddenly to glare at Tracy. "And as fer you. Yuh know right well how bad yuh wanted to stay with Caleb. Right from the start. Only yuh wouldn't never let on. Mebbe even to yerself. Yuh kept tellin' yerself he wasn't good enough fer yuh. Why yuh ain't bin woman enough to be let wash his pants. Like's not yer squawkin' now about his comin' arter yuh with Injuns. Yuh ain't got the wit to notice thet only goes to show one time more the size man he is. He traded with them Wyandot no more'n one month all of three years back but they remember him so well they come runnin' like dogs when yuh whistle the minute he let 'em know they was a way they might help him a little. And thet's something else thet could stick in yer craw. Whut the Injuns think about him is a-goin' to cost us all plenty 'fore we're through. Oncet the war gits started up next summer every no-good buck Injun north o' the Ohio is a-goin' to figger they ain't no better way to make a big name fer hisself than to try to take this place away from Caleb Lewis. Goddam' if I kin figger whut a man like him wants with you."

Polly grunted, spat, and swung around to stalk back to her ash-shifting. Tracy sprang in front of her.

"Look at me," she demanded. "Maybe you can tell something by that."

Polly stared, gulped and gathered her to her ample, soot-streaked bosom.

"Do yuh some good," she declared, "to take a stick to me, I'll find yuh a big one right quick. I git so used to takin' the hide off thet no-count Olen and them turnip-headed boys o' mine thet I'm allus a-blattin' out nine times more'n I mean."

Tracy clung to her. "If I can't even find words to tell you, whatever can I say to him? After all we've done to each other, how can I make him understand?"

"Will yuh fer Gawd's sake leave off talkin'," cried Polly. She gave Tracy a push and watched, beginning to sniffle and to dab at her eyes, as Tracy walked slowly down to the bridge.

Daisy was sitting on the edge of the flat rock, dangling her feet in the water. Beside her on the rock was a basket containing her few personal belongings. Covertly she watched Tracy's approach. It was apparent that she was waiting, with philosophic docility, for some indication of the next move that might be expected of her. Tracy met her glance, gave her an impersonally friendly smile, and kept on across the bridge. Daisy scrambled to her feet, snatched up her basket and ran eagerly up the slope to the stockade gateway.

Tracy could hear the rustling of the bending cornstalks and the rasp of the knife. Caleb was at work directly between her and the cabin. The sounds ceased. Breathing faster, she kept on through the corn and pushed between the last two stalks separating them. Once more they were face to face. He looked at her gravely and turned toward the cabin. She followed. At the doorstep he faced her again. He was still grave.

"I knew you would need another dress," he said. "But there was no chance in Louisville for me to buy you one. So I told Daisy to make you something to wear out of that cloth you wove. It might not look just the way you like but it will be better than nothing."

He went back to his harvesting. She went into the cabin. Spread out on the bed was the dress. She held it up. It hung from her hands in the straight lines of one of Daisy's own deerskin garments, but its stark white simplicity was relieved by touches of neat red and green embroidering at the hem of the skirt and about the neck. On the hearth was a kettle of warm water and on the stool beside it a strip of clean blanketing to serve as a towel. She striped off her bedraggled clothing and devoted a luxurious and leisurely hour to bathing, combing her hair, and, at last, to arraying herself in the new white dress. White, she reflected with a forced smile, was traditionally a bride's color.

She paused in the doorway. Caleb was at the end of a row at the farther edge of the clearing. He was working away as steadily as ever. She wondered if beneath his outward calm he could be in anything like such a state as she. Her heart began to beat so hard she choked. She slipped around the corner of the cabin and, cravenly temporizing, pretended to make an interested inspection of the stockpens. The young chickens and turkeys were almost grown, the calves had put on weight, there were nineteen pigs; but all of these familiar images were blurred. Then she heard Spec's squeaking whimper. He had been tied by a leather thong just inside the barn door. She released him and he cavorted about her feet as, at last, she walked steadily toward Caleb. He stopped work and watched her as she slowly approached, but she was unable to look up at him.

"I had to tie up the coon," he said, "else he would never have let you sleep last night. Then I forgot to untie him."

She regarded the windrows of corn on the ground.

"Shouldn't I get a basket and start picking them up?" she proposed.

He placed his hands on her shoulders but still she could not look up at him.

"You have made up your mind?"

"Yes," she whispered.

"I am not much for talk."

"Yes, I know." She was trying to smile. "According to you it's only what people do that counts."

"But I have something to say and I am going to try to say it. You have to believe I want you. Twice I have proved that by taking you when you did not want to be taken. But that is not what I am trying to say. There is something more that you have to believe."

She pushed his extended arms aside, threw herself against him, and wrapped her own arms about him.

"There's only one thing I have to believe," she declared, "that it had to be like this—that it could never have been any other way."